THE WORLD'S
GREAT THINKERS

MAN AND THE UNIVERSE:

The Philosophers
of Science

Man and the Universe:

THE

PHILOSOPHERS

OF SCIENCE

Edited by SAXE COMMINS & ROBERT N. LINSCOTT

RANDOM HOUSE · NEW YORK

ACKNOWLEDGMENTS ৶ৡ FOR PERMISSION TO REPRINT COPY-
RIGHTED SECTIONS OF THIS VOLUME, ACKNOWLEDGMENT IS
HERE MADE TO: *Encyclopædia Britannica, Inc., and the Estate of
Charles Glenn Wallis, Charles S. Glenn, Executor, for the transla-
tion of "On the Revolution of the Celestial Spheres" by Nicholas
Copernicus.* COPYRIGHT, 1939, BY CHARLES GLENN WALLIS.
Henry Holt and Company, Inc., for "The Evolution of Life" from
CREATIVE EVOLUTION *by Henri Bergson.* COPYRIGHT, 1911,
BY HENRY HOLT AND COMPANY. COPYRIGHT, 1938, BY
ARTHUR MITCHELL. *Random House, Inc., for "The Method of
Dream-Interpretation" and "The Dream As Wish-Fulfillment"
from* THE BASIC WRITINGS OF SIGMUND FREUD. COPYRIGHT,
1938, BY RANDOM HOUSE, INC. *The Macmillan Company for
"Science and Philosophy" from* SCIENCE AND THE MODERN
WORLD *by A. N. Whitehead,* COPYRIGHT, 1925, BY THE MAC-
MILLAN COMPANY; *"Some Problems of Philosophy" from*
PHYSICS AND PHILOSOPHY *by Sir James Jeans,* COPYRIGHT,
1943, BY THE MACMILLAN COMPANY; *"Reality, Causation,
Science and Mysticism" from* THE NATURE OF THE PHYSICAL
WORLD *by A. S. Eddington,* COPYRIGHT, 1928, BY THE MAC-
MILLAN COMPANY. *Cambridge University Press for "Science
and Philosophy" by A. N. Whitehead; "Some Problems of Philos-
ophy" by Sir James Jeans; "Reality, Causation, Science and Mysti-
cism" by A. S. Eddington. Crown Publishers for "The Problem of
Space, Ether and the Field in Physics" from* THE WORLD AS I
SEE IT *by Albert Einstein.* COPYRIGHT, 1934, BY COVICI,
FRIEDE, INC.

CONTENTS

Lucretius

ON THE NATURE OF

THINGS

(BOOK V)

Lucretius
[99–55 B.C.]

So little is known about the life of Lucretius beyond his birth and death dates that even scholars, with their zeal for filling in lacunae, can only surmise from some casual phrases that he went insane, that his work was edited by Cicero and that he committed suicide. What remains undisputed is the existence of *De Rerum Natura* (*On the Nature of Things*). Two centuries after the death of Epicurus, the doctrines of Epicureanism, especially those which emphasize the liberation of mankind from superstition and the fear of death, found reaffirmation in Lucretius. Fundamentally a treatise on science, the first four Books of this poem examine atoms and the void, the soul, sense-perception, psychology and the will. The fifth Book, which is given here in toto, considers the origin of the world, astronomy, a study of species and their development, human institutions, language, art and religion, and is a summary of prevailing scientific concepts just before the beginning of the Christian era.

ON THE NATURE OF THINGS

(BOOK V)

LUCRETIUS

Who is able with powerful genius to frame a poem worthy
of the grandeur of the things and these discoveries? Or who
is so great a master of words as to be able to devise praises
equal to the deserts of him who left to us such prizes won
and earned by his own genius? None methinks who is formed
of mortal body. For if we must speak as the acknowledged
grandeur of the things itself demands, a god he was, a god,
most noble Memmius, who first found out that plan of life
which is now termed wisdom, and who by trained skill rescued life from such great billows and such thick darkness and
moored it in so perfect a calm and in so brilliant a light. Compare the godlike discoveries of others in old times: Ceres is
famed to have pointed out to mortals corn, and Liber the
vine-born juice of the grape; though life might well have sub-
sisted without these things, as we are told some nations even
now live without them. But a happy life was not possible
without a clean breast; wherefore with more reason this man
is deemed by us a god, from whom come those sweet solaces
of existence which even now are distributed over great nations and gently soothe men's minds. Then if you shall suppose that the deeds of Hercules surpass his, you will be carried still farther away from true reason. For what would yon
great gaping maw of Nemean lion now harm us and the bris-
tled Arcadian boar? Ay or what could the bull of Crete do
and the hydra plague of Lerna, fenced round with its en-

3

venomed snakes? Or how could the triple-breasted might of
threefold Geryon, how could the birds with brazen arrowy
feathers that dwelt in the Stymphalian swamps do us such
mighty injury, and the horses of Thracian Diomede breathing fire from their nostrils along the Bistonian borders and
Ismara? And the serpent which guards the bright golden
apples of the Hesperides, fierce, dangerous of aspect, girding
the tree's stem with his enormous body, what harm pray
could he do us beside the Atlantic shore and its sounding
main, which none of us goes near and no barbarian ventures
to approach? And all other monsters of the kind which have
been destroyed, if they had not been vanquished, what harm
could they do, I ask, though now alive? None methinks: the
earth even now so abounds to repletion in wild beasts and
is filled with troublous terror throughout woods and great
mountains and deep forests; places which we have it for the
most part in our own power to shun. But unless the breast is
cleared, what battles and dangers must then find their way
into us in our own despite! What poignant cares inspired by
lust then rend the distressful man, and then also what mighty
fears! And pride, filthy lust and wantonness? What disasters
they occasion, and luxury and all sorts of sloth? He therefore
who shall have subdued all these and banished them from the
mind by words, not arms, shall he not have a just title to be
ranked among the gods? And all the more so that he was
wont to deliver many precepts in beautiful and god-like
phrase about the immortal gods themselves and to open up
by his teachings all the nature of things.

    While walking in his footsteps I follow out his reasonings
and teach by my verses, by what law all things are made,
what necessity there is then for them to continue in that law,
and how impotent they are to annul the binding statutes of
time: foremost in which class of things the nature of the mind
has been proved to be formed of a body that had birth and to
be unable to endure unscathed through great time, mere idols
being wont to mock the mind in sleep, when we seem to see
him whom life has abandoned: to continue, che order of my
design has now brought me to this point, where I must pro-

ceed to show that the world is formed of a mortal body and
at the same time had birth; to show too in what way that
union of matter founded earth, heaven, sea, stars, sun, and the
ball of the moon; also what living creatures sprang out of
the earth, as well as those which never at any time were born;
in what way too mankind began to use with one another
varied speech by the names conferred on things; and also in
what ways yon fear of the gods gained an entry into men's
breasts, and now throughout the world maintains as holy
fanes, lakes, groves, altars, and idols of the gods. Furthermore
I shall make clear by what force piloting nature guides the
courses of the sun and the wanderings of the moon; lest haply
we imagine that these of their own free will between heaven
and earth traverse their everlasting orbits, graciously further-
ing the increase of crops and living creatures, or we think
they roll on by any forethought of the gods. For they who
have been rightly taught that the gods lead a life without care,
if nevertheless they wonder by what plan all things can be
carried on, above all in regard to those things which are seen
overhead in the ethereal borders, are borne back again into
their old religious scruples and take unto themselves hard
taskmasters, whom they poor wretches believe to be almighty,
not knowing what can, what cannot be, in short by what
system each thing has its powers defined, its deep-set boundary mark.

Well then not to detain you any longer by mere promises,
look before all on seas and lands and heaven: their threefold
nature, their three bodies, Memmius, three forms so unlike,
three such wondrous textures a single day shall give over to
destruction; and the mass and fabric of the world upheld for
many years shall tumble to ruin. Nor can I fail to perceive
with what a novel and strange effect it falls upon the mind,
this destruction of heaven and earth that is to be, and how
hard it is for me to produce a full conviction of it by words;
as is the case when you bring to the ears a thing hitherto un-
exampled, and yet you cannot submit it to the eyesight nor
put it into the hands; through which the straightest highway
of belief leads into the human breast and quarters of the mind.

But yet I will speak out: it well may be that the reality itself will bring credit to my words and that you will see earthquakes arise and all things grievously shattered to pieces in short time. But this may pilot fortune guide far away from us, and may reason rather than the reality convince that all things may be overpowered and tumble in with a frightful crash.

But before I shall begin on this question to pour forth decrees of fate with more sanctity and much more certainty than the Pythia who speaks out from the tripod and laurel of Phoebus, I will clearly set forth to you many comforting topics in learned language; lest held in the yoke of religion you haply suppose that earth and sun and heaven, sea, stars, and moon must last for ever with divine body; and therefore think it right that they after the fashion of the giants should all suffer punishment for their monstrous guilt, who by their reasoning displace the walls of the world and seek to quench the glorious sun of heaven, branding immortal things in mortal speech; though in truth these things are so far from possessing divinity and are so unworthy of being reckoned in the number of gods, that they may be thought to afford a notable instance of what is quite without vital motion and sense. For it is quite impossible to suppose that the nature and judgment of the mind can exist with any body whatever; even as a tree cannot exist in the ether nor clouds in the salt sea, nor can fishes live in the fields nor blood exist in woods nor sap in stones. Where each thing can grow and abide is fixed and ordained. Thus the nature of the mind cannot come into being alone without the body nor exist far away from the sinews and blood. But if (for this would be much more likely to happen than that) the force itself of the mind might be in the head or shoulders or heels or might be born in any other part of the body, it would after all be wont to abide in one and the same man or vessel. But since in our body even it is fixed and seen to be ordained where the soul and the mind can severally be and grow, it must still more strenuously be denied that it can abide out of the body and the living room altogether in crumbling clods of earth or in the fire of the sun or in water or in the high borders of ether. These things therefore are not possessed of divine sense, since they cannot be quickened with the vital feeling.

This too you may not possibly believe, that the holy seats of the gods exist in any parts of the world: the fine nature of the gods far withdrawn from our senses is hardly seen by the thought of the mind; and since it has ever eluded the touch and stroke of the hands, it must touch nothing which is tangible for us; for that cannot touch which does not admit of being touched in turn. And therefore their seats as well must be unlike our seats, fine, even as their bodies are fine. All which I will prove to you later in copious argument. To say again that for the sake of men they have willed to set in order the glorious nature of the world and therefore it is meet to praise the work of the gods calling as it does for all praise, and to believe that it will be eternal and immortal, and that it is an unholy thing ever to shake by any force from its fixed seats that which by the forethought of the gods in ancient days has been established on everlasting foundations for mankind, or to assail it by speech and utterly overturn it from top to bottom; and to invent and add other figments of the kind, Memmius, is all sheer folly. For what advantage can our gratitude bestow on immortal and blessed beings, that for our sakes they should take in hand to administer aught? And what novel incident should have induced them hitherto at rest so long after to desire to change their former life? For it seems natural he should rejoice in a new state of things, whom old things annoy; but for him whom no ill has befallen in times gone by, when he passed a pleasant existence, what could have kindled in such a one a love of change? Did life lie grovelling in darkness and sorrow, until the first dawn of the birth-time of things? Or what evil had it been for us never to have been born? Whoever has been born must want to continue in life, so long as fond pleasure shall keep him; but for him who has never tasted the love, never been on the lists, of life, what harm not to have been born? Whence again was first implanted in the gods a pattern for begetting things in general as well as the preconception of what men are, so that they knew and saw in mind what they wanted to make? And in what way was the power of first-beginnings ever ascertained, and what they could effect by a change in their mutual arrangements, unless nature herself gave the model for making things? For in suchwise the first-beginnings of things many in number in many ways impelled by blows for infinite ages back and kept in motion by their own weights have been wont to be carried along and to unite in all manner of ways and thoroughly test every kind of production possible by their mutual combinations; that it is not strange if they have also fallen into arrangements and have come into courses like to those out of which this sum of things is now carried on by constant renewing.

But if I did not know what first-beginnings of things are, yet this judging by the very arrangements of heaven I would venture to affirm, and led by many other facts to maintain, that the nature of things has by no means been made for us by divine power: so great are the defects with which it is encumbered. In the first place of all the space which the vast reach of heaven covers, a portion greedy mountains and forests of wild beasts have occupied, rocks and wasteful pools take up and the sea which holds wide apart the coasts of different lands. Next of nearly two thirds burning heat and the constant fall of frost rob mortals. What is left for tillage, even that nature by its power would overrun with thorns, unless the force of man made head against it, accustomed for the sake of a livelihood to groan beneath the strong hoe and to cut through the earth by pressing down the plough. Unless by turning up the fruitful clods with the share and labouring the soil of the earth we stimulate things to rise, they could not spontaneously come up into the clear air; and even then sometimes when things earned with great toil now put forth their leaves over the lands and are all in blossom, either the ethereal sun burns them up with excessive heats or sudden rains and cold frosts cut them off, and the blasts of the winds waste them by a furious hurricane. Again why does nature give food and increase to the frightful race of wild beasts dangerous to mankind both by sea and land? Why do the seasons of the year bring diseases in their train? Why stalks abroad untimely death? Then too the baby, like to a sailor cast away by the cruel waves, lies naked on the ground, speechless, wanting every furtherance of life, soon as nature by the throes of birth has shed him forth from his mother's womb into the borders of light: he fills the room with a rueful wauling, as well he may whose destiny it is to go through in life so many ills. But the different flocks, herds, and wild beasts grow up; they want no rattles; to none of them need be addressed the fond broken accents of the fostering nurse; they ask not different dresses according to the season; no nor do they want arms or lofty walls, whereby to protect their own, the earth itself and nature manifold in her works producing in plenty all things for all.

First of all, since the body of the earth and water and the light breath of air and burning heats, out of which this sum of things is seen to be formed, do all consist of a body that had a birth and is mortal, the whole nature of the world must be reckoned of a like body. For those things whose parts and members we see to be of a body that had a birth and of forms that are mortal, we perceive to be likewise without exception mortal, and at the same time to have had a birth. Since therefore I see that the chiefest members and parts of the world are destroyed and begotten anew, I may be sure that for heaven and earth as well there has been a time of beginning and there will be a time of destruction.

And herein that you may not think I have unfairly seized on this point for myself, because I have assumed that earth and fire are mortal and have not doubted that water and air perish, and have said that these are likewise begotten and grow afresh, mark the proofs: first of all some portion of the earth, burnt up by constant suns, trampled by a multitude of feet, sends forth a cloud and flying eddies of dust, which the strong winds disperse over the whole air. Part too of the soil is put under water by rains, and rivers graze against and eat into the banks. Again whatever increases something else, is in its turn replenished; and since beyond a doubt earth the universal mother is found at the same time to be the general tomb of things, therefore you see she is lessened and increases and grows again.

Furthermore, that sea, rivers, fountains always stream over

with new moisture and that waters well up without ceasing,
it needs no words to prove: the great flow of waters from all
sides clearly shows it. But then the water on the surface is
always taken off, and thus it is that on the whole there is no
overflow, partly because the seas are lessened by the strong
winds sweeping over them and by the ethereal sun decomposing them with his rays; partly, because the water is diffused below the surface over all lands; for the salt is strained
off and the matter of liquid streams back again to the source
and all meets together at the river heads, and then flows over
the lands in a fresh current, where a channel once scooped out
has carried down the waters with liquid foot.

And next I will speak of the air which is changed over its
whole body every hour in countless ways. For whatever
ebbs from things, is all borne always into the great sea of air;
and unless it in return were to give back bodies to things and
to recruit them as they ebb, all things ere now would have
been dissolved and changed into air. It therefore ceases not to
be begotten from things and to go back into things, since it is
a fact that all things constantly ebb.

Likewise the abundant source of clear light, the ethereal
sun, constantly floods heaven with fresh brightness and supplies the place of light on the instant by new light; for every
previous emission of brightness is quite lost to it, wherever it
falls. This you may know from the following examples: as
soon as ever clouds begin to pass below the sun and to break
off so to say the rays of light, forthwith their lower part is
wholly lost, and the earth is over-shadowed wherever the
clouds pass over; so that you may know that things constantly
require new irradiation and that all the preceding emissions
of light are lost, and in no other way can things be seen in
the sun, unless the fountain head of light itself send a supply.
Moreover, you see, nightly lights which belong to earth, such
as hanging lamps and torches bright with darting flames,
hasten in like fashion amid great darkness with ministering
heat to supply new light; are eager to bicker with fires, ay
eager; nor is the light ever broken off nor does it quit the
spots illuminated: with such suddenness is its destruction

concealed by the swift birth of flame from all the fires at once. In the same way then we must believe that sun, moon, and stars emit light from fresh and ever fresh supplies rising up, and always lose every previous discharge of flames; that you may not haply believe that these flourish indestructible.

Again see you not that even stones are conquered by time, that high towers fall and rocks moulder away, that shrines and idols of gods are worn out with decay, and that the holy divinity cannot prolong the bounds of fate or struggle against the fixed laws of nature? Then see we not the monuments of men, fallen to ruin, ask for themselves as well whether you'd believe that *they* decay with years? See we not basalt rocks tumble down river away from high mountains and unable to endure and suffer the strong might of finite age? Surely they would never fall suddenly thus riven away, if for infinite time past they had held out against all the batteries of age without a crash.

Again gaze on this, which about and above holds in its embrace all the earth: if it begets all things out of itself, as some say, and takes them back when they are destroyed, then the whole of it has had a birth and is of a mortal body; for whatever gives increase and food out of itself to other things, must be lessened; and must be replenished, when it takes things back.

Again if there was no birth-time of earth and heaven and they have been from everlasting, why before the Theban war and the destruction of Troy have not other poets as well sung other themes? Whither have so many deeds of men so often passed away, why live they nowhere embodied in lasting records of fame? The truth methinks is that the sum has but a recent date and the nature of the world is new and has but lately had its commencement. Wherefore even now some arts are receiving their last polish, some are even in course of growth: just now many improvements have been made in ships; only yesterday musicians have given birth to tuneful melodies; then too this nature or system of things has been discovered lately, and I the very first of all have only now been found able to transfer it into native words. But if haply you believe that before this all things have existed just the same, but that the generations of men have perished by burning heat, or that cities have fallen by some great concussion of the world, or that after constant rains devouring rivers have gone forth over the earth and have whelmed towns, so much the more you must yield and admit that there will be entire destruction too of earth and heaven; for when things were tried by so great distempers and so great dangers, at that time had a more disastrous cause pressed upon them, they would far and wide have gone to destruction and mighty ruin. And in no other way are we proved to be mortals, except because we all alike in turn fall sick of the same diseases which those had whom nature has withdrawn from life.

Again whatever things last for ever, must either, because they are of solid body, repel strokes and not suffer aught to pass into them, sufficient to disunite the closely massed parts within: such are the bodies of matter whose nature we have shown before: or they must be able to endure through all time for this reason, because they are exempt from blows, as void is which remains untouched and suffers not a jot from any stroke; or else because there is no extent of room around, into which things so to say may depart and be broken up: in this way the sum of sums is eternal and there is no place outside into which things may spring asunder, nor are there any bodies which can fall upon them and dissolve them by a powerful blow. But the nature of the world, as I have shown, is neither of solid body, since void is mixed up in things, nor is it again like void, no nor is there lack of bodies that may haply rise up in mass out of the infinite and overthrow this sum of things with furious tornado or bring upon them some other perilous disaster; nor further is the nature of room or the space of deep void wanting, into which the walls of the world may be scattered abroad; or they may be assailed and perish by some other force. Therefore the gate of death is not closed against heaven or sun or earth or the deep waters of the sea, but stands open and looks towards them with huge wide-gaping maw. And therefore also you must admit that these things likewise had a birth; for things which are of mortal body could not for an infinite time back up to the present have been able to set at naught the puissant strength of immeasurable age.

Again since the chiefest members of the world fight so hotly together, fiercely stirred by no hallowed civil warfare, see you not that some limit may be set to their long struggle? Either when the sun and all heat shall have drunk up all the waters and gotten the mastery: this they are ever striving to do, but as yet are unable to accomplish their endeavours: such abundant supplies the rivers furnish, and threaten to turn aggressors and flood all things with a deluge from the deep gulfs of ocean; all in vain, since the winds sweeping over the seas and the ethereal sun decomposing them with his rays do lessen them, and trust to be able to dry all things up before water can attain the end of its endeavour. Such a war do they breathe out with undecided issue, and strive with each other to determine it for mighty ends; though once by the way fire got the upper hand and once, as the story goes, water reigned paramount in the fields. Fire gained the mastery and licked and burnt up many things, when the headstrong might of the horses of the sun dashed from the course and hurried Phaethon through the whole sky and over all lands. But the almighty father, stirred then to fierce wrath, with a sudden thunderstroke dashed Phaethon down from his horses to earth, and the sun meeting him as he fell caught from him the everburning lamp of the world and got in hand the scattered steeds and yoked them shaking all over; then guided them on their proper course and gave fresh life to all things. Thus to wit have the old poets of the Greeks sung; though it is all too widely at variance with true reason. Fire may gain the mastery when more bodies of matter than usual have gathered themselves up out of the infinite; and then its powers decay, vanquished in some way or other, or else things perish burnt up by the torrid air. Water too of yore gathered itself and began to get the mastery, as the story goes, when it whelmed many cities of men; and then when all that force that had gathered itself up out of the infinite, by some means or other was turned aside and withdrew, the rains were stayed and the rivers abated their fury.

But in what ways yon concourse of matter founded earth

and heaven and the deeps of the sea, the courses of the sun and moon, I will next in order describe. For verily not by design did the first-beginnings of things station themselves each in its right place by keen intelligence, nor did they bargain sooth to say what motions each should assume, but because the first-beginnings of things many in number in many ways impelled by blows for infinite ages back and kept in motion by their own weights have been wont to be carried along and to unite in all manner of ways and thoroughly to test every kind of production possible by their mutual combinations, therefore it is that spread abroad through great time after trying unions and motions of every kind they at length meet together in those masses which suddenly brought together become often the rudiments of great things, of earth, sea, and heaven and the race of living things.

At this time then neither could the sun's disc be discerned flying aloft with its abundant light, nor the stars of great ether, nor sea nor heaven, no nor earth nor air, nor could any thing be seen like to our things, but only a strange stormy crisis and medley, gathered together out of first-beginnings of every kind, whose state of discord joining battle disordered their interspaces, passages, connexions, weights, blows, clashings, and motions, because by reason of their unlike forms and varied shapes they could not all remain thus joined together nor fall into mutually harmonious motions. Then next the several parts began to fly asunder and things to be joined like with like and to mark off the world and portion out its members and arrange its mighty parts, that is to say, to separate high heaven from earth, and let the sea spread itself out apart with its unmixed water, and likewise let the fires of ether spread apart pure and unmixed.

For first the several bodies of earth, because they were heavy and closely entangled, met together in the middle and took up all of them the lowest positions; and the more they got entangled and the closer their union, the more they squeezed out those particles which were to make up sea, stars, sun, and moon and the walls of the great world. All these are of smooth and round seeds and of much smaller

elements than the earth. Therefore the fire-laden ether first
burst out from the different parts of the earth through all the
porous openings and lightly bore off with itself many fires;
much in the same way as we often see, so soon as the morning
light of the beaming sun blushes golden over the grass
jewelled with dew, and the pools and the ever-running rivers
exhale a mist, and even as the earth itself is sometimes seen
to smoke; and when all these are gathered together aloft, then
do clouds on high with a now cohering body weave a covering beneath heaven. In this way therefore then the light and
expansive ether with its now cohering body swept round and
arched itself on all sides and expanding widely in all directions
round in this way fenced all other things in with its greedy
grasp. After it followed the rudiments of sun and moon, whose
spheres turn round in air midway between earth and ether:
these neither earth has taken unto itself nor greatest ether,
because they were neither heavy enough to sink and settle
down nor light enough to glide along the uppermost borders;
they yet however are so placed between the two as to wheel
along their life-like bodies and still to be parts of the whole
world; just as in us some members may be at rest, while
others at the same time are in motion. These things then being
withdrawn, the earth in those parts where the vast azure level
of ocean now spreads, in a moment sank in and drenched with
salt flood the hollows. At every day the more the heats of
ether round and the rays of the sun on all sides compressed
the earth into a close mass by oft-repeated blows on all its
outer edges, so that thus buffeted it was condensed and drawn
together about its centre, ever the more did the salt sweat
squeezed out of its body increase by its oozings the sea and
floating fields, and ever the more did those many bodies of
heat and air escape and fly abroad and condense far away from
earth the high glittering quarters of heaven. The plains sank
down, the high hills grew in elevation; for the rocks could not
settle down nor all the parts sink to one uniform level.

Thus then the ponderous mass of earth was formed with
close-cohering body and all the slime of the world so to speak
slid down by its weight to the lowest point and settled at the

bottom like dregs. Then the sea, then the air, then the fire-laden ether itself, all are left unmixed with their clear bodies; and some are lighter than others, and clearest and lightest of all ether floats upon the airy currents, and blends not its clear body with the troubled airs; it suffers all these things below to be upset with furious hurricanes, suffer them to be troubled by wayward storms; while it carries along its own fires gliding with a changeless onward sweep. For that ether may stream on gently and with one uniform effort the Pontos shows, a sea which streams with a changeless current, ever preserving one uniform gliding course.

Let us now sing what causes the motions of the stars. In the first place, if the great sphere of heaven revolves, we must say that an air presses on the pole at each end and confines it on the outside and closes it in at both ends; and then that a third air streams above and moves in the same direction in which roll on as they shine the stars of the eternal world; or else that this third air streams below in order to carry up the sphere in the contrary direction; just as we see rivers turn wheels and water-scoops. It is likewise quite possible too that all the heaven remains at rest, while at the same time the glittering signs are carried on; either because rapid heats of ether are shut in and whirl round while seeking a way out and roll their fires in all directions through heaven's Summanian quarters; or else an air streaming from some part from another source outside drives and whirls the fires; or else they may glide on of themselves going withersoever the food of each calls and invites them, feeding their flamy bodies everywhere throughout heaven. For which of these causes is in operation in this world, it is not easy to affirm for certain; but what can be and is done throughout the universe in various worlds formed on various plans, this I teach, and I go on to set forth several causes which may exist throughout the universe for the motions of stars; one of which however must in this world also be the cause that imparts lively motion to the signs; but to dictate which of them it is, is by no means the duty of the man who advances step by step.

And in order that the earth may rest in the middle of the

world, it is proper that its weight should gradually pass away and be lessened, and that it should have another nature underneath it conjoined from the beginning of its existence and formed into one being with the airy portions of the world in which it is embodied and lives. For this reason it is no burden and does not weigh down the air; just as his limbs are of no weight to a man nor is his head a burden to his neck, nor do we feel that the whole weight of the body rests on the feet; but whatever weights come from without and are laid upon us, hurt us though they are often very much smaller: of such great moment it is what function each thing has to perform. Thus then the earth is not an alien body suddenly brought in and forced from some other quarter on air alien to it, but was conceived together with it at the first birth of the world and is a fixed portion of that world, just as our limbs are seen to be to us. Again the earth when suddenly shaken by loud thunder shakes by its motion all the things which are above it; and this it could in no wise do, unless it had been fast bound with the airy portions of the world and with heaven. For the earth and they cohere with one another by common roots, conjoined and formed into a single being from the beginning of their existence. See you not too that great as is the weight of our body, the force of the soul, though of the extremest fineness, supports it, because it is so closely conjoined and formed into a single being with it? Then too what is able to lift the body with a nimble bound save the force of the mind which guides the limbs? Now do you see what power a subtle nature may have, when it is conjoined with a heavy body, as the air is conjoined with the earth and the force of the mind with us?

Again the disc of the sun cannot be much larger nor its body of heat much smaller, than they appear to be to our senses. For from whatever distances fires can reach us with their light and breathe on our limbs burning heat, those distances take away nothing by such spaces between from the body of the flames, the fire is not in the least narrowed in appearance. Therefore since the heat of the sun and the light which it sheds reach our senses and stroke the proper places, the form too and size of the sun must be seen from this earth in their real dimensions, so that you may not add anything whatever more or less. And whether the moon as it is borne on illuminates places with a borrowed light, or emits its own light from its own body, whatever that is, the form with which it is thus borne on is not at all larger than the one which it presents to our eyes seems to us to be. For all things which we see at a great distance through much air, look dimmed in appearance before their size is diminished. Therefore since the moon presents a bright aspect and well-defined form, it must be seen on high by us from this earth precisely such as it is in the outline which defines it, and of the size it actually is. Lastly in the case of all those fires of ether which you observe from this earth—since in the case of fires which we see here on earth, so long as their flickering is distinct, so long as their heat is perceived, their size is seen sometimes to change to a very very small extent either way, according to the distance at which they are—you may infer that the fires of ether may be smaller than they look in an extremely minute degree, or larger by a very small and insignificant fraction.

This likewise need not excite wonder, how it is that so small a body as yon sun can emit so great a light, enough to flood completely seas and all lands and heaven and to steep all things in its burning heat. It well may be that a single spring for the whole world may open up from this spot and gush out in plenteous stream and shoot forth light, because elements of heat meet together from all sides out of the whole world in such manner and the mass of them thrown together streams to a point in such manner, that this heat wells forth from a single source. See you not too what a breadth of meadowland a small spring of water sometimes floods, streaming out over the fields? It is likewise possible that heat from the sun's flame though not at all great may infect the whole air with fervent fires, if haply the air is in a suitable and susceptible state, so that it can be kindled when struck by small bodies of heat; thus we see sometimes a general conflagration from a single spark catch fields of corn and stubble. Perhaps too the sun as he shines aloft with rosy lamp has round about him much fire with heats that are not visible, and

thus the fire may be marked by no radiance, so that fraught
with heat it increases to such a degree the stroke of the rays.

Nor with regard to the sun is there one single explanation,
certain and manifest, of the way in which he passes from his
summer positions to the midwinter turning-point of Capricorn and then coming back from thence bends his course to
the solstitial goal of Cancer, and how the moon is seen once
a month to pass over that space, in traversing which the sun
spends the period of a year. No single plain cause, I say, has
been assigned for these things. It seems highly probable that
that may be the truth which the revered judgment of the
worthy man Democritus maintains: the nearer the different
constellations are to the earth, the less they can be carried
along with the whirl of heaven; for the velocity of its force,
he says, passes away and the intensity diminishes in the lower
parts, and therefore the sun is gradually left behind with the
rearward signs, because he is much lower than the burning
signs. And the moon more than the sun: the lower her path
is and the more distant she is from heaven and the nearer she
approaches to earth, the less she can keep pace with the signs.
For the fainter the whirl is in which she is borne along, being
as she is lower than the sun, so much the more all the signs
around overtake and pass her. Therefore it is that she appears
to come back to every sign more quickly, because the signs go
more quickly back to her. It is quite possible too that from
quarters of the world crossing the sun's path two airs may
stream each in its turn at a fixed time; one of which may force
the sun away from the summer signs so far as his midwinter
turning-point and freezing cold, and the other may force him
back from the freezing shades of cold as far as the heat-laden
quarters and burning signs. And in like manner we must suppose that the moon, and the stars which make revolutions of
great years in great orbits may pass by means of airs from
opposite quarters in turn. See you not too that clouds from
contrary winds pass in contrary directions, the upper in a
contrary way to the lower? Why may not yon stars just as
well be borne on through their great orbits in ether by currents contrary one to the other?

But night buries the earth in thick darkness, either when the sun after his long course has struck upon the utmost parts of heaven and now exhausted has blown forth all his fires shaken by their journey and weakened by passing through much air: or else because the same force which has carried on his orb above the earth, compels him to change his course and pass below the earth.

At a fixed time too Matuta spreads rosy morning over the borders of ether and opens up their light, either because the same sun, coming back below the earth, seizes heaven before his time trying to kindle it with his rays; or because fires meet together and many seeds of heat are accustomed to stream together at a fixed time, which cause new sunlight to be born every day. Thus they tell that from the high mountains of Ida scattered fires are seen at day-break, that these then unite as it were into a single ball and make up an orb. And herein it ought to cause no surprise that these seeds of fire stream together at a time so surely fixed and reproduce the radiance of the sun. For we see many occurrences which take place at a fixed time in all things. At a fixed time trees blossom and at a fixed time shed their blossoms; and at a time no less surely fixed age bids the teeth be shed and the boy put on the soft dress of puberty and let a soft beard fall down equally from each cheek. Lastly lightnings, snow, rains, clouds, and winds take place at not very irregular seasons of year. For where causes from their very first-beginnings have been in this way and things have thus fallen out from the first birth of the world, in due sequence too they now come round after a fixed order.

Likewise days may lengthen and nights wane, and days shorten when the nights receive increase, either because the same sun running his course below the earth and above in curves of unlike length parts the borders of ether and divides his orbit into unequal halves; and as he comes round adds on in the opposite half just as much as he has subtracted from the other of the two halves, until he has arrived at that sign of heaven, where the node of the year makes the shades of night of the same length as the daylight. For when the sun's course lies midway between the blast of the north and of the south, heaven keeps his two goals apart at distances now rendered exactly equal on account of the position of the whole starry circle, in gliding through which the sun takes up the period of a year, lighting with slanting rays earth and heaven; as is clearly shown by the plans of those who have mapped out all the quarters of heaven as they are set off with their array of signs. Or else because the air is denser in certain parts, therefore the quivering beam of fire is retarded below the earth and cannot easily pass through and force its way out to its place of rising: for this reason in wintertime nights linger long, ere the beamy badge of day arrive. Or else, because in the way just mentioned at alternate parts of the year fires are accustomed to stream together more slowly and more quickly, which cause the sun to rise in a certain point, therefore it is that those appear to speak the truth who suppose a fresh sun to be born every day.

The moon may shine because struck by the sun's rays, and turn that light every day more and more directly towards our sight, in proportion as she recedes from the sun's orb, until just opposite to him she has shone out with full light and at her rising as she soars aloft has beheld his setting; and then by slow steps reversing as it were her course she must in the same way hide her light, the nearer and nearer she now glides to the sun from a different quarter through the circle of the signs; according to the theory of those who suppose the moon to be like a ball and to hold on her course under the sun. She may also very possibly revolve with her own light and display various phases of brightness; for there may well be another body which is carried on and glides in her company getting before her path and obstructing her in all manner of ways and yet cannot be seen, because it glides on without light. She may also revolve, like it may be to a spherical ball steeped over one half in shining light, and as she rolls round this sphere she may present changing phases, until she has turned that half which is illuminated full towards our sight and open eyes; then by slow steps she whirls back and withdraws the light-fraught half of the spherical ball; as the Babylonian science of the Chaldees refuting the system of the astronomers essays to prove in opposition to them; just as though that which each party fights for might not be equally true, or there were any reason why you should venture to embrace the one theory less than the other. Again, why a new moon should not be born every day after a regular succession of forms and regular phases, and each day the one which is born perish and another be produced in its room and stead, it is not easy to teach by reasoning or prove by words, since so many things can be born in such a regular succession. Spring and Venus go their way, and the winged harbinger of Venus steps on before; and close on Zephyr's footprints mother Flora strews all the way before them and covers it over with the choicest colours and odours. Next in order follows parching heat, and in its company dusty Ceres and the Etesian blasts of the north winds. Next autumn advances and Euhius Euan steps on together. Then other seasons and winds follow, loud-roaring Volturnus and the southwind stored with lightning. At last midwinter brings with it snows and gives back benumbing cold; after it follows winter with teeth chattering with cold. It is therefore the less strange that a moon is begotten at a fixed time and at a fixed time is destroyed again, since many things may take place at a time so surely fixed.

The eclipses of the sun likewise and the obscurations of the moon you may suppose to take place from many different causes. For why should the moon be able to shut the earth out from the sun's light and on the earthward side put in his way her high-exalted head, placing her dark orb before his burning rays; and yet at the same time it be thought that another body gliding on ever without light cannot do the same? Why too should not the sun be able, quite exhausted, to lose his fires at a fixed time, and again reproduce his light when in his journey through the air he has passed by spots fatal to his flames, which cause his fires to be quenched and to perish? And why should the earth be able in turn to rob the moon of light and moreover herself to keep the sun suppressed, while in her monthly course she glides through the well-defined shadows of the cone; and yet at the same time another body not be able to pass under the moon or glide above the sun's orb, breaking off its rays and the light it sheds forth? Yes and if the moon shines with her own brightness, why should she not be able to grow faint in a certain part of the world, while she is passing through spots hostile to her own light?

And now further since I have explained in what way everything might take place throughout the blue of the great heaven; how we might know what force and cause set in motion the varied courses of the sun and wanderings of the moon; and in what way their light might be intercepted and they be lost to us and spread darkness over the earth little expecting it, when so to speak they close their eye of light and opening it again survey all places shining in bright radiance, I now go back to the infancy of the world and the tender age of the fields of earth and show what first in their early essays of production they resolved to raise into the borders of light and give in charge to the wayward winds.

In the beginning the earth gave forth all kinds of herbage and verdant sheen about the hills and over all the plains; the flowery meadows glittered with the bright green hue, and next in order to the different trees was given a strong and emulous desire of growing up into the air with full unbridled powers. As feathers and hairs and bristles are first born on the limbs of four-footed beasts and the body of the strong of wing, thus the new earth then first put forth grass and bushes, and next gave birth to the races of mortal creatures springing up many in number in many ways after divers fashions. For no living creatures can have dropped from heaven nor can those belonging to the land have come out of the salt pools. It follows that with good reason the earth has gotten the name of mother, since all things have been produced out of the earth. And many living creatures even now spring out of the earth taking form by rains and the heat of the sun. It is therefore the less strange if at that time they sprang up more in number and larger in size, having come to maturity in the freshness of earth and ether. First of all the race of fowls and the various birds would leave their eggs, hatched in the springtime, just as now in summer the cicades leave spontaneously their gossamer coats in quest of a living and life. Then you must know did the earth first give forth races of mortal men. For much heat and moisture would then abound in the fields; and therefore wherever a suitable spot offered, wombs would grow attached to the earth by roots; and when the warmth of the infants, flying the wet and craving the air, had opened these in the fulness of time, nature would turn to that spot the pores of the earth and constrain it to yield from its opened veins a liquid most like to milk, even as now-a-days every woman when she has borne, is filled with sweet milk, because all that current of nutriment streams towards the breasts. To the children the earth would furnish food, the heat raiment, the grass a bed rich in abundance of soft down. Then the fresh youth of the world would give forth neither severe colds nor excessive heats nor gales of great violence; for all things grow and acquire strength in a like proportion.

Wherefore again and again I say the earth with good title has gotten and keeps the name of mother, since she of herself gave birth to mankind and at a time nearly fixed shed forth every beast that ranges wildly over the great mountains, and at the same time the fowls of the air with all their varied shapes. But because she must have some limit set to her bearing, she ceased like a woman worn out by length of days. For time changes the nature of the whole world and all things must pass on from one condition to another, and nothing continues like to itself: all things quit their bounds, all things nature changes and compels to alter. One thing crumbles away and is worn and enfeebled with age, then another comes unto honour and issues out of its state of contempt. In this way then time changes the nature of the whole world and the earth passes out of one condition into another: what once it could, it can bear no more, in order to be able to bear what before it did not bear.

And many monsters too the earth at that time essayed to produce, things coming up with strange face and limbs, the man-woman, a thing between the two and neither the one sex nor the other, widely differing from both; some things deprived of feet, others again destitute of hands, others too proving dumb without mouth, or blind without eyes, and things bound fast by the adhesion of their limbs over all the body, so that they could not do anything nor go anywhere nor avoid the evil nor take what their needs required. Every other monster and portent of this kind she would produce, but all in vain, since nature set a ban on their increase and they could not reach the coveted flower of age nor find food nor be united in marriage. For we see that many conditions must meet together in things in order that they may beget and continue their kinds; first a supply of food, then a way by which the bird-producing seeds throughout the frame may stream from the relaxed limbs; also in order that the woman may be united with the male, the possession of organs whereby they may each interchange mutual joys.

And many races of living things must then have died out and been unable to beget and continue their breed. For in the case of all things which you see breathing the breath of life, either craft or courage or else speed has from the beginning of its existence protected and preserved each particular race. And there are many things which, recommended to us by their useful services, continue to exist consigned to our protection. In the first place the fierce breed of lions and the savage races their courage has protected, foxes their craft and stags their proneness to fight. But light-sleeping dogs with faithful heart in breast and every kind which is born of the seed of beasts of burden and at the same time the woolly flocks and the horned herds are all consigned, Memmius, to the protection of man. For they have ever fled with eagerness from wild beasts and have ensued peace and plenty of food obtained without their own labour, as we give it in requital of their useful services. But those to whom nature has granted none of these qualities, so that they could neither live by their own means nor perform for us any useful service in return for which we should suffer their kind to feed and be safe under our protection, those, you are to know, would lie exposed as a prey and booty of others, hampered all in their own death-bringing shackles, until nature brought that kind to utter destruction.

But Centaurs never have existed, and at no time can there exist things of twofold nature and double body formed into one frame out of limbs of alien kinds, such that the faculties and powers of this and that portion cannot be sufficiently like. This however dull of understanding you may learn from what follows. To begin, a horse when three years have gone round is in the prime of his vigour, far different the boy: often even at that age he will call in his sleep for the milk of the breast. Afterwards when in advanced age his lusty strength and limbs now faint with ebbing life fail the horse, then and not till then youth in the flower of age commences for that boy and clothes his cheeks in soft down; that you may not haply believe that out of a man and the burden-carrying seed of horses Centaurs can be formed and have being; or that Scyllas with bodies half those of fishes girdled round with raving dogs can exist, and all other things of the kind, whose limbs we see cannot harmonize together; as they neither come to their flower at the same time nor reach the fulness of their bodily strength nor lose it in advanced old age, nor burn with similar passions nor have compatible manners, nor feel the same things give pleasure throughout their frames. Thus we may see bearded goats often fatten on hemlock which for man is rank poison. Since flame moreover is wont to scorch and burn the tawny bodies of lions just as much as any other kind of flesh and blood existing on earth, how could it be that a single chimera with triple body, in front a lion, behind a dragon, in the middle the goat whose name it bears, could breathe out at the mouth fierce flame from its body? Wherefore also he who fables that in the new time of the earth and the fresh youth of heaven such living creatures could have been begotten, resting upon this one futile term new, may babble out many things in like fashion, may say that rivers then ran with gold over all parts of the earth and that trees were wont to blossom with precious stones, or that man was born with such giant force of frame that he could wade on foot across deep seas and whirl the whole heaven about him with his hands. For the fact that there were many seeds of things in the earth what time it first shed forth living creatures, is yet no proof that there could have been produced beasts of different kinds mixed together, and limbs of different living things formed into a single frame, because the kinds of herbage and corn and joyous trees which even now spring in plenty out of the earth yet cannot be produced with the several sorts plaited into one, but each thing goes on after its own fashion, and all preserve their distinctive differences according to a fixed law of nature.

But the race of man then in the fields was much hardier, as beseemed it to be, since the hard earth had produced it; and built on a groundwork of larger and more solid bones within, knit with powerful sinews throughout the frame of flesh; not lightly to be disabled by heat or cold or strange kinds of food or any malady of body. And during the revolution of many lustres of the sun through heaven they led a life after the roving fashion of wild beasts. No one then was a sturdy guider of the bent plough or knew how to labour the fields with iron or plant in the ground young saplings or lop with pruning-hooks old boughs from the high trees. What the sun and rains had given, what the earth had produced spontaneously, was guerdon sufficient to content their hearts. Among acorn-bearing oaks they would refresh their bodies for the most part; and the arbute-berries which you now see in the winter-time ripen with a bright scarlet hue, the earth would then bear in greatest plenty and of a larger size; and many coarse kinds of food besides the teeming freshness of the world then bare, more than enough for poor wretched men. But rivers and springs invited to slake thirst, even as now a rush of water down from the great hills summons with clear plash far and wide the thirsty races of wild beasts. Then too as they ranged about they would occupy the well-known woodland haunts of the nymphs, out of which they knew that smooth-gliding streams of water with a copious gush bathed the dripping rocks, the dripping rocks, trickling down over the green moss; and in parts welled and bubbled out over the level plain. And as yet they knew not how to apply fire to their purposes or to make use of skins and clothe their body in the spoils of wild beasts, but they would dwell in woods and mountain-caves and forests and shelter in the brushwood their squalid limbs when driven to shun the buffeting of the winds and the rains. And they were unable to look to the general weal and knew not how to make a common use of any customs or laws. Whatever prize fortune threw in his way, each man would bear off, trained at his own discretion to think of himself and live for himself alone. And Venus would join the bodies of lovers in the woods; for each woman was gained over either by mutual desire or the head-strong violence and vehement lust of the man or a bribe of some acorns and arbute-berries or choice pears. And trusting to the marvellous powers of their hands and feet they would pursue the forest-haunting races of wild beasts with showers of stones and club of ponderous weight; and many they would conquer, a few they would avoid in hiding-places; and like to bristly swine just as they were they would throw their savage limbs all naked on the ground, when overtaken by night, covering themselves up with leaves and boughs. Yet never with loud wailings would they call for the daylight and the sun, wandering terror-stricken over the fields in the shadows of night, but silent and buried in sleep they would wait, till the sun with rosy torch carried light into heaven; for ac-customed as they had been from childhood always to see darkness and light begotten time about, never could any wonder come over them, nor any misgiving that never-ending night would cover the earth and the light of the sun be with-drawn for evermore. But what gave them trouble was rather the races of wild beasts which would often render repose fatal to the poor wretches. And driven from their home they would fly from their rocky shelters on the approach of a foaming bear or a strong lion, and in the dead of night they would surrender in terror to their savage guests their sleep-ing-places strewn with leaves.

Nor then much more than now would the races of mortal men leave the sweet light of ebbing life. For then this one or that other one of them would be more likely to be seized, and torn open by their teeth would furnish to the wild beasts a living food, and would fill with his moaning woods and mountains and forests as he looked on his living flesh buried in a living grave. But those whom flight had saved with body eaten into, holding ever after their quivering palms over the noisome sores would summon death with appalling cries, until cruel grippings had rid them of life, forlorn of help, unwitting what wounds wanted. But then a single day gave not over to death many thousands of men marching with banners spread, nor did the stormy waters of the sea dash on the rocks men and ships. At this time the sea would often rise up and rage without aim, without purpose, without result, and just as lightly put off its empty threats; nor could the winning wiles of the calm sea treacherously entice any one to his ruin with laughing waters, when the reckless craft of the skipper had not yet risen into the light. Then too want of food would consign to death their fainting frames, now on the contrary 'tis plenty sinks into ruin. They unwittingly would often pour out poison for themselves; now with nicer skill men give it to their son's wife instead.

Next after they had got themselves huts and skins and fire, and the woman united with the man passed with him into one domicile and the duties of wedlock were learnt by the two, and they saw an offspring born from them, then first mankind began to soften. For fire made their chilled bodies less able now to bear the frost beneath the canopy of heaven, and Venus impaired their strength and children with their caresses soon broke down the haughty temper of parents. Then too neighbours began to join in a league of friendship mutually desiring neither to do nor suffer harm; and asked for indulgence to children and womankind, when with cries and gestures they declared in stammering speech that meet it is for all to have mercy on the weak. And though harmony could not be established without exception, yet a very large portion observed their agreements with good faith, or else the race of man would then have been wholly cut off, nor could breeding have continued their generations to this day.

But nature impelled them to utter the various sounds of the tongue and use struck out the names of things, much in the same way as the inability to speak is seen in its turn to drive children to the use of gestures, when it forces them to point with the finger at the things which are before them. For every one feels how far he can make use of his peculiar powers. Ere the horns of a calf are formed and project from his forehead, he butts with it when angry and pushes out in his rage. Then whelps of panthers and cubs of lions fight with claws and feet and teeth at a time when teeth and claws are hardly yet formed. Again we see every kind of fowl trust to wings and seek from pinions a fluttering succour. Therefore to suppose that some one man at that time apportioned names to things and that men from him learnt their first words, is sheer folly. For why should this particular man be able to denote all things by words and to utter the various sounds of the tongue, and yet at the same time others be supposed not to have been able to do so? Again if others as well as he had not made use of words among themselves, whence was implanted in this man the previous conception of its use and whence was given to him the original faculty, to know and perceive in mind what he wanted to do? Again one man could not constrain and subdue and force many to choose to learn the names of things. It is no easy thing in any way to teach and convince the deaf of what is needful to be done; for they never would suffer nor in any way endure sounds of voice hitherto unheard to continue to be dinned fruitlessly into their ears. Lastly what is there so passing strange in this circumstance, that the race of men whose voice and tongue were in full force, should denote things by different words as different feelings prompted? Since dumb brutes, yes and the races of wild beasts are accustomed to give forth distinct and varied sounds, when they have fear or pain and when joys are rife. This you may learn from facts plain to sense: when the large spongy open lips of Molossian dogs begin to growl enraged and bare their hard teeth, thus drawn back in rage they threaten in a tone far different from that in which they bark outright and fill with sounds all the places round. Again when they essay fondly to lick their whelps with their tongue or when they toss them with their feet and snapping at them make a feint with lightly closing teeth of swallowing though

with gentle forbearance, they caress them with a yelping
sound of a sort greatly different from that which they utter
when, left alone in a house, they bay or when they slink away
howling from blows with a crouching body. Again is not
the neigh too seen to differ, when a young stallion in the
flower of age rages among the mares smitten by the goads of
winged love, and when with wide-stretched nostrils he snorts
out the signal to arms, and when as it chances on any other
occasion he neighs with limbs all shaking? Lastly the race of
fowls and various birds, hawks and ospreys and gulls seeking
their living in the salt water mid the waves of the sea, utter
at a different time noises widely different from those they
make when they are fighting for food and struggling with
their prey. And some of them change together with the
weather their harsh croakings, as the long-lived races of
crows and flocks of rooks when they are said to be calling for
water and rain and sometimes to be summoning winds and
gales. Therefore if different sensations compel creatures,
dumb though they be, to utter different sounds, how much
more natural it is that mortal men in those times should have
been able to denote dissimilar things by many different words!

And lest haply on this head you ask in silent thought this
question, it was lightning that brought fire down on earth for
mortals in the beginning; thence the whole heat of flames is
spread abroad. Thus we see many things shine dyed in heavenly flames, when the stroke from heaven has stored them
with its heat. Ay and without this when a branching tree
sways to and fro and tosses about under the buffeting of the
winds, pressing against the boughs of another tree, fire is
forced out by the power of the violent friction, and sometimes the burning heat of flame flashes out, the boughs and
stems rubbing against each other. Now either of these accidents may have given fire to men. Next the sun taught them
to cook food and soften it with the heat of flame, since they
would see many things grow mellow, when subdued by the
strokes of the rays and by heat throughout the land.

And more and more every day men who excelled in intellect and were of vigorous understanding, would kindly show

them how to exchange their former way of living for new methods. Kings began to build towns and lay out a citadel as a place of strength and of refuge for themselves, and divided cattle and lands and gave to each man in proportion to his personal beauty and strength and intellect; for beauty and vigorous strength were much esteemed. Afterwards wealth was discovered and gold found out, which soon robbed of their honours strong and beautiful alike; for men however valiant and beautiful of person generally follow in the train of the richer man. But were a man to order his life by the rules of true reason, a frugal subsistence joined to a contented mind is for him great riches; for never is there any lack of a little. But men desired to be famous and powerful, in order that their fortunes might rest on a firm foundation and they might be able by their wealth to lead a tranquil life; but in vain, since in their struggle to mount up to the highest dignities they rendered their path one full of danger; and even if they reach it, yet envy like a thunderbolt sometimes strikes and dashes men down from the highest point with ignominy into noisome Tartarus; since the highest summits and those elevated above the level of other things are mostly blasted by envy as by a thunderbolt; so that far better it is to obey in peace and quiet than to wish to rule with power supreme and be the master of kingdoms. Therefore let men wear themselves out to no purpose and sweat drops of blood, as they struggle on along the strait road of ambition, since they gather their knowledge from the mouths of others and follow after things from hearsay rather than the dictates of their own feelings; and this prevails not now nor will prevail by and by any more than it has prevailed before.

Kings therefore being slain the old majesty of thrones and proud sceptres were overthrown and laid in the dust, and the glorious badge of the sovereign head bloodstained beneath the feet of the rabble mourned for its high prerogative; for that is greedily trampled on which before was too much dreaded. It would come then in the end to the lees of uttermost disorder, each man seeking for himself empire and sovereignty. Next a portion of them taught men to elect legal officers, and drew up codes, to induce men to obey the laws. For mankind, tired out with a life of brute force, lay exhausted from its feuds; and therefore the more readily it submitted of its own freewill to laws and stringent codes. For as each one moved by anger took measures to avenge himself with more severity than is now permitted by equitable laws, for this reason men grew sick of a life of brute force. Thence fear of punishment mars the prizes of life; for violence and wrong enclose all who commit them in their meshes and do mostly recoil on him from whom they began; and it is not easy for him who by his deeds trangresses the terms of the public peace to pass a tranquil and a peaceful existence. For though he eludes God and man, yet he cannot but feel a misgiving that his secret can be kept for ever; seeing that many by speaking in their dreams or in the wanderings of disease have often we are told betrayed themselves and have disclosed their hidden deeds of evil and their sins.

And now what cause has spread over great nations the worship of the divinities of the gods and filled towns with altars and led to the performance of stated sacred rites, rites now in fashion on solemn occasions and in solemn places, from which even now is implanted in mortals a shuddering awe which raises new temples of the gods over the whole earth and prompts men to crowd them on festive days, all this it is not so difficult to explain in words. Even then in sooth the races of mortal men would see in waking mind glorious forms, would see them in sleep of yet more marvellous size of body. To these then they would attribute sense, because they seemed to move their limbs and to utter lofty words suitable to their glorious aspect and surpassing powers. And they would give them life everlasting, because their face would ever appear before them and their form abide; yes and yet without all this, because they would not believe that beings possessed of such powers could lightly be overcome by any force. And they would believe them to be preeminent in bliss, because none of them was ever troubled with the fear of death, and because at the same time in sleep they would see them perform many miracles, yet feel on their part no fatigue from the effort. Again they would see the system of heaven and the different seasons of the years come round in regular succession, and could not find out by what causes this was done; therefore they would seek a refuge in handing over all things to the gods and supposing all things to be guided by their nod. And they placed in heaven the abodes and realms of the gods, because night and moon are seen to roll through heaven, moon, day, and night and night's austere constellations and night-wandering meteors of the sky and flying bodies of flame, clouds, sun, rains, snow, winds, light-nings, hail, and rapid rumblings and loud threatful thunder-claps.

O hapless race of men, when that they charged the gods with such acts and coupled with them bitter wrath! What groanings did they then beget for themselves, what wounds for us, what tears for our children's children! No act is it of piety to be often seen with veiled head to turn to a stone and approach every altar and fall prostrate on the ground and spread out the palms before the statues of the gods and sprinkle the altars with much blood of beasts and link vow on to vow, but rather to be able to look on all things with a mind at peace. For when we turn our gaze on the heavenly quarters of the great upper world and ether fast above the glittering stars, and direct our thoughts to the courses of the sun and moon, then into our breasts burdened with other ills that fear as well begins to exalt its reawakened head, the fear that we may haply find the power of the gods to be unlimited, able to wheel the bright stars in their varied motion; for lack of power to solve the question troubles the mind with doubts, whether there was ever a birthtime of the world, and whether likewise there is to be any end; how far the walls of the world can endure this strain of restless motion; or whether gifted by the grace of the gods with an everlasting existence they may glide on through a never-ending tract of time and defy the strong powers of immeasurable ages. Again who is there whose mind does not shrink into itself with fear of the gods, whose limbs do not cower in terror, when the parched earth rocks with the appalling thunderstroke and rattlings run through the great heaven? Do not peoples and nations quake, and proud monarchs shrink into themselves smitten with fear of the gods, lest for any foul transgression or over-weening word the heavy time of reckoning has arrived at its fulness? When too the utmost fury of the headstrong wind passes over the sea and sweeps over its waters the commander of a fleet together with his mighty legions and elephants, does he not draw near with vows to seek the mercy of the gods and ask in prayer with fear and trembling a lull in the winds and propitious gales; but all in vain, since often caught up in the furious hurricane he is borne none the less to the shoals of death? so constantly does some hidden power trample on human grandeur and is seen to tread under its heel and make sport for itself of the renowned rods and cruel axes. Again when the whole earth rocks under their feet and towns tumble with the shock or doubtfully threaten to fall, what wonder that mortal men abase themselves and make over to the gods in things here on earth high prerogatives and marvellous powers, sufficient to govern all things?

To proceed, copper and gold and iron were discovered and at the same time weighty silver and the substance of lead, when fire with its heat had burnt up vast forests on the great hills, either by a discharge of heaven's lightning, or else because men waging with one another a forest-war had carried fire among the enemy in order to strike terror, or because drawn on by the goodness of the soil they would wish to clear rich fields and bring the country into pasture, or else to destroy wild beasts and enrich themselves with the booty; for hunting with the pitfall and with fire came into use before the practice of enclosing the lawn with toils and stirring it with dogs. Whatever the fact is, from whatever cause the heat of flame had swallowed up the forests with a frightful crackling from their very roots and had thoroughly baked the earth with fire, there would run from the boiling veins and collect into the hollows of the ground a stream of silver and gold, as well as of copper and lead. And when they saw these afterwards cool into lumps and glitter on the earth with a brilliant gleam, they would lift them up attracted by the bright and polished lustre, and they would see them to be moulded in a shape the same as the outline of the cavities in which each lay. Then it would strike them that these might be melted by heat and cast in any form or shape soever, and might by hammering out be brought to tapering points of any degree of sharpness and fineness, so as to furnish them with tools and enable them to cut the forests and hew timber and plane smooth the planks, and also to drill and pierce and bore. And they would set about these works just as much with silver and gold at first as with the overpowering strength of stout copper, but in vain, since their force would fail and give way and not be able like copper to stand the severe strain. At that time copper was in higher esteem and gold would lie neglected on account of its uselessness, with its dull blunted edge: now copper lies neglected, gold has mounted up to the highest place of honour. Thus time as it goes round changes the seasons of things. That which was in esteem, falls at length into utter disrepute; and then another thing mounts up and issues out of its degraded state and every day is more and more coveted and blossoms forth high in honour when discovered and is in marvellous repute with men.

And now, Memmius, it is easy for you to find out by yourself in what way the nature of iron was discovered. Arms of old were hands, nails, and teeth and stones and boughs broken off from the forests, and flame and fire, as soon as they had become known. Afterwards the force of iron and copper was discovered; and the use of copper was known before that of iron, as its nature is easier to work and it is found in greater quantity. With copper they would labour the soil of the earth, with copper stir up the billows of war and deal about wide-gaping wounds and seize cattle and lands; for every thing defenceless and unarmed would readily yield to them with arms in hand. Then by slow steps the sword of iron gained ground and the make of the copper sickle became a byword; and with iron they began to plough through the earth's soil, and the struggles of wavering war were rendered equal. And the custom of mounting in arms on the back of a horse and guiding him with reins and showing prowess with the right hand is older than that of tempting the risks of war in a two-horsed chariot; and yoking a pair of horses is older than yoking four or mounting in arms scythed chariots. Next the Poeni taught the lucan kine with towered body, hideous of aspect, with snake-like hand, to endure the wounds of war and to disorder the mighty ranks of Mars. Thus sad discord begat one thing after another, to affright nations of men under arms, and every day made some addition to the terrors of war.

They made trial of bulls too in the service of war and essayed to send savage boars against the enemy. And some sent before them valorous lions with armed trainers and courageous keepers to guide them and to hold them in chains; but in vain, since heated with promiscuous slaughter they would disorder in their rage the troops without distinction, shaking all about the frightful crests upon their heads; and the horsemen were not able to calm the breasts of the horses scared by the roaring and turn them with the bridle upon the enemy. The lionesses with a spring would throw their enraged bodies on all sides and would attack in the face those who met them, and others off their guard they would tear down from behind and twining round them would bring them to the ground overpowered by the wound, fastening on them with firm bite and with hooked claws. The bulls would toss their own friends and trample them under foot, and gore with their horns the flanks and bellies of the horses underneath and turn up the earth with threatening front. The boars too would rend their friends with powerful tusks, in their rage dyeing with their blood the weapons broken in them, ay dyeing with their blood the weapons broken in their own bodies; and would put to promiscuous rout horse and foot; for the tame beasts would try to avoid by shying to the side the cruel push of the tusk, or would rear up and paw the winds, all in vain, since you might see them tumble down with their tendons severed and strew the ground in their heavy fall. Those whom they believed before to have been sufficiently broken in at home, they would see lash themselves into fury in the heat of action from wounds and shouting, flight, panic, and uproar; and they could not rally any portion of them; for all the different kinds of wild beasts would fly all abroad; just as now the lucan kine when cruelly mangled by the steel fly often all abroad, after inflicting on their friends many cruel sufferings. But men chose thus to act not so much in any hope of victory, as from a wish to give the enemy something to rue at the cost of their own lives, when they mistrusted their numbers and were in want of arms.

A garment tied on the body was in use before a dress of woven stuff. Woven stuff comes after iron, because iron is needed for weaving a web; and in no other way can such finely polished things be made, as heddles and spindles, shuttles and ringing yarn-beams. And nature impelled men to work up the wool before womankind: for the male sex in general far excels the other in skill and is much more ingenious; until the rugged countrymen so upbraided them with it, that they were glad to give it over into the hands of the women and take their share in supporting hard toil, and in such hard work hardened body and hands.

But nature parent of things was herself the first model of sowing and first gave rise to grafting, since berries and acorns dropping from the trees would put forth in due season swarms of young shoots underneath; and hence also came the fashion of inserting grafts in their stocks and planting in the ground young saplings over the fields. Next they would try another and yet another kind of tillage for their loved piece of land and would see the earth better the wild fruits through genial fostering and kindly cultivation. And they would force the forests to recede every day higher and higher up the hillside and yield the ground below to tilth, in order to have on the uplands and plains meadows, tanks, runnels, corn-fields, and glad vineyards, and allow a grey-green strip of olives to run between and mark the divisions, spreading itself over hillocks and valleys and plains; just as you now see richly dight with varied beauty all the ground which they lay out and plant with rows of sweet fruit-trees and enclose all round with plantations of other goodly trees.

But imitating with the mouth the clear notes of birds was

in use long before men were able to sing in tune smooth-
running verses and give pleasure to the ear. And the whistlings
of the zephyr through the hollows of reeds first taught peas-
ants to blow into hollow stalks. Then step by step they learned
sweet plaintive ditties, which the pipe pours forth pressed by
the fingers of the players, heard through pathless woods and
forests and lawns, through the unfrequented haunts of shep-
herds and abodes of unearthly calm. These things would
soothe and gratify their minds when sated with food; for
then all things of this kind are welcome. Often therefore
stretched in groups on the soft grass beside a stream of water
under the boughs of a high tree at no great cost they would
pleasantly refresh their bodies, above all when the weather
smiled and the seasons of the year painted the green grass
with flowers. Then went round the jest, the tale, the peals of
merry laughter; for the peasant muse was then in its glory;
then frolick mirth would prompt to entwine head and shoulders with garlands plaited with flowers and leaves, and to
advance in the dance out of step and move the limbs clumsily
and with clumsy foot beat mother earth; which would occasion smiles and peals of merry laughter, because all these
things then from their greater novelty and strangeness were
in high repute. And the wakeful found a solace for want of
sleep in this, in drawing out a variety of notes and going
through tunes and running over the reeds with curving lip;
whence even at the present day watchmen observe these traditions and have lately learned to keep the proper tune; and
yet for all this receive not a jot more of enjoyment, than
erst the rugged race of sons of earth received. For that which
we have in our hands, if we have known before nothing pleas-
anter, pleases above all and is thought to be the best; and as a
rule the later discovery of something better spoils the taste
for the former things and changes the feelings in regard to
all that has gone before. Thus began distaste for the acorn,
thus were abandoned those sleeping-places strewn with grass
and enriched with leaves. The dress too of wild beasts' skin
fell into neglect; though I can fancy that in those days it was
found to arouse such jealousy that he who first wore it met

his death by an ambuscade, and after all it was torn in pieces among them and drenched in blood was utterly destroyed and could not be turned to any use. In those times therefore skins, now gold and purple plague men's lives with cares and wear them out with war. And in this methinks the greater blame rests with us; for cold would torture the naked sons of earth without their skins; but us it harms not in the least to do without a robe of purple, spangled with gold and large figures, if only we have a dress of the people to protect us. Mankind therefore ever toils vainly and to no purpose and wastes life in groundless cares, because sure enough they have not learnt what is the true end of getting and up to what point genuine pleasure goes on increasing: this by slow degrees has carried life out into the deep sea and stirred up from their lowest depths the mighty billows of war.

But those watchful guardians, sun and moon, traversing with their light all round the great revolving sphere of heaven taught men that the seasons of the year came round and that the system was carried on after a fixed plan and fixed order.

Already they would pass their life fenced about with strong towers, and the land, portioned out and marked off by boundaries, be tilled; the sea would be filled with ships scudding under sail; towns have auxiliaries and allies as stipulated by treaty, when poets began to consign the deeds of men to verse; and letters had not been invented long before. For this reason our age cannot look back to what has gone before, save where reason points out any traces.

Ships and tillage, walls, laws, arms, roads, dress and all such like things, all the prizes, all the elegancies too of life without exception, poems, pictures and the chiselling of fine-wrought statues, all these things practiced together with the acquired knowledge of the untiring mind taught men by slow degrees as they advanced on the way step by step. Thus time by degrees brings each several thing forth before men's eyes and reason raises it up into the borders of light; for things must be brought to light one after the other and in due order in the different arts, until these have reached their highest point of development.

Nicholas Copernicus

ON THE REVOLUTIONS OF

THE CELESTIAL SPHERES

Nicholas Copernicus
[1473–1543]

Modern astronomy rests upon the foundation of the Copernican system. The Polish physician who devoted himself to the
treatment of the poor and whose learning in canon law made
him one of the foremost authorities of his land dedicated a
major portion of his life to the study of mathematics and astronomy. Copernicus succeeded in proving, against all previous misconceptions, that the sun is the center of a great
system, with the earth, one of its planets, rotating on its axis
around it. His pioneer work, *On the Revolution of the Celestial Spheres*, was completed in 1540, but the first printed
copies could not be made ready until the author was on his
deathbed. The passage here given is from Book One and sets
forth the main aspects of Copernicus's heliocentric theories.

ON THE REVOLUTIONS OF
THE CELESTIAL SPHERES

NICHOLAS COPERNICUS

Among the many and varied literary and artistic studies upon which the natural talent of man is nourished, I think that those above all should be embraced and pursued with the greatest zeal which have to do with things that are very beautiful and very worthy of knowledge. Such studies are those which deal with the godlike circular movements of the world, the course of the stars, their magnitudes, distances, risings and settings, and the causes of the other celestial phenomena; and which finally explicate the whole form. For what could be more beautiful than the heavens which contain all beautiful things? Their very names make this clear: *Caelum* (heavens) by naming that which is beautifully carved; and *Mundus* (world) purity and elegance. Many philosophers have called the world a visible god on account of its extraordinary excellence. So if the worth of the arts were measured by the subject-matter with which they deal, this art—which some call astronomy, others astrology, and many of the ancients the consummation of mathematics—would be by far the most outstanding. This art which is as it were the head of all the arts and the one most worthy of a free man has nearly all the other branches of mathematics to support it. Arithmetic, geometry, optics, geodesy, mechanics, and whatever others, all assist it. And since a property of all good arts is to draw the mind of man away from vice and direct it to better things, these arts can do that more plentifully on account of the unbelievable pleasure of mind which they furnish. For who, after applying himself to things which he sees established in the best order and directed by divine ruling would not through contemplation of them and through a certain habituation be awakened to that which is best and would not admire the artificer of all things, in whom is all happiness and every good? For the divine psalmist surely did not say gratuitously that he took pleasure in the workings of God and rejoiced in the works of his hands, unless by means of these things as by some sort of vehicle we are transported to the contemplation of the highest good?

Now as regards the utility and ornament which they confer upon a commonwealth—to pass over the innumerable advantages they give to private citizens—Plato calls our attention to the right things, for in the seventh book of the *Laws* he says that this study should be pursued especially in order that through it the divisions of time into days, months, and years and the determination of solemnities and sacrifices should keep the state alive and watchful; and he says that if anyone denies that this study is necessary for a man who is going to take up any of the highest branches of learning, then such a person is thinking foolishly; and he thinks that it is impossible for anyone to become godlike or be called so who has no necessary knowledge of the sun, moon, and the other stars.

However, this more divine than human science, which inquires into the highest things, is not lacking in difficulties. And in particular we see that as regards its principles and postulates, which the Greeks call hypotheses, many of those who undertook to deal with them were not in accord and hence did not support themselves with the same reasons. In addition, the courses of the planets and the revolution of the stars cannot be determined by exact calculations and reduced to perfect knowledge except through the passage of time and with the help of many prior observations, transmitted so to speak by hand to posterity. For even if Claud Ptolemy of

Alexandria, who stands far in front of all the others on account of his admirable care and industry, with the help of more than forty years of observations brought this art to such a high point that there seemed to be nothing left which he had not touched upon; nevertheless we see that very many things are not in accord with the movements which should follow from his doctrine but rather with movements which were discovered later and were unknown to him. Whence even Plutarch in speaking of the revolving solar year says, "So far the movement of the stars has overcome the ingenuity of the mathematicians." Now to take the year itself as my example, I believe it is well known how many different opinions there are about it, so that many people have given up hope of making an exact determination of it. Similarly, in the case of the other stars I shall try,—with the help of God, without whom we can do nothing—to make a more detailed inquiry concerning them since the greater the interval of time between us and the founding fathers of this art—whose discoveries we can compare with the new ones made by us—the more means we have of supporting our own theory. Furthermore I confess that I shall expound many things differently from my predecessors,—although with their aid, for it was they who first opened the road of inquiry into these things.

The World Is Spherical

In the beginning we should remark that the world is like a globe; whether because this form is the most perfect of all, as it is an integral whole and needs no joints; or because it is the figure having the greatest volume and so would be especially suitable for comprehending and conserving all things; or even because the separate parts of the world, i.e., the sun, moon, and stars are seen under such a form; or because all things seek to be delimited by such a form, as is

apparent in the case of drops of water and other liquid
bodies, when they become delimited through themselves.
And so no one would hesitate to say that this form belongs
to the heavenly bodies.

The Earth Is Spherical Too

The earth is like a globe too, since on every side it rests upon
its center. But that it is a perfect sphere is not seen right
away on account of the great height of its mountains and the
lowness of its vallies, though they modify its universal round-
ness to only a very small extent. That is made clear in this
way. For when people journey northward from any region,
the northern vertex of the axis of daily revolution gradually
moves overhead, and the other moves downward to the same
extent; and many stars situated in the north do not seem to
set and many in the south do not seem to rise any more. So
Italy does not see Canopus, which is visible in Egypt. And
Italy sees the last star of Fluvius which is not visible in this
region situated in a more frigid zone. Conversely for people
who travel southward, the second group of stars become
higher in the sky; while others become lower, which to us
seem high up. Moreover, the inclinations of the poles have
everywhere the same ratio with the measured spaces of the
earth, and that happens in no other figure except the spherical.
Whence it is manifest that the earth itself is contained between the vertices and is therefore a globe. Add to this the
fact that the inhabitants of the East do not perceive the
eclipses of the sun and moon when they occur in the evening;
and the inhabitants of the West, when they occur in the
morning; while of those who live in the middle region—some
see them earlier and some later. The navigators have perceived that the waters too are fixed within this figure: for
example, when land is not visible from the deck of a ship, it
may be seen from the top of the mast, and conversely, if

something shining is attached to the top of the mast, it appears to those remaining on the shore to come down gradually, as the ship moves from land, until finally it disappears, as if setting. Moreover it is admitted that water, which by its nature flows, always seeks lower places—the same way as earth—and does not climb up the shore any farther than the convexity of the shore allows. That is why the land is so much higher where it rises up from the ocean.

How Land and Water Make Up
a Single Globe

And so the ocean encircling the land pours forth its waters everywhere and fills up the deeper hollows with them. Accordingly it was necessary for there to be less water than land, so as not to have the whole earth soaked with water,— since both of them tend toward the same center on account of their weight—and so as to leave some portions of land— such as the islands discernible here and there—for the preservation of living creatures. For what is the continent itself and the *orbis terrarum* except an island which is larger than the rest? We should not listen to certain peripaticians who maintain that there is ten times more water than land, because— according to this conclusion which they accept—in the transmutation of the elements the liquefaction of one part of earth results in ten parts of water. And they say that land has emerged for a certain distance because, having hollow spaces inside, it does not balance everywhere with respect to weight and so the center of gravity is different from the center of magnitude. But they fall into error through ignorance of geometry; for they do not know that there cannot be seven times more water than land and some part of the land still remain dry, unless the land abandon its center of gravity and give place to the waters as being heavier. For spheres are to

one another in the triplicate ratio of their diameters. If therefore there were seven parts of water and one part of land
the diameter of the land could not be greater than the distance
from the center to the circumference of the waters. So it is
even less possible that the water should be ten times greater.
It can be seen that there is no difference between the centers
of magnitude and of gravity of the earth from the fact that
the convexity of the land spreading out from the ocean does
not swell continuously, for in that case it would have re-
pulsed the seawaters completely and would not in any way
have allowed interior seas and huge gulfs to break through.
Moreover, from the seashore outward the depth of the abyss
would not stop increasing, and so no island or reef or any
spot of land would be met with by people voyaging out very
far. Now it is well known that there is not quite the distance
of two miles—at practically the center of the *orbis terrarum*
—between the Egyptian and the Red Sea. And on the contrary Ptolemy in his *Cosmography* extends inhabited lands as
far as the median circle, and he leaves that part of the earth
as unknown, where the moderns have added Cathay and
other vast regions as far as 60° longitude, so that inhabited
land extends in longitude farther than the rest of the ocean
does. And if you add to these the islands discovered in our
time under the princes of Spain and Portugal and especially
America—named after the ship's captain who discovered her
—which they consider a second *orbis terrarum* on account of
her sofar unmeasured extent—besides many other islands
heretofore unknown, we would not be greatly surprised if
there were antipodes or antichthones. For reasons of geometry
compel us to believe that America is situated diametrically
opposite to the India of the Ganges. And from that I think
it is manifest that the land and the water rest upon one center
of gravity; that this is the same as the center of magnitude of
the land, since land is the heavier; that parts of land which
are as it were yawning are filled with water; and that accordingly there is little water in comparison with the land, even
if more of the surface appears to be covered by water. For
it is necessary that the land and the surrounding waters have

the figure which the shadow of the earth casts, for at the time of an eclipse it projects on the moon the circumference of a perfect circle. Therefore the earth is not a plane, as Empedocles and Anaximenes opined; or a tympanoid, as Leucippus; or a scaphoid, as Heracleitus; or hollowed out in any other way, as Democritus; or again a cylinder, as Anaximander; and it is not infinite in its lower part, with the sediment deposited at the bottom, as Zenophanes thought; but it is perfectly round, as the philosophers perceived.

The Movement of the Celestial Bodies Is Regular, Circular, and Everlasting—or Else Compounded of Circular Movements

After this we will recall that the movement of the celestial bodies is circular. For the motion of a sphere is to turn in a circle; by this very act expressing its form, in the most simple body, where beginning and end cannot be discovered or distinguished from one another, while it moves through the same parts in itself. But there are many movements on account of the multitude of spheres or orbital circles. The most obvious of all is the daily revolution,—which the Greeks call νυχθύμερον i.e., having the temporal span of a day and a night.

The total world—with the exception of the earth—is supposed to be carried from east to west by this movement. This movement is taken as the common measure of all movements, since we measure even time itself principally by the number of days. Next, we perceive other as it were antagonistic movements, i.e., from west to east, of the sun, moon, and the wandering stars. In this way the sun gives us the year, the moon the months—the most common periods of time; and each of the other five planets makes its circuit. Nevertheless these bodies have movements manifoldly different from the first

movement. First, in that they do not revolve around the
same poles as the first movement but go obliquely through
the ecliptic; next, in that they do not seem to be borne in
their circuit regularly. For the sun and moon are caught moving at times more slowly and at times more quickly. And we
perceive the five wandering stars sometimes even to retro-
grade and to come to a stop between these two movements.
And though the sun always proceeds straight ahead along its
route, they wander in various ways, straying sometimes towards the south, and at other times towards the north—
whence they are called planets. Add to this the fact that
sometimes they are nearer the earth—and are then said to be
in their perigee—and at other times are farther away—and
are said to be in their apogee. We must however confess that
these movements are circular or are composed of many circular movements, in that they maintain these irregularities in
accordance with a constant law and with fixed periodic returns: and that could not take place, if they were not circular.
For it is only the circle which can bring back what is past
and over with: and in this way, for example, the sun by a
movement composed of circular movements brings back to
us the inequality of days and nights and the four seasons of
the year. Many movements are recognized in that movement, since it is impossible that a simple heavenly body
should be moved irregularly by a single sphere. For that
would have to take place either on account of the inconstancy of the motive power—whether by reason of an extrinsic cause or its intrinsic nature—or on account of the
disparity between it and the moved body. But since the mind
shudders at either of these suppositions, and since it is quite
unsuitable to suppose that such a state of affairs exists among
things which are established in the best system, it is agreed
that their regular movements appear to us as irregular,
whether on account of their circles having different poles
or even because the earth is not in the midpoint of the circles
in which they revolve. And so for us watching from the
earth, it happens that the transits of the stars, on account of
being at unequal distances from the earth, appear greater

when they are nearer than when they are farther away, as has been demonstrated in optics; thus in the case of equal arcs of an orbital circle which are seen at different distances there will appear to be unequal movements in equal times. For this reason I think it necessary above all that we should note carefully what the relation of the heavens to the earth is, so as not—when we wish to scrutinize the highest things— to be ignorant of those which are nearest to us and so as not —by the same error—to attribute to the celestial bodies what belongs to the earth.

Does the Earth Have a Circular Movement? And of Its Place

It has been shown that the earth has the form of a globe. I think we must see whether or not a movement follows from its form and what the place of the earth is in the universe. For without doing that it will not be possible to find a sure reason for the celestial phenomena. Although there are so many authorities for saying that the earth rests in the center of the world that people think the contrary supposition is ridiculous and inopinable; if, however, we consider the thing attentively, we will see that the question has not yet been decided and is by no means to be scorned. For every apparent change in place occurs on account of either the movement of the thing seen or of the seer or on account of the unequal movement of both. For the motion of things moved equally in the same respects—I mean that of the thing seen and the seer—is not perceptible. Now it is from the earth that the celestial circuit is beheld and presented to our sight. Therefore if some movement should belong to the earth it will appear, in the parts of the universe which are outside, as the same movement but in the opposite direction, as though the things outside were passing over; and the daily revolution in especial is such a movement. For the daily revolution appears to carry the whole universe along, with the exception of the earth and the things around it. And if you admit that the heavens possess none of this movement but that the earth turns from west to east, you will find—if you make a serious examination—that as regards the apparent rising and setting of the sun, moon, and stars the case is so. And since it is the heavens which contain and embrace all things as the place common to the universe, it will not be clear at once why movement should not be attributed to the contained rather than to the container, to the thing placed rather than to the thing providing the place.

As a matter of fact the Pythagoreans Herakleides and Ekphantus were of this opinion and so was Nicetas the Syracusan in Cicero: they made the earth to revolve at the midpoint of the world. For they believed that the stars set by reason of the interposition of the earth and that with cessation of that they rose again. Now with this assumption there follows other things, and a no lesser difficulty concerning the place of the earth, though it is taken for granted and believed by nearly all that the earth is the midpoint of the world. For if any one denied that the earth is located at the midpoint or center of the world and did not admit that the distance (between the two) was great enough to be compared with (the distance to) the sphere of the fixed stars but was considerable and quite apparent in relation to the spheres of the sun and the planets; and if for that reason he thought that their movements appeared irregular because they were organized around a different center from the center of the earth, he might perhaps be able to give a perfectly sound reason for irregular apparent movement. For the fact that the wandering stars are seen to be sometimes nearer the earth and at other times farther away necessarily argues that the center of the earth is not the center of their circles. It is not yet clear whether the earth draws near to them and moves away or they draw near to the earth and move away.

And so it would not be very surprising if some one attributed some other movement to the earth in addition to the daily revolution. As a matter of fact Philolaus the Pythagorean

—a mathematician of no ordinary ability, whom Plato's biographers say Plato went to Italy for the sake of seeing—is supposed to have held that the earth moved in a circle and wandered in some other movements and was one of the stars.

Many however have believed that they could show by geometrical reasoning that the earth is in the midpoint of the world; that it has the proportionality of a point in relation to the immensity of the heavens, occupies the central position, and for this reason is immovable because, when the universe moves, the center remains unmoved and the things which are closest to the center are moved the most slowly.

On the Immensity of the Heavens in Relation to the Magnitude of the Earth

It can be understood that this great mass which is the earth is not commensurable with the magnitude of the heavens from the fact that the boundary circles—for that is the translation of the Greek ὁρίζοντες—cut the whole celestial sphere into two halves; for that could not take place if the magnitude of the earth in comparison with the heavens or if its distance from the center of the world were considerable. For the circle bisecting a sphere goes through the center of the sphere, and is the greatest circle which it is possible to circumscribe.

Now let the horizon be the circle ABCD and the earth—from where the horizon is seen by us—be E the center of the horizon by which the visible stars are separated from those which are not visible. Now if, with a dioptra or horoscope or level placed at E, the beginning of Cancer is seen to rise at point C; at the same moment the setting of Capricorn will be seen at A. Therefore since AEC is in a straight line with the dioptra, it is clear that this line is a diameter of the ecliptic because the six signs bound a semicircle, whose center

E is the same as that of the horizon. But when the circular movement has taken place and the beginning of Capricorn arises at B, then the setting of Cancer at D will be visible, and BED will be a straight line and a diameter of the ecliptic. But

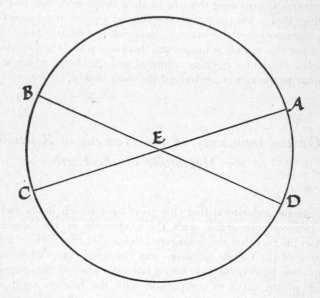

it has already been seen that the line AEC is a diameter of the same circle; therefore the center will be at their common section. So in this way the horizon always bisects the ecliptic, which is a great circle of the sphere. But on a sphere, if a circle bisects one of the great circles, then the circle bisecting is a great circle; therefore the horizon is a great circle; and its center is the same as that of the ecliptic, as far as appearance goes; although nevertheless the line passing through the center of the earth and the line touching to the surface are necessarily different; but on account of their immensity in comparison with the earth they are like parallel lines, which on account of the great distance between the termini appear to be one line, when the space contained between them is in no sensible ratio to their length, as has been shown in optics.

From this argument it is certainly clear enough that the heavens are immense or beyond commensurability in comparison with the earth and present the aspect of an infinite magnitude and that in the judgment of sense-perception the earth is to the heavens as a point to a body and as a finite to an infinite magnitude. But nothing more than that has been shown, and it does not follow that the earth necessarily rests at the midpoint of the world. And we should be even more surprised if such a vast world should wheel completely around during the space of twenty-four hours rather than that its least part, the earth, should. For saying that the center is immobile and that those things which are closest to the center are moved least does not argue that the earth rests at the midpoint of the world. It is no different from saying that the heavens revolve but the poles are at rest and those things which are closest to the poles are moved least. In this way the pole star is seen to move much more slowly than Aquila or Canicula because being very near to the pole it describes a smaller circle. For they are all contained within a single sphere, the movement of which stops at its axis and which does not allow any of its parts to have movements which are equal to one another: and nevertheless the revolution of the whole brings them round in equal times but not over equal spaces. This is the position to which the argument advances that maintains that the earth, as a part of the celestial sphere and therefore sharing in its form and movement, moves very little because very near to its center: therefore the earth will move, as being a body and not a center, and will describe in the same time arcs similar to, but smaller than, the arcs of the celestial circle. It is clearer than daylight how false that is, for there would necessarily always be noon at one place and midnight at another, and so the daily risings and settings could not take place, since the movement of the whole and the part would be one and inseparable. But the ratio between things separated by diversity of nature is so entirely different that those which describe a smaller circle turn more quickly than those which describe a greater circle. In this way Saturn, the highest of the wandering stars, completes its revolution in thirty years, and the moon which is without doubt the closest to the earth completes its circuit in a month, and finally the earth itself will be considered to have a circular movement completed during the space of a day and a night. So this same difficulty concerning the daily revolution returns. And also the question about the place of the earth becomes even less certain on account of what was just said. For that demonstration proves nothing except that the heavens are of an indefinite magnitude with respect to the earth. On the contrary, it is not at all clear how far this immensity stretches out. For, on the contrary, as the monimal and indivisible corpuscles, which are called atoms, when taken in twos or in some small number, do not, since they are not perceptible to sense, compose a visible body, but they can be taken in such a large quantity that there will at last be enough to form a visible magnitude; in the same way as regards the place of the earth, for although it is not at the center of the world, nevertheless the distance is not measurable, particularly in comparison with the sphere of the fixed stars.

Why the Ancients Thought the Earth Was at Rest at the Middle of the World as Its Center

Wherefore for other reasons the ancient philosophers tried to force the earth to remain at rest at the midpoint of the world and as principal cause they put forward heaviness and lightness. For earth is the heaviest element; and all things of any weight are borne towards it and strive to move towards the very center of it.

For since the earth is a globe towards which from every direction heavy things by their own nature are borne along lines making right angles with its surface, the heavy things would fall on one another at the center if they were not held back at the surface: For a straight line making right angles with a plane surface where it touches sphere leads to the center. And those things which are borne toward the center seem to follow along in order to be at rest at the center. All the more then will the earth be at rest at the center and, being the receptacle for falling bodies, will remain immobile because of its weight.

They strive similarly to prove this by reason of movement and its nature. For Aristotle says that the movement of a body which is one and simple is simple and the simple movements are the rectilineal and the circular. And of rectilineal movements, one is upward, and the other is downward. As a consequence every simple movement is either toward the center, i.e., downward, or away from the center, i.e., upward, or around the center, i.e., is circular. It is a property of earth and water only, which are heavy, to be borne downward, i.e., to seek the center: for air and fire, which possess lightness, move upward, i.e., away from the center. It seems fitting to attribute rectilineal movement to the four elements and to give the heavenly bodies a circular movement around the center. So Aristotle. Therefore, said Ptolemy of Alexandria, if the earth moved, even if only by its daily rotation, the contrary of what was said above would necessarily take place. For this movement which would traverse the total circuit of the earth in twenty-four hours would necessarily be very headlong and of an unsurpassable velocity. Now things which are suddenly and violently whirled around are seen to be utterly unfitted for reuniting, and the more unified are seen to become dispersed, unless some constant force constrains them to stick together. And a long time ago, he says, the scattered earth would have passed beyond the heavens, as is certainly ridiculous; and *a fortori* so would all the living creatures and all the other separate masses which could by no means remain unshaken. Moreover, freely falling bodies would not arrive at their destination, and certainly not along the perpendicular line which they assume so quickly. And we would see clouds and other things floating in the air always borne toward the west.

Answer to the Aforesaid Reasons and Their Inadequacy

For these and similar reasons they say that the earth remains at rest at the midpoint of the world and that there is no doubt about this. But if some one opines that the earth moves, he will also say that the movement is natural and not violent. Now things which take place naturally produce effects contrary to those which take place violently. For things which are moved by force or vehemence necessarily get broken up and are unable to subsist for a long time. But things which are caused by nature are in a right condition and are kept in their best organization. Therefore Ptolemy had no reason to fear that the earth and all things on the earth would be scattered in a revolution caused by the efficacy of nature, which is greatly different from that of art or from that which can result from the genius of man. But why didn't he feel anxiety about the world instead, whose movement must necessarily be of greater velocity, the greater the heavens are than the earth? or have the heavens become so immense, because an unspeakably vehement motion has pulled the heavens away from the center, and because the heavens would fall if they came to rest anywhere else?

Surely if this reasoning were tenable, the magnitude of the heavens would extend infinitely. For the farther the movement is borne upward by the vehement force, the greater will be the velocity of the movement, on account of the increasing circumference which must be traversed every twenty-four hours: and conversely, the immensity of the sky would increase with the increase in movement. In this way the velocity would make the magnitude increase infinitely. And in accordance with the axiom of physics that "that which is infinite cannot be traversed or moved in any way," then the heavens will necessarily come to rest.

But they say that beyond the heavens there isn't any body or place or void or anything at all, and accordingly it is not possible for the heavens to move outward: in that case it is rather surprising that something can be held together by nothing. But if the heavens were infinite and were finite only with respect to a hollow space inside, then it will be said with more truth that there is nothing outside the heavens, since anything which occupied any space would be in them; but the heavens will remain immobile. For movement is the most powerful reason wherewith they try to conclude that the universe is finite.

But let us leave to the philosophers of nature the dispute as to whether the world is finite or infinite, and let us hold as certain that the earth held together between its two poles terminates in a spherical surface. Why therefore should we hesitate any longer to grant to it the movement which accords naturally with its form, rather than put the whole world in a commotion—the world whose limits we do not and cannot know? And why not admit that the appearance of diurnal revolution belongs to the heavens but the reality (*veritatem*) belongs to the earth? And things are as when Aeneas said in Virgil: "We sail out of the harbor, the land and cities move away." As a matter of fact, when a ship floats on over a tranquil sea, all the things outside seem to the voyagers to be moving in a movement which is the image of their own, and they think on the contrary that they themselves and all the things with them are at rest. So it can easily happen in the case of the movement of the earth that the whole world should be believed to be moving in a circle. Then what will we say about the clouds and the other things floating in the air or falling or rising up, except that not only the earth and the watery element with which it is conjoined are moved in this way but also no small part of the air and whatever other things have a similar connection with the earth? whether because the air close by, which is mixed with earthy and watery matter, shares in the same nature as the earth or because the movement of the air is an acquired one, in which it participates without resistance on account of the contiguity and perpetual rotation of the earth. Conversely, it is no less astonishing for them to say that the highest region of the air follows the celestial movement, as is shown by those stars which appear suddenly—I mean those called comets or bearded stars by the Greeks. For that place is assigned for their generation; and like all the other stars they rise and set. We can say that that part of the air is deprived of terrestrial motion on account of its great distance from the earth. Hence the air which is nearest to the earth and the things floating in it will appear tranquil, unless they are driven to and fro by the wind or some other force, as happens. For how is the wind in the air different from a current in the sea? But we must confess that in comparison with the world the movement of falling and of rising bodies is twofold and is in general compounded of the rectilineal and the circular. As regards things which move downward on account of their weight, because they have very much earth in them, doubtlessly their parts possess the same nature as the whole, and it is for the same reason that fiery bodies are drawn upward with force. For even this earthly fire feeds principally on earthly matter; and they define flame as burning smoke. Now it is a property of fire to make that which it invades to expand; and it does this with such force that it can be stopped by no means or contrivance from breaking prison and completing its job. Now expanding movement moves away from the center to the circumference; and so if some part of earth were set on fire, it would be borne away from the center upward. Accordingly, as they say, a simple body possesses a simple movement—this is first verified in the case of circular movement —as long as the simple body remains in its unity in its natural place. In this place, in fact, its movement is none other than the circular, which remains entirely in itself, as though at rest. Rectilineal movement however belongs to those which journey away from their natural place or are shoved out of it or are outside it somehow. But nothing is more repugnant to the order of the whole and to the form of the world than for anything to be outside of its place. Therefore rectilineal movement belongs only to things which are not in the right condition and are not perfectly conformed to their nature—when they are separated from their whole and abandon its unity. Furthermore, bodies which are moved upward or downward do not possess a simple, uniform and regular movement—even without taking into account circular movement. For they cannot be in conformity with their lightness or their force of weight. And those which fall possess a slow movement at the beginning but increase their velocity as they fall. And conversely we note that this earthly fire,—and we see no other—when carried high up immediately dies down, as though manifesting the violence of earthly matter.

Now circular movement always goes on regularly, for it has an unfailing cause; but (in rectilineal movement) the acceleration stops, because, when the bodies have reached their place, they are no longer heavy or light, and so the motion ends. Therefore since circular movement belongs to wholes and rectilineal to parts, we can say that the circular movement abides with the rectilineal, as animal with sick. And the fact that Aristotle divided simple movement into three genera: away from the center, toward the center, and around the center, should be considered merely as an act of reason, just as we distinguish between line, point, and surface, though none of them can subsist without the others or without body. In addition there is the fact that the state of immobility is regarded as more noble and godlike than that of change and instability, which for that reason should belong to the earth rather than to the world. I will add that it seems rather absurd to attribute movement to the container or to that which provides the place and not rather to that which is contained and has a place, i.e., the earth; and lastly, since it is clear that the wandering stars are sometimes nearer and sometimes farther away from the earth, then the movement of one and the same body around the center—and they mean the center of the earth—will be both away from the center and toward the center. Therefore it is necessary that movement around the center should be taken more generally; and it should be enough if each movement is in accord with its own center. You see therefore that for all these reasons it is more probable that the earth moves than that it is at rest—especially in the case of the diurnal revolution, as it is most proper to the earth. And I think that is enough as regards the first part of the question.

Whether Many Movements Can Be Attributed to the Earth, and Concerning the Center of the World

Therefore since nothing hinders the mobility of the earth, I think we should now see whether more than one movement belongs to it, so that it could be regarded as one of the wandering stars. For the apparently irregular movement of the planets and their variable distances from the earth—which cannot be understood as occurring in circles which are homocentric with the earth—show that the earth is not the center of their circular movements. Therefore since there are many centers, it does not require audacity to doubt whether the center of gravity of the earth rather than some other is the center of the world. I myself think that gravity or heaviness is nothing except a certain natural appetency implanted in the parts by the divine providence of the universal artisan, in order that they should unite in their oneness and wholeness, coming together in the form of a globe. It is believable that this affect is present in the sun, moon, and the other bright planets and that through its efficacy they remain in the spherical figure in which they are visible, though they nevertheless accomplish their circular movements in many different ways. Therefore if the earth too possesses movements different from the one around its center, then they will necessarily be movements which similarly appear on the outside and in many things; and we find the annual revolution among these movements. For if the annual revolution were changed from being solar to being terrestrial, and immobility were granted to the sun, (7B) the risings and setting of the signs and of the fixed stars—by reason of which the stars are mattutinal or vespertine—will appear in the same way; and it will be seen that the stoppings, retrogressions and progressions of the wandering stars are not theirs, but are a movement of the earth and that they borrow the appearances of this movement. Lastly, the sun will be regarded as occupying the mid-point of the world. The reason for the order in which all these things succeed one another and the harmony of the whole world teaches us their truth, if only—as they say—we would look at the thing with both eyes.

On the Order of the Celestial Orbital Circles [1]

I know of no one who doubts that the heaven of the fixed stars is the highest up of all visible things. We know that the ancient philosophers wished to take the order of the planets according to the magnitude of their revolutions, for the reason that among things which are moved with equal speed those which are the more distant seem to be borne along more slowly, as Euclid proves in his *Optics*. And so they thought that the moon traversed its circle in the shortest period of time because, being next to the earth, it revolved in the smallest circle. But Saturn, which completes the longest circuit in the longest period of time, is the highest. Beneath Saturn, Jupiter. After Jupiter, Mars. There are different opinions about Venus and Mercury, because they do not have the total (angular) elongation from the sun that the others do. Wherefore some place them above the sun, as Timaeus does in Plato; some, beneath the sun, as Ptolemy and a good many moderns. Alpetragius makes Venus higher than the sun and Mercury lower. Accordingly as the followers of Plato

---

[1] The great circle on the sphere in which the planet moves.

suppose that all the planets—which are otherwise dark bodies
—shine with light received from the sun, they think that if
the planets were below the sun, they would on account of
their slight distance from the sun be seen as only half—or at
any rate as only partly—spherical. For they reflect mostly
upward, i.e., toward the sun, the light which they receive,
as we see in the case of the new moon or the old. Moreover
they say that necessarily the sun would sometimes be obscured through their interposition and that its light would be
eclipsed in proportion to their size: and as that is not a celestial phenomenon, they think that these planets cannot by
any means be below the sun. On the contrary, those who
place Venus and Mercury below the sun, claim as a reason
the amplitude of the space found between the sun and the
moon. For they find that the greatest distance between the
earth and the moon, i.e., 64⅙ parts, whereof the radius of
the earth is the unit part, is contained almost eighteen times in
the least distance between the sun and the earth. This distance
is 1060 such unit parts, and therefore the distance between
the sun and the moon is 1096 such unit parts. And then, in
order for such a vast space not to remain empty, they find
that approximately the same numbers are filled out by the
intervals between their apsides—according to which they
reason out the width of their orbital circles—so that the
highest apsis of the moon is succeeded by the lowest apsis of
Mercury, so that the highest apsis of Mercury is followed by
the nearest of Venus, and so that finally the highest apsis of
Mercury is followed by the nearest of Venus, and so that
finally the highest apsis of Venus nearly touches the lowest
apsis of the sun. In fact they calculate that the interval between the apsides of Mercury contains approximately 177½
of the aforesaid unit parts and that the remaining space is
nearly filled by the 910 unit parts of the interval between
the apsides of Venus. Therefore they do not admit that these
planets have a certain opacity, like that of the moon; but that
they shine either by their own proper light or because their
entire bodies are impregnated with sunlight, and that accordingly they do not obscure the sun, because it is an extremely
rare occurrence for them to be interposed between our vision

and the sun, as they usually withdraw (from the sun) latitudinally. In addition there is the fact that they are small bodies in comparison with the sun, since Venus even though larger than Mercury can cover scarcely 1/100 of the sun, as Al Battani the Aratensian maintains, who holds that the diameter of the sun is ten times greater, and therefore it would not be easy to see such a little speck in the midst of such beaming light. Averroes however in his paraphrase of Ptolemy records having seen something blackish, when he observed the conjunction of the sun and Mercury which he had computed. And so they judge that these two stars move below the solar circle. But how uncertain and shaky this reasoning is, is clear from the fact that though the shortest distance of the moon is 38 parts whereof the radius of the earth is the unit part—according to Ptolemy, but more than forty-nine such unit parts by a truer evaluation, as will be shown below—nevertheless we do not know that this great space contains anything except air, or if you prefer, what they call the fiery element. Moreover there is the fact that the diameter of the circle of Venus—by reason of which Venus has an elongation of approximately 45° on either side of the sun—would have to have been 6 times greater than the distance from the center of the earth to its lowest apsis, as will be shown in the proper place. Then what will they say is contained in all this space, which is so great as to take in the earth, air, ether, moon and Mercury, and which moreover the vast epicycle of Venus would occupy if it revolved around an immobile earth? Furthermore, how unconvincing is Ptolemy's argument that the sun must occupy the middle position between those planets which have a very great elongation from the sun and those which do not is clear from the fact that the moon's very great elongation proves its falsity.

But what cause will those who place Venus below the sun, and Mercury next, or separate them in some other order— what cause will they allege why these planets do not also make circuits separate and independent of the sun, like the other planets, unless the ratio of speed or slowness falsifies the order? Therefore it will be necessary either for the earth not to be the center to which the order of the planets and orbital circles is referred, or for there to be no sure reason for their order and for it not to be apparent why the highest place is due to Saturn rather than to Jupiter or some other planet. Wherefore I judge that what Martianus Capella—who wrote the *Encyclopedia*—and some other Latins took to be the case is by no means to be despised. For they hold that Venus and Mercury describe a circle around the sun as a center, and they think that for that reason Venus and Mercury do not have any farther elongation from the sun than the convexity of their orbital circles permits; for they do not make a circle around the earth as do the others, but have converse apsides. Now what do they wish to signify except that the center of their orbital circles is at the sun? Thus the orbital circle of Mercury will be enclosed within the orbital circle of Venus—which would have to be more than twice as large—and will obtain an adequate place within that amplitude. Therefore if any one should take this as an occasion to refer Saturn, Jupiter, and Mars also to this same center, provided he understands the dimensions of these orbital circles to be such as to comprehend and encircle the earth remaining within them, he would not be in error, as the table of ratios of their movements shows. For it is manifest that the planets are nearer to the earth at the time of their vespertine rising, i.e., when they are opposite to the sun and the earth is in the middle between them and the sun. But they are farthest away from the earth at the time of their vespertine setting, i.e., when they are occulted in the neighborhood of the sun, namely when we have the sun between them and the earth. All that shows clearly enough that their center is more directly related to the sun and is the same as that to which Venus and Mercury refer their revolutions. But as they all have one common center, it is necessary that the space left between the convex orbital circle of Venus and the concave orbital circle of Mars should be viewed as an orbital circle or sphere homocentric with them in respect to both surfaces, and that it should receive the earth and its satellite the moon and whatever is enclosed by the lunar globe. For we can by no means separate the moon from the earth, as the moon is incontestably very close to the earth,—especially since we find in this space a place for the moon which is proper enough and sufficiently large. Therefore we are not ashamed to maintain that this totality—which the moon em-

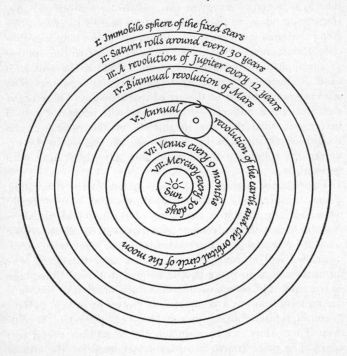

braces—, and the center of the earth too traverse that great orbital circle among the other wandering stars in an annual revolution around the sun; and that the center of the world is around the sun. I also say that the sun remains forever immobile and that whatever apparent movement belongs to it can be verified as due to the mobility of the earth; that the magnitude of the world is such that, although the distance from the sun to the earth in relation to the orbital circles of the planets possesses magnitude which is sufficiently manifest in proportion to those dimensions, this distance, as compared with the sphere of the fixed stars, is imperceptible. I find it much more easy to grant that than to unhinge the understanding by an almost infinite multitude of spheres—which is what those who keep the earth at the center of the world are forced to do. But we should rather follow the wisdom of nature, which, as it takes very great care not to have produced anything superfluous or useless, so it often prefers to endow one thing with many effects. And though all these things are difficult, almost inconceivable, and quite contrary to the opinion of the multitude, nevertheless in what follows we will with God's help make them clearer than day—at least for those who are not ignorant of the art of mathematics. Therefore if the first law is still safe—for no one will bring forward a better one than that the magnitude of the orbital circles should be measured by the magnitude of time—then the order of the spheres will follow in this way—beginning with the highest:

The first and highest of all is the sphere of the fixed stars, which comprehends itself and all things, and is accordingly immovable. In fact it is the place of the universe, i.e., it is that to which the movement and position of all the other stars are referred. For in the deduction of terrestrial movement, we will however give the cause why there are phenomena such as to make people believe that even the sphere of the fixed stars somehow moves. Saturn the first of the wandering stars follows; it completes its circuit in 30 years. After it comes Jupiter moving in a twelve-year period of revolution. Then Mars, which completes a revolution every two years. The place fourth in order is occupied by the annual revolution in which we said the earth together with the orbital circle of the moon as an epicycle is comprehended. In the fifth place, Venus, which comes around in nine months. The sixth and final place is occupied by Mercury, which completes its revolution in a period of eighty days. In the center of all rests the sun. For who would place this lamp of a very beautiful temple in another or better place than this wherefrom it can illuminate everything at the same time? As a matter of fact, not unhappily do some call it the lantern; others, the mind and still others, the pilot of the world. Trismegistus calls it a "visible god"; Sophocles' Electra, "that which gazes at all things." And so the sun, as if resting on a kingly throne, governs the family of stars which wheel around. Moreover, the earth is by no means cheated of the services of the moon; but, as Aristotle says in the *De Animalibus* the earth has the closest connection (*cognationem*) with the moon. The earth moreover is fertilized by the sun and conceives offspring every year.

Therefore in this ordering we find a wonderfully symmetrical world and a sure bond of harmony for the movement and magnitude of the orbital circles such as cannot be found in any other way. For now the careful observer can see why progression and retrogradation appear greater in Jupiter than in Saturn and less than in Mars; and in turn greater in Venus than in Mercury; and why these reciprocal events appear more often in Saturn than in Jupiter, and even less often in Mars and Venus than in Mercury; in addition, why when Saturn, Jupiter, and Mars are in opposition (to the mean position of the sun) they are nearer to the earth than at the time of their occultation and their reappearance; and especially why at the times when Mars is in opposition to the sun, it seems to equal Jupiter in magnitude and to be distinguished from Jupiter only by a reddish color, but when discovered through careful observation by means of a sextant is found with difficulty among the stars of second magnitude? All these things proceed from the same cause, which resides in the movement of the earth. But that there are no such phenomena among the fixed stars argues that they are at an immense height away, which makes the circle of annual movement or its image disappear from before our eyes, since every visible thing has a certain distance beyond which it is no longer seen, as is shown in optics. For the brilliance of their lights shows that there is a very great distance between Saturn the highest of the planets and the sphere of the fixed stars. It is by this mark in particular that they are distinguished from the planets, as it is proper to have the greatest difference between the moved and the unmoved. How exceedingly fine is the godlike work of the best and greatest artist!

Francis Bacon

NOVUM ORGANUM

(BOOK I)

Francis Bacon
[1561–1626]

A lawyer and member of Parliament during the reign of Queen Elizabeth, Francis Bacon's star did not rise until after her death, when he became, following a succession of high offices, Lord Chancellor under King James. Even in so crowded a legal and political career, he undertook the colossal task of surveying and reorganizing the then-prevailing concepts of science. His *Advancement of Learning*, issued in 1605 as the first part of *The Great Instauration*, classified the sciences. Fifteen years later, his master work, *Novum Organum*, established a new methodology in the experimental interpretation of nature. It was Bacon's conviction that the mind, freed from the impediments of prejudices and generalizations, can by knowledge attain sovereignty over nature. Hardly had his great work appeared when Bacon found himself in serious political trouble and under a charge of bribery. His downfall followed his confession. He was heavily fined, sentenced to the Tower of London, excluded from Parliament and barred from ever holding office again. After his pardon and for the last five years of his life, he devoted himself exclusively to writing, and it is to this period that the world owes his famous *Essays*. Book One of *Novum Organum* is offered as Bacon's most representative contribution to the philosophy of science.

NOVUM ORGANUM

(BOOK I)

FRANCIS BACON

Preface

Those who have taken upon them to lay down the law of nature as a thing already searched out and understood, whether they have spoken in simple assurance or professional affectation, have therein done philosophy and the sciences great injury. For as they have been successful in inducing belief, so they have been effective in quenching and stopping inquiry; and have done more harm by spoiling and putting an end to other men's efforts than good by their own. Those on the other hand who have taken a contrary course, and asserted that absolutely nothing can be known—whether it were from hatred of the ancient sophists, or from uncertainty and fluctuation of mind, or even from a kind of fulness of learning, that they fell upon this opinion,—have certainly advanced reasons for it that are not to be despised; but yet they have neither started from true principles nor rested in the just conclusion, zeal and affection having carried them much too far. The more ancient of the Greeks (whose writings are lost) took up with better judgment a position between these two extremes,—between the presumption of pronouncing on everything, and the despair of comprehending anything; and though frequently and bitterly complaining of the difficulty of inquiry and the obscurity of things, and like impatient horses champing the bit, they did not the less follow up their object and engage with nature; thinking (it seems) that this very question—viz., whether or no anything can be known— was to be settled not by arguing, but by trying. And yet they too, trusting entirely to the force of their understanding, applied no rule, but made everything turn upon hard thinking and perpetual working and exercise of the mind.

Now my method, though hard to practice, is easy to explain; and it is this. I propose to establish progressive stages of certainty. The evidence of the sense, helped and guarded by a certain process of correction, I retain. But the mental operation which follows the act of sense I for the most part reject; and instead of it, I open and lay out a new and certain path for the mind to proceed in, starting directly from the simple sensuous perception. The necessity of this was felt no doubt by those who attributed so much importance to logic; showing thereby that they were in search of helps for the understanding, and had no confidence in the native and spontaneous process of the mind. But this remedy comes too late to do any good, when the mind is already, through the daily intercourse and conversation of life, occupied with unsound doctrines and beset on all sides by vain imaginations. And therefore that art of logic, coming (as I said) too late to the rescue, and no way able to set matters right again, has had the effect of fixing errors rather than disclosing truth. There remains but one course for the recovery of a sound and healthy condition,— namely, that the entire work of the understanding be commenced afresh, and the mind itself be from the very outset not left to take its own course, but guided at every step; and the business be done as if by machinery. Certainly if in things mechanical men had set to work with their naked hands, without help or force of instruments, just as in things intellectual they have set to work with little else than the naked forces of the understanding, very small would the matters have been which, even with their best efforts applied in conjunction, they could have attempted or accomplished. Now (to pause awhile upon this example and look in it as in a glass) let us suppose that some vast obelisk were (for the decoration of a triumph or some such magnificence) to be removed from its place, and that men should set to work upon it with their naked hands; would not any sober spectator think them mad? And if they should then send for more people, thinking that in that way they might manage it, would he not think them all the madder? And if they then proceeded to make a selection, putting away the weaker hands, and using only the strong and vigorous, would he not think them madder than ever? And if lastly, not content with this, they resolved to call in aid the art of athletics, and required all their men to come with hands, arms, and sinews well anointed and medicated according to the rules of art, would he not cry out that they were only taking pains to show a kind of method and discretion in their madness? Yet just so it is that men proceed in matters intellectual,—with just the same kind of mad effort and useless combination of forces,—when they hope great things either from the number and cooperation or from the excellency and acuteness of individual wits; yea, and when they endeavor by logic (which may be considered as a kind of athletic art) to strengthen the sinews of the understanding: and yet with all this study and endeavor it is apparent to any true judgment that they are but applying the naked intellect all the time; whereas in every great work to be done by the hand of man it is manifestly impossible, without instruments and machinery, either for the strength of each to be exerted or the strength of all to be united.

Upon these premises two things occur to me of which, that they may not be overlooked, I would have men reminded. First it falls out fortunately as I think for the allaying of contradictions and heart-burnings, that the honor and reverence due to the ancients remains untouched and undiminished; while I may carry out my designs and at the same time reap the fruit of my modesty. For if I should profess that I, going the same road as the ancients, have something better to produce, there must needs have been some comparison or rivalry between us (not to be avoided by any art of words) in respect of excellency or ability of wit; and though in this there would be nothing unlawful or new (for if there be anything misapprehended by them, or falsely laid down, why may not I, using a liberty common to all, take exception to it?), yet the contest, however just and allowable, would have been an unequal one perhaps, in respect of the measure of my own powers. As it is, however,—my object being to open a new way for the understanding, a way by them untried and unknown,—the case is altered; party zeal and emulation are at an end; and I appear merely as a guide to point out the road; an office of small authority, and depending more upon a kind of luck than upon any ability or excellency. And thus much relates to the persons only. The other point of which I would have men reminded relates to the matter itself.

Be it remembered then that I am far from wishing to interfere with the philosophy which now flourishes, or with any other philosophy more correct and complete than this which has been or may hereafter be propounded. For I do not object to the use of this received philosophy, or others like it, for supplying matter for disputations or ornaments for discourse, —for the professor's lecture and for the business of life. Nay more, I declare openly that for these uses the philosophy which I bring forward will not be much available. It does not lie in the way. It cannot be caught up in passage. It does not flatter the understanding by conformity with preconceived notions. Nor will it come down to the apprehension of the vulgar except by its utility and effects.

Let there be therefore (and may it be for the benefit of both) two streams and two dispensations of knowledge; and in like manner two tribes or kindreds of students in philoso-

phy—tribes not hostile or alien to each other, but bound together by mutual services;—let there in short be one method
for the cultivation, another for the invention, of knowledge.

And for those who prefer the former, either from hurry or
from considerations of business or for want of mental power
to take in and embrace the other (which must needs be most
men's case), I wish that they may succeed to their desire in
what they are about, and obtain what they are pursuing. But
if any man there be who, not content to rest in and use the
knowledge which has already been discovered, aspires to
penetrate further; to overcome, not an adversary in argument, but nature in action; to seek, not pretty and probable
conjectures, but certain and demonstrable knowledge;—I
invite all such to join themselves, as true sons of knowledge,
with me, that passing by the outer courts of nature, which
numbers have trodden, we may find a way at length into her
inner chambers. And to make my meaning clearer and to
familiarize the thing by giving it a name, I have chosen to call
one of these methods or ways *Anticipation of the Mind*, the
other *interpretation of Nature*.

Moreover I have one request to make. I have on my own
part made it my care and study that the things which I shall
propound should not only be true, but should also be presented to men's minds, how strangely soever preoccupied and
obstructed, in a manner not harsh or unpleasant. It is but
reasonable however (especially in so great a restoration of
learning and knowledge) that I should claim of men one favor
in return; which is this:—If anyone would form an opinion or
judgment either out of his own observation, or out of the
crowd of authorities, or out of the forms of demonstration
(which have now acquired a sanction like that of judicial
laws), concerning these speculations of mine, let him not
hope that he can do it in passage or by the by; but let him
examine the thing thoroughly; let him make some little trial
for himself of the way which I describe and lay out; let him
familiarize his thoughts with that subtlety of nature to which
experience bears witness; let him correct by seasonable pa-

tience and due delay the depraved and deep-rooted habits of his mind; and when all this is done and he has begun to be his own master, let him (if he will) use his own judgment.

Aphorisms
Concerning the Interpretation of Nature and the Kingdom of Man

I

MAN, being the servant and interpreter of nature, can do and understand so much and so much only as he has observed in fact or in thought of the course of nature: beyond this he neither knows anything nor can do anything.

II

Neither the naked hand nor the understanding left to itself can effect much. It is by instruments and helps that the work is done, which are as much wanted for the understanding as for the hand. And as the instruments of the hand either give motion or guide it, so the instruments of the mind supply either suggestions for the understanding or cautions.

III

Human knowledge and human power meet in one; for where the cause is not known the effect cannot be produced. Nature to be commanded must be obeyed; and that which in contemplation is as the cause is in operation as the rule.

IV

Towards the effecting of works, all that man can do is to put together or put asunder natural bodies. The rest is done by nature working within.

V

The study of nature with a view to works is engaged in by the mechanic, the mathematician, the physician, the alchemist, and the magician; but by all (as things now are) with slight endeavor and scanty success.

VI

It would be an unsound fancy and self-contradictory to expect that things which have never yet been done can be done except by means which have never yet been tried.

VII

The productions of the mind and hand seem very numerous in books and manufactures. But all this variety lies in an exquisite subtlety and derivations from a few things already known; not in the number of axioms.

VIII

Moreover the works already known are due to chance and experiment rather than to sciences; for the sciences we now possess are merely systems for the nice ordering and setting forth of things already invented; not methods of invention or directions for new works.

IX

The cause and root of nearly all evils in the sciences is this —that while we falsely admire and extol the powers of the human mind we neglect to seek for its true helps.

X

The subtlety of nature is greater many times over than the subtlety of the senses and understanding; so that all those specious meditations, speculations, and glosses in which men indulge are quite from the purpose, only there is no one by to observe it.

XI

As the sciences which we now have do not help us in finding out new works, so neither does the logic which we now have help us in finding out new sciences.

XII

The logic now in use serves rather to fix and give stability to the errors which have their foundation in commonly received notions, than to help the search after truth. So it does more harm than good.

XIII

The syllogism is not applied to the first principles of sciences, and is applied in vain to intermediate axioms; being no match for the subtlety of nature. It commands assent therefore to the proposition, but does not take hold of the thing.

XIV

The syllogism consists of propositions, propositions consist of words, words are symbols of notions. Therefore if the notions themselves (which is the root of the matter) are confused and overhastily abstracted from the facts, there can be no firmness in the superstructure. Our only hope therefore lies in a true induction.

XV

There is no soundness in our notions whether logical or physical. Substance, Quality, Action, Passion, Essence itself, are not sound notions: much less are Heavy, Light, Dense, Rare, Moist, Dry, Generation, Corruption, Attraction, Repulsion, Element, Matter, Form, and the like; but all are fantastical and ill defined.

XVI

Our notions of less general species as Man, Dog, Dove, and of the immediate perceptions of the sense, as Hot, Cold, Black, White, do not materially mislead us; yet even these are sometimes confused by the flux and alteration of matter and the mixing of one thing with another. All the others which men have hitherto adopted are but wanderings, not being abstracted and formed from things by proper methods.

XVII

Nor is there less of willfulness and wandering in the construction of axioms than in the formations of notions; not excepting even those very principles which are obtained by common induction; but much more in the axioms and lower propositions educed by the syllogism.

XVIII

The discoveries which have hitherto been made in the sciences are such as lie close to vulgar notions, scarcely beneath the surface. In order to penetrate into the inner and further recesses of nature, it is necessary that both notions and axioms be derived from things by a more sure and guarded way; and that a method of intellectual operation be introduced altogether better and more certain.

XIX

There are and can be only two ways of searching into and discovering truth. The one flies from the senses and particulars to the most general axioms, and from these principles, the truth of which it takes for settled and immovable, proceeds to judgment and to the discovery of middle axioms. And this way is now in fashion. The other derives axioms from the senses and particulars, rising by a gradual and unbroken ascent, so that it arrives at the most general axioms last of all. This is the true way, but as yet untried.

XX

The understanding left to itself takes the same course (namely, the former) which it takes in accordance with logical order. For the mind longs to spring up to positions of higher generality, that it may find rest there; and so after a little while wearies of experiment. But this evil is increased

by logic, because of the order and solemnity of its disputations.

XXI

The understanding left to itself, in a sober, patient, and
grave mind, especially if it be not hindered by received doctrines, tries a little that other way, which is the right one,
but with little progress; since the understanding, unless directed and assisted, is a thing unequal, and quite unfit to con-
tend with the obscurity of things.

XXII

Both ways set out from the senses and particulars, and rest
in the highest generalities; but the difference between them is
infinite. For the one just glances at experiment and particulars
in passing, the other dwells duly and orderly among them.
The one, again, begins at once by establishing certain abstract
and useless generalities, the other rises by gradual steps to
that which is prior and better known in the order of nature.

XXIII

There is a great difference between the *Idols* of the human
mind and the *Ideas* of the divine. That is to say, between certain empty dogmas, and the true signatures and marks set
upon the works of creation as they are found in nature.

XXIV

It cannot be that axioms established by argumentation
should avail for the discovery of new works; since the subtlety
of nature is greater many times over than the subtlety of argument. But axioms duly and orderly formed from particulars
easily discover the way to new particulars, and thus render
sciences active.

XXV

The axioms now in use, having been suggested by a scanty
and manipular experience and a few particulars of most general occurrence, are made for the most part just large enough

to fit and take these in: and therefore it is no wonder if they do not lead to new particulars. And if some opposite instance, not observed or not known before, chance to come in the way, the axiom is rescued and preserved by some frivolous distinction; whereas the truer course would be to correct the axiom itself.

XXVI

The conclusions of human reason as ordinarily applied in matter of nature, I call for the sake of distinction *Anticipations of Nature* (as a thing rash or premature). That reason which is elicited from facts by a just and methodical process, I call *Interpretation of Nature*.

XXVII

Anticipations are a ground sufficiently firm for consent; for even if men went mad all after the same fashion, they might agree one with another well enough.

XXVIII

For the winning of assent, indeed, anticipations are far more powerful than interpretations; because being collected from a few instances, and those for the most part of familiar occurrence, they straightway touch the understanding and fill the imagination; whereas interpretations on the other hand, being gathered here and there from very various and widely dispersed facts, cannot suddenly strike the understanding; and therefore they must needs, in respect of the opinions of the time, seem harsh and out of tune; much as the mysteries of faith do.

XXIX

In sciences founded on opinions and dogmas, the use of anticipations and logic is good; for in them the object is to command assent to the proposition, not to master the thing.

XXX

Though all the wits of all the ages should meet together

and combine and transmit their labors, yet will no great
progress ever be made in science by means of anticipations;
because radical errors in the first concoction of the mind are
not to be cured by the excellence of functions and remedies
subsequent.

XXXI

It is idle to expect any great advancement in science from
the superinducing and engrafting of new things upon old. We
must begin anew from the very foundations, unless we would
revolve forever in a circle with mean and contemptible progress.

XXXII

The honor of the ancient authors, and indeed of all, remains
untouched; since the comparison I challenge is not of wits or
faculties, but of ways and methods, and the part I take upon
myself is not that of a judge, but of a guide.

XXXIII

This must be plainly avowed: no judgment can be rightly
formed either of my method or of the discoveries to which it
leads, by means of anticipations (that is to say, of the reasoning which is now in use); since I cannot be called on to abide
by the sentence of a tribunal which is itself on its trial.

XXXIV

Even to deliver and explain what I bring forward is no easy
matter; for things in themselves new will yet be apprehended
with reference to what is old.

XXXV

It was said by Borgia of the expedition of the French into
Italy, that they came with chalk in their hands to mark out
their lodgings, not with arms to force their way in. I in like
manner would have my doctrine enter quietly into the minds
that are fit and capable of receiving it; for confutations cannot
be employed, when the difference is upon first principles and
very notions and even upon forms of demonstration.

XXXVI

One method of delivery alone remains to us; which is simply this: we must lead men to the particulars themselves, and their series and order; while men on their side must force themselves for awhile to lay their notions by and begin to familiarize themselves with facts.

XXXVII

The doctrine of those who have denied that certainty could be attained at all, has some agreement with my way of proceeding at the first setting out; but they end in being infinitely separated and opposed. For the holders of that doctrine assert simply that nothing can be known; I also assert that not much can be known in nature by the way which is now in use. But then they go on to destroy the authority of the senses and understanding; whereas I proceed to devise and supply helps for the same.

XXXVIII

The idols and false notions which are now in possession of the human understanding, and have taken deep root therein, not only so beset men's minds that truth can hardly find entrance, but even after entrance obtained, they will again in the very instauration of the sciences meet and trouble us, unless men being forewarned of the danger fortify themselves as far as may be against their assaults.

XXXIX

There are four classes of idols which beset men's minds. To these for distinction's sake I have assigned names,—calling the first class *Idols of the Tribe;* the second, *Idols of the Cave;* the third, *Idols of the Market-place;* the fourth, *Idols of the Theater.*

XL

The formation of ideas and axioms by true induction is no doubt the proper remedy to be applied for the keeping off and clearing away of idols. To point them out, however, is of great use, for the doctrine of idols is to the interpretation of nature what the doctrine of the refutation of sophisms is to common logic.

XLI

The Idols of the Tribe have their foundation in human nature itself, and in the tribe or race of men. For it is a false assertion that the sense of man is the measure of things. On the contrary, all perceptions, as well of the sense as of the mind, are according to the measure of the individual and not according to the measure of the universe. And the human understanding is like a false mirror, which, receiving rays irregularly, distorts and discolors the nature of things by mingling its own nature with it.

XLII

The Idols of the Cave are the idols of the individual man. For everyone (besides the errors common to human nature in general) has a cave or den of his own, which refracts and discolors the light of nature; owing either to his own proper and peculiar nature or to his education and conversation with others; or to the reading of books, and the authority of those whom he esteems and admires; or to the differences of impressions, accordingly as they take place in a mind preoccupied and predisposed or in a mind indifferent and settled; or the like. So that the spirit of man (according as it is meted out to different individuals) is in fact a thing variable and full of perturbation, and governed as it were by chance. Whence it was well observed by Heraclitus that men look for sciences in their own lesser worlds, and not in the greater or common world.

XLIII

There are also idols formed by the intercourse and association of men with each other, which I call Idols of the Marketplace, on account of the commerce and consort of men there. For it is by discourse that men associate; and words are imposed according to the apprehension of the vulgar. And therefore the ill and unfit choice of words wonderfully obstructs the understanding. Nor do the definitions or explanations wherewith in some things learned men are wont to guard and defend themselves, by any means set the matter right. But words plainly force and overrule the understanding, and throw all into confusion, and lead men away into numberless empty controversies and idle fancies.

XLIV

Lastly, there are idols which have immigrated into men's minds from the various dogmas of philosophies, and also from wrong laws of demonstration. These I call Idols of the Theater; because in my judgment all the received systems are but so many stage-plays, representing worlds of their own creation after an unreal and scenic fashion. Nor is it only of the systems now in vogue, or only of the ancient sects and philosophies, that I speak: for many more plays of the same kind may yet be composed and in like artificial manner set forth; seeing that errors the most widely different have nevertheless causes for the most part alike. Neither again do I mean this only of entire systems, but also of many principles and axioms in science, which by tradition, credulity, and negligence have come to be received.

But of these several kinds of idols I must speak more largely and exactly, that the understanding may be duly cautioned.

XLV

The human understanding is of its own nature prone to suppose the existence of more order and regularity in the world than it finds. And though there be many things in nature which are singular and unmatched, yet it devises for them parallels and conjugates and relatives which do not exist. Hence the fiction that all celestial bodies move in perfect circles; spirals and dragons being (except in name) utterly rejected. Hence too the element of fire with its orb is brought in, to make up the square with the other three which the sense perceives. Hence also the ratio of density of the so-called elements is arbitrarily fixed at ten to one. And so on of other dreams. And these fancies affect not dogmas only, but simple notions also.

XLVI

The human understanding when it has once adopted an opinion (either as being the received opinion or as being agreeable to itself) draws all things else to support and agree with it. And though there be a greater number and weight of instances to be found on the other side, yet these it either neglects and despises, or else by some distinction sets aside and rejects; in order that by this great and pernicious predetermination the authority of its former conclusions may remain inviolate. And therefore it was a good answer that was made by one who when they showed him hanging in a temple a picture of those who had paid their vows as having escaped shipwreck, and would have him say whether he did not now acknowledge the power of the gods,—"Aye," asked he again, "but where are they painted that were drowned after their vows?" And such is the way of all superstition, whether in astrology, dreams, omens, divine judgments, or the like; wherein men, having a delight in such vanities, mark the events where they are fulfilled, but where they fail, though this happen much oftener, neglect and pass them by. But with far more subtlety does this mischief insinuate itself into philosophy and the sciences; in which the first conclusion colors and brings into conformity with itself all that come after, though far sounder and better. Besides, independently of that delight and vanity which I have described, it is the peculiar and perpetual error of the human intellect to be more moved and excited by affirmatives than by negatives; whereas it ought properly to hold itself indifferently disposed towards both alike. Indeed in the establishment of any true axiom, the negative instance is the more forcible of the two.

XLVII

The human understanding is moved by those things most

which strike and enter the mind simultaneously and suddenly, and so fill the imagination; and then it feigns and supposes all other things to be somehow, though it cannot see how, similar to those few things by which it is surrounded. But for that going to and fro to remote and heterogeneous instances, by which axioms are tried as in the fire, the intellect is altogether slow and unfit, unless it be forced thereto by severe laws and overruling authority.

XLVIII

The human understanding is unquiet; it cannot stop or rest, and still presses onward, but in vain. Therefore it is that we cannot conceive of any end or limit to the world; but always as of necessity it occurs to us that there is something beyond. Neither again can it be conceived how eternity has flowed down to the present day: for that distinction which is commonly received of infinity in time past and in time to come can by no means hold; for it would thence follow that one infinity is greater than another, and that infinity is wasting away and tending to become finite. The like subtlety arises touching the infinite divisibility of lines, from the same inability of thought to stop. But this inability interferes more mischievously in the discovery of causes: for although the most general principles in nature ought to be held merely positive, as they are discovered, and cannot with truth be referred to a cause; nevertheless the human understanding being unable to rest still seeks something prior in the order of nature. And then it is that in struggling towards that which is further off it falls back upon that which is more nigh at hand, —namely, on final causes; which have relation clearly to the nature of man rather than to the nature of the universe, and from this source have strangely defined philosophy. But he is no less an unskilled and shallow philosopher who seeks causes of that which is most general, than he who in things subordinate and subaltern omits to do so.

XLIX

The human understanding is no dry light, but receives an

infusion from the will and affections; whence proceed sciences which may be called "sciences as one would." For what a man had rather were true he more readily believes. Therefore he rejects difficult things from impatience of research; sober things, because they narrow hope; the deeper things of nature, from superstition; the light of experience, from arrogance and pride, lest his mind should seem to be occupied with things mean and transitory; things not commonly believed, out of deference to the opinion of the vulgar. Numberless in short are the ways, and sometimes imperceptible, in which the affections color and infect the understanding.

L

But by far the greatest hindrance and aberration of the human understanding proceeds from the dullness, incompetency, and deceptions of the senses; in that things which strike the sense outweigh things which do not immediately strike it, though they be more important. Hence it is that speculation commonly ceases where sight ceases, insomuch that of things invisible there is little or no observation. Hence all the working of the spirits inclosed in tangible bodies lies hid and unobserved of men. So also all the more subtle changes of form in the parts of coarser substances (which they commonly call alteration, though it is in truth local motion through exceedingly small spaces) is in like manner unobserved. And yet unless these two things just mentioned be searched out and brought to light, nothing great can be achieved in nature, as far as the production of works is concerned. So again the essential nature of our common air, and of all bodies less dense than air (which are very many), is almost unknown. For the sense by itself is a thing infirm and erring; neither can instruments for enlarging or sharpening the senses do much: but all the truer kind of interpretation of nature is effected by instances and experiments fit and apposite; wherein the sense decides touching the experiment only, and the experiment touching the point in nature and the thing itself.

LI

The human understanding is of its own nature prone to abstractions and gives a substance and reality to things which are fleeting. But to resolve nature into abstractions is less to our purpose than to dissect her into parts; as did the school of Democritus, which went further into nature than the rest. Matter rather than forms should be the object of our attention, its configurations and changes of configuration, and simple action, and law of action or motion; for forms are figments of the human mind, unless you will call those laws of action forms.

LII

Such then are the idols which I call *Idols of the Tribe;* and which take their rise either from the homogeneity of the substance of the human spirit, or from its preoccupation, or from its narrowness, or from its restless motion, or from an infusion of the affections, or from the incompetency of the senses, or from the mode of impression.

LIII

The *Idols of the Cave* take their rise in the peculiar constitution, mental or bodily, of each individual; and also in education, habit, and accident. Of this kind there is a great number and variety; but I will instance those the pointing out of which contains the most important caution, and which have most effect in disturbing the clearness of the understanding.

LIV

Men become attached to certain particular sciences and speculations, either because they fancy themselves the authors and inventors thereof, or because they have bestowed the greatest pains upon them and become most habituated to them. But men of this kind, if they betake themselves to philosophy and contemplations of a general character, distort and color them in obedience to their former fancies; a thing especially to be noticed in Aristotle, who made his natural philosophy a mere bondservant to his logic, thereby render-

ing it contentious and well nigh useless. The race of chemists
again out of a few experiments of the furnace have built up a
fantastic philosophy, framed with reference to a few things;
and Gilbert also, after he had employed himself most laboriously in the study and observation of the lodestone, proceeded
at once to construct an entire system in accordance with his
favorite subject.

LV

There is one principal and as it were radical distinction between different minds, in respect of philosophy and the
sciences; which is this: that some minds are stronger and apter
to mark the differences of things, others to mark their resemblances. The steady and acute mind can fix its contemplations and dwell and fasten on the subtlest distinctions; the
lofty and discursive mind recognizes and puts together the
finest and most general resemblances. Both kinds however
easily err in excess, by catching the one at gradations the
other at shadows.

LVI

There are found some minds given to an extreme admiration of antiquity, others to an extreme love and appetite for
novelty; but few so duly tempered that they can hold the
mean, neither carping at what has been well laid down by the
ancients, nor despising what is well introduced by the moderns. This however turns to the great injury of the sciences
and philosophy: since these affectations of antiquity and
novelty are the humors of partisans rather than judgments;
and truth is to be sought for not in the felicity of any age,
which is an unstable thing, but in the light of nature and experience, which is eternal. These factions therefore must be
abjured, and care must be taken that the intellect be not hurried by them into assent.

LVII

Contemplations of nature and of bodies in their simple
form break up and distract the understanding, while con-

templations of nature and bodies in their composition and configuration overpower and dissolve the understanding: a distinction well seen in the school of Leucippus and Democritus as compared with the other philosophies. For that school is so busied with the particles that it hardly attends to the structure; while the others are so lost in admiration of the structure that they do not penetrate to the simplicity of nature. These kinds of contemplation should therefore be alternated and taken by turns; that so the understanding may be rendered at once penetrating and comprehensive, and the inconveniences above mentioned, with the idols which proceed from them, may be avoided.

LVIII

Let such then be our provision and contemplative prudence for keeping off and dislodging the Idols of the Cave, which grow for the most part either out of the predominance of a favorite subject, or out of an excessive tendency to compare or to distinguish, or out of partiality for particular ages, or out of the largeness or minuteness of the objects contemplated. And generally let every student of nature take this as a rule,—that whatever his mind seizes and dwells upon with peculiar satisfaction is to be held in suspicion, and that so much the more care is to be taken in dealing with such questions to keep the understanding even and clear.

LIX

But the *Idols of the Market-place* are the most troublesome of all: idols which have crept into the understanding through the alliances of words and names. For men believe that their reason governs words; but it is also true that words react on the understanding; and this it is that has rendered philosophy and the sciences sophistical and inactive. Now words, being commonly framed and applied according to the capacity of the vulgar, follow those lines of division which are most obvious to the vulgar understanding. And whenever an understanding of greater acuteness or a more diligent observation would alter those lines to suit the true divisions of nature, words stand in the way and resist the change. Whence it comes to pass that the high and formal discussions of learned men end oftentimes in disputes about words and names; with which (according to the use and wisdom of the mathematicians) it would be more prudent to begin, and so by means of definitions reduce them to order. Yet even definitions cannot cure this evil in dealing with natural and material things; since the definitions themselves consist of words, and those words beget others: so that it is necessary to recur to individual instances, and those in due series and order; as I shall say presently when I come to the method and scheme for the formation of notions and axioms.

LX

The idols imposed by words on the understanding are of two kinds. They are either names of things which do not exist (for as there are things left unnamed through lack of observation, so likewise are there names which result from fantastic suppositions and to which nothing in reality corresponds), or they are names of things which exist, but yet confused and ill-defined, and hastily and irregularly derived from realities. Of the former kind are Fortune, the Prime Mover, Planetary Orbits, Elements of Fire, and like fictions which owe their origin to false and idle theories. And this class of idols is more easily expelled, because to get rid of them it is only necessary that all theories should be steadily rejected and dismissed as obsolete.

But the other class, which springs out of a faulty and unskillful abstraction, is intricate and deeply rooted. Let us take for example such a word as *humid*, and see how far the several things which the word is used to signify agree with each other; and we shall find the word *humid* to be nothing else than a mark loosely and confusedly applied to denote a variety of actions which will not bear to be reduced to any constant meaning. For it both signifies that which easily spreads itself round any other body; and that which in itself is indeterminate and cannot solidize; and that which readily yields in every direction; and that which easily divides and scatters itself; and that which easily unites and collects itself; and that which readily flows and is put in motion; and that which readily clings to another body and wets it; and that which is easily reduced to a liquid, or being solid easily melts. Accordingly when you come to apply the word,—if you take it in one sense, flame is humid; if in another, air is not humid; if in another, fine dust is humid; if in another, glass is humid. So that it is easy to see that the notion is taken by abstraction only from water and common and ordinary liquids, without any due verification.

There are however in words certain degrees of distortion and error. One of the least faulty kinds is that of names of substances, especially of lowest species and well-deduced (for the notion of *chalk* and of *mud* is good, of *earth* bad); a more faulty kind is that of actions, as *to generate, to corrupt, to alter;* the most faulty is of qualities (except such as are the immediate objects of the sense) as *heavy, light, rare, dense,* and the like. Yet in all these cases some notions are of necessity a little better than others, in proportion to the greater variety of subjects that fall within the range of the human sense.

LXI

But the *Idols of the Theater* are not innate, nor do they steal into the understanding secretly, but are plainly impressed and received into the mind from the play-books of philosophical systems and the perverted rules of demonstration. To attempt refutations in this case would be merely inconsistent with what I have already said: for since we agree neither upon principles nor upon demonstrations there is no place for argument. And this is so far well, inasmuch as it leaves the honor of the ancients untouched. For they are no wise disparaged—the question between them and me being only as to the way. For as the saying is, the lame man who keeps the right road outstrips the runner who takes a wrong one. Nay it is obvious that when a man runs the wrong way, the more active and swift he is the further he will go astray.

But the course I propose for the discovery of sciences is such as leaves but little to the acuteness and strength of wits, but places all wits and understandings nearly on a level. For as in the drawing of a straight line or a perfect circle, much depends on the steadiness and practice of the hand, if it be done by aim of hand only, but if with the aid of rule or compass, little or nothing; so is it exactly with my plan. But though particular confutations would be of no avail, yet touching the sects and general divisions of such systems I must say something; something also touching the external signs which show that they are unsound; and finally something touching the causes of such great infelicity and of such lasting and general agreement in error; that so the access to truth may be made less difficult, and the human understanding may the more willingly submit to its purgation and dismiss its idols.

LXII

Idols of the Theater, or of Systems, are many, and there can be and perhaps will be yet many more. For were it not that now for many ages men's minds have been busied with religion and theology; and were it not that civil governments, especially monarchies, have been averse to such novelties, even in matters speculative; so that men labor therein to the peril and harming of their fortunes,—not only unrewarded, but exposed also to contempt and envy: doubtless there would have arisen many other philosophical sects like to those which in great variety flourished once among the Greeks. For as on the phenomena of the heavens many hypotheses may be constructed, so likewise (and more also) many various dogmas may be set up and established on the phenomena of philosophy. And in the plays of this philosophical theater you may observe the same thing which is found in the theater of the poets, that stories invented for the stage are more compact and elegant, and more as one would wish them to be, than true stories out of history.

In general however there is taken for the material of philosophy either a great deal out of a few things, or a very little out of many things; so that on both sides philosophy is based on too narrow a foundation of experiment and natural history, and decides on the authority of too few cases. For the rational school of philosophers snatches from experience a variety of common instances, neither duly ascertained nor diligently examined and weighed, and leaves all the rest to meditation and agitation of wit.

There is also another class of philosophers, who having bestowed much diligent and careful labor on a few experiments, have thence made bold to educe and construct systems; wresting all other facts in a strange fashion to conformity therewith.

And there is yet a third class, consisting of those who out of faith and veneration mix their philosophy with theology and traditions; among whom the vanity of some has gone so far aside as to seek the origin of science among spirits and genii. So that this parent stock of errors—this false philosophy—is of three kinds; the *sophistical*, the *empirical*, and the *superstitious*.

LXIII

The most conspicuous example of the first class was Aristotle, who corrupted natural philosophy by his logic: fashioning the world out of categories; assigning to the human soul, the noblest of substances, a genus from words of the second intention; doing the business of density and rarity (which is to make bodies of greater or less dimensions, that is, occupy greater or less spaces), by the frigid distinction of act and power; asserting that single bodies have each a single and proper motion, and that if they participate in any other, then this results from an external cause; and imposing countless other arbitrary restrictions on the nature of things: being always more solicitous to provide an answer to the question and affirm something positive in words, than about the inner truth of things; a failing best shown when his philosophy is compared with other systems of note among the Greeks. For the *homœomera* of Anaxagoras; the atoms of Leucippus and Democritius; the Heaven and Earth of Parmenides; the Strife and Friendship of Empedocles; Heraclitus's doctrine how bodies are resolved into the indifferent nature of fire, and remolded into solids; have all of them some taste of the natural philosopher,—some savor of the nature of things, and experience, and bodies; whereas in the physics of Aristotle you hear hardly anything but the words of logic; which in his metaphysics also, under a more imposing name, and more forsooth as a realist than a nominalist, he has handled over again. Nor let any weight be given to the fact that in his books on animals, and his *Problems*, and other of his treatises, there is frequent dealing with experiments. For he had come to his conclusion before: he did not consult experience, as he should have done, in order to the framing of his decisions and axioms; but having first determined the question according to his will, he then resorts to experience, and bending her into conformity with his placets leads her about like a captive in a procession: so that even on this count he is more guilty than his modern followers, the schoolmen, who have abandoned experience altogether.

LXIV

But the empirical school of philosophy gives birth to dogmas more deformed and monstrous than the sophistical or rational school. For it has its foundations not in the light of common notions (which, though it be a faint and superficial light, is yet in a manner universal, and has reference to many things) but in the narrowness and darkness of a few experiments. To those therefore who are daily busied with these experiments, and have infected their imagination with them, such a philosophy seems probable and all but certain; to all men else incredible and vain. Of this there is a notable instance in the alchemists and their dogmas; though it is hardly to be found elsewhere in these times, except perhaps in the philosophy of Gilbert. Nevertheless with regard to philosophies of this kind there is one caution not to be omitted; for I foresee that if ever men are roused by my admonitions to betake themselves seriously to experiment and bid farewell to sophistical doctrines, then indeed through the premature hurry of the understanding to leap or fly to universals and principles of things, great danger may be apprehended from philosophies of this kind; against which evil we ought even now to prepare.

LXV

But the corruption of philosophy by superstition and an admixture of theology is far more widely spread, and does the greatest harm, whether to entire systems or to their parts. For the human understanding is obnoxious to the influence of the imagination no less than to the influence of common notions. For the contentious and sophistical kind of philosophy ensnares the understanding; but this kind, being fanciful and tumid and half poetical, misleads it more by flattery. For there is in man an ambition of the understanding, no less than of the will, especially in high and lofty spirits.

Of this kind we have among the Greeks a striking example in Pythagoras, though he united with it a coarser and more cumbrous superstition; another in Plato and his school, more dangerous and subtle. It shows itself likewise in parts of other philosophies, in the introduction of abstract forms and final causes and first causes, with the omission in most cases of causes intermediate, and the like. Upon this point the greatest caution should be used. For nothing is so mischievous as the apotheosis of error; and it is a very plague of the understanding for vanity to become the object of veneration. Yet in this vanity some of the moderns have with extreme levity indulged so far as to attempt to found a system of natural philosophy on the first chapters of Genesis, on the book of Job, and other parts of the sacred writings; seeking for the dead among the living: which also makes the inhibition and repression of it the more important, because from this unwholesome mixture of things human and divine there arises not only a fantastic philosophy but also an heretical religion. Very meet it is therefore that we be sober-minded, and give to faith that only which is faith's.

LXVI

So much then for the mischievous authorities of systems,

which are founded either on common notions, or on a few experiments, or on superstition. It remains to speak of the faulty subject-matter of contemplations, especially in natural philosophy. Now the human understanding is infected by the sight of what takes place in the mechanical arts, in which the alteration of bodies proceeds chiefly by composition or separation, and so imagines that something similar goes on in the universal nature of things. From this source has flowed the fiction of elements, and of their concourse for the formation of natural bodies. Again, when man contemplates nature working freely, he meets with different species of things, of animals, of plants, of minerals; whence he readily passes into the opinion that there are in nature certain primary forms which nature intends to educe, and that the remaining variety proceeds from hindrances and aberrations of nature in the fulfillment of her work, or from the collision of different species and the transplanting of one into another. To the first of these speculations we owe our primary qualities of the elements; to the other our occult properties and specific virtues; and both of them belong to those empty *compendia* of thought wherein the mind rests, and whereby it is diverted from more solid pursuits. It is to better purpose that the physicians bestow their labor on the secondary qualities of matter, and the operations of attraction, repulsion, attenuation, conspissation, dilatation, astriction, dissipation, maturation, and the like; and were it not that by those two compendia which I have mentioned (elementary qualities, to wit, and specific virtues) they corrupted their correct observations in these other matters,—either reducing them to first qualities and their subtle and incommensurable mixtures, or not following them out with greater and more diligent observation to third and fourth qualities, but breaking off the scrutiny prematurely,—they had made much greater progress. Nor are powers of this kind (I do not say the same, but similar) to be sought for only in the medicines of the human body, but also in the changes of all other bodies.

But it is a far greater evil that they make the quiescent principles, *wherefrom*, and not the moving principles, *whereby*, things are produced, the object of their contemplation and inquiry. For the former tend to discourse, the latter to works. Nor is there any value in those vulgar distinctions of motion which are observed in the received system of natural philosophy, as generation, corruption, augmentation, diminution, alteration, and local motion. What they mean no doubt is this: If a body, in other respects not changed, be moved from its place, this is *local motion;* if without change of place or essence, it be changed in quality, this is *alteration;* if by reason of the change the mass and quantity of the body do not remain the same, this is *augmentation* or *diminution;* if they be changed to such a degree that they change their very essence and substance and turn to something else, this is *generation* and *corruption.* But all this is merely popular, and does not at all go deep into nature; for these are only measures and limits, not kinds of motion. What they intimate is *how far,* not *by what means,* or *from what source.* For they do not suggest anything with regard either to the desires of bodies or to the development of their parts: it is only when that motion presents the thing grossly and palpably to the sense as different from what it was, that they begin to mark the division. Even when they wish to suggest something with regard to the causes of motion, and to establish a division with reference to them, they introduce with the greatest negligence a distinction between motion natural and violent; a distinction which is itself drawn entirely from a vulgar notion, since all violent motion is also in fact natural; the external efficient simply setting nature working otherwise than it was before. But if, leaving all this, anyone shall observe (for instance) that there is in bodies a desire of mutual contact, so as not to suffer the unity of nature to be quite separated or broken and a vacuum thus made; or if anyone say that there is in bodies a desire of resuming their natural dimensions or tension, so that if compressed within or extended beyond them, they immediately strive to recover themselves, and fall back to their old volume and extent; or if anyone say that there is in bodies a desire of congregating towards masses of kindred nature,—of dense bodies, for instance, towards the globe of the earth, of thin and rare bodies towards the compass of the sky; all these and the like are truly physical kinds of motion;—but those others are entirely logical and scholastic, as is abundantly manifest from this comparison.

Nor again is it a less evil, that in their philosophies and contemplations their labor is spent in investigating and handling the first principles of things and the highest generalities of nature; whereas utility and the means of working result entirely from things intermediate. Hence it is that men cease not from abstracting nature till they come to potential and uninformed matter, nor on the other hand from dissecting nature till they reach the atom; things which, even if true, can do but little for the welfare of mankind.

LXVII

A caution must also be given to the understanding against the intemperance which systems of philosophy manifest in giving or withholding assent; because intemperance of this kind seems to establish idols and in some sort to perpetuate them, leaving no way open to reach and dislodge them.

This excess is of two kinds: the first being manifest in those who are ready in deciding; and render sciences dogmatic and magisterial; the other in those who deny that we can know anything, and so introduce a wandering kind of inquiry that leads to nothing; of which kinds the former subdues, the latter weakens the understanding. For the philosophy of Aristotle, after having by hostile confutations destroyed all the rest (as the Ottomans serve their brothers), has laid down the law on all points: which done, he proceeds himself to raise new questions of his own suggestion, and dispose of them likewise; so that nothing may remain that is not certain and decided,—a practice which holds and is in use among his successors.

The school of Plato, on the other hand, introduced *Acatalepsia*, at first in jest and irony, and in disdain of the older sophists, Protagoras, Hippias, and the rest, who were of nothing else so much ashamed as of seeming to doubt about anything. But the New Academy made a dogma of it, and held it as a tenet. And though theirs is a fairer seeming way than arbitrary decisions; since they say that they by no means destroy all investigation, like Pyrrho and his Refrainers, but allow of some things to be followed as probable, though of none to be maintained as true; yet still when the human mind has once despaired of finding truth, its interest in all things grows fainter; and the result is that men turn aside to pleasant disputations and discourses and roam as it were from object to object, rather than keep on a course of severe inquisition. But, as I said at the beginning and am ever urging, the human senses and understanding, weak as they are, are not to be deprived of their authority, but to be supplied with helps.

LXVIII

So much concerning the several classes of idols, and their equipage: all of which must be renounced and put away with a fixed and solemn determination, and the understanding thoroughly freed and cleansed; the entrance into the kingdom of man, founded on the sciences, being not much other than the entrance into the kingdom of heaven, whereinto none may enter except as a little child.

LXIX

But vicious demonstrations are as the strongholds and defenses of idols; and those we have in logic do little else than make the world the bond-slave of human thought, and human thought the bond-slave of words. Demonstrations truly are in effect the philosophies themselves and the sciences. For such as *they* are, well or ill established, such are the systems of philosophy and the contemplations which follow. Now in the whole of the process which leads from the sense and objects to axioms and conclusions, the demonstrations which we use are deceptive and incompetent. This process consists of four parts, and has as many faults. In the first place, the impressions of the sense itself are faulty; for the sense both fails us and deceives us. But its shortcomings are to be supplied, and its deceptions to be corrected. Secondly, notions are ill drawn from the impressions of the senses, and are indefinite and confused, whereas they should be definite and distinctly bounded. Thirdly, the induction is amiss which infers the principles of sciences by simple enumeration, and does not, as it ought, employ exclusions and solutions (or separations) of nature. Lastly, that method of discovery and proof according to which the most general principles are first established, and then intermediate axioms are tried and proved by them, is the parent of error and the curse of all science. Of these things however, which now I do but touch upon, I will speak more largely, when, having performed these expiations and purgings of the mind, I come to set forth the true way for the interpretation of nature.

LXX

But the best demonstration by far is experience, if it go not beyond the actual experiment. For if it be transferred to other cases which are deemed similar, unless such transfer be made by a just and orderly process, it is a fallacious thing. But the manner of making experiments which men now use is blind and stupid. And therefore, wandering and straying as they do with no settled course, and taking counsel only from things as they fall out, they fetch a wide circuit and meet with many matters, but make little progress; and sometimes are full of hope, sometimes are distracted; and always find that there is something beyond to be sought. For it generally happens that men make their trials carelessly, and as it were in play; slightly varying experiments already known, and, if the thing does not answer, growing weary and abandoning the attempt. And even if they apply themselves to experiments more seriously and earnestly and laboriously, still they spend their labor in working out some one experiment, as Gilbert with the magnet, and the chemists with gold,—a course of proceeding not less unskillful in the design than small in the attempt. For no one successfully investigates the nature of a thing in the thing itself; the inquiry must be enlarged, so as to become more general.

And even when they seek to educe some science or theory

from their experiments, they nevertheless almost always turn aside with overhasty and unseasonable eagerness to practice; not only for the sake of the uses and fruits of the practice, but from impatience to obtain in the shape of some new work an assurance for themselves that it is worth their while to go on; and also to show themselves off to the world, and so raise the credit of the business in which they are engaged. Thus, like Atalanta, they go aside to pick up the golden apple, but meanwhile they interrupt their course, and let the victory escape them. But in the true course of experience, and in carrying it on to the effecting of new works, the divine wisdom and order must be our pattern. Now God on the first day of creation created light only, giving to that work an entire day, in which no material substance was created. So must we likewise from experience of every kind first endeavor to discover true causes and axioms; and seek for experiments of Light, not for experiments of Fruit. For axioms rightly discovered and established supply practice with its instruments, not one by one, but in clusters, and draw after them trains and troops of works. Of the paths however of experience, which no less than the paths of judgment are impeded and beset, I will speak hereafter; here I have only mentioned ordinary experimental research as a bad kind of demonstration. But now the order of the matter in hand leads me to add something both as to those *signs* which I lately mentioned,—signs that the system of philosophy and contemplation in use are in a bad condition,—and also as to the *causes* of what seems at first so strange and incredible. For a knowledge of the signs prepares assent; an explanation of the causes removes the marvel: which two things will do much to render the extirpation of idols from the understanding more easy and gentle.

LXXI

The sciences which we possess come for the most part from the Greeks. For what has been added by Roman, Arabic, or later writers is not much nor of much importance; and whatever it is, it is built on the foundation of Greek discoveries.

Now the wisdom of the Greeks was professorial and much given to disputations; a kind of wisdom most adverse to the inquisition of truth. Thus that name of Sophists, which by those who would be thought philosophers was in contempt cast back upon and so transferred to the ancient rhetoricians, Gorgias, Protagoras, Hippias, Polus, does indeed suit the entire class, Plato, Aristotle, Zeno, Epicurus, Theophrastus, and their successors Chrysippus, Carnades, and the rest. There was this difference only, that the former class was wandering and mercenary, going about from town to town, putting up their wisdom to sale, and taking a price for it; while the latter was more pompous and dignified, as composed of men who had fixed abodes, and who opened schools and taught their philosophy without reward. Still both sorts, though in other respects unequal, were professorial; both turned the matter into disputations, and set up and battled for philosophical sects and heresies; so that their doctrines were for the most part (as Dionysius not unaptly rallied Plato) "the talk of idle old men to ignorant youths." But the elder of the Greek philosophers, Empedocles, Anaxagoras, Leucippus, Democritus, Parmenides, Heraclitus, Xenophanes, Philolaus, and the rest (I omit Pythagoras as a mystic), did not, so far as we know, open schools; but more silently and severely and simply,—that is, with less affectation and parade,—betook themselves to the inquisition of truth. And therefore they were in my judgment more successful; only that their works were in the course of time obscured by those slighter persons who had more which suits and pleases the capacity and tastes of the vulgar: time, like a river, bringing down to us things which are light and puffed up, but letting weighty matters sink. Still even they were not altogether free from the failing of their nation; but leaned too much to the ambition and vanity of founding a sect and catching popular applause. But the inquisition of truth must be despaired of when it turns aside to trifles of this kind. Nor should we omit that judgment, or rather divination, which was given concerning the Greeks by the Egyptian priest,—that "they were always boys, without antiquity of knowledge or knowledge of antiquity."

Assuredly they have that which is characteristic of boys; they are prompt to prattle, but cannot generate; for their wisdom abounds in words but is barren of works. And therefore the signs which are taken from the origin and birthplace of the received philosophy are not good.

LXXII

Nor does the character of the time and age yield much better signs than the character of the country and nation. For at that period there was but a narrow and meager knowledge either of time or place; which is the worst thing that can be, especially for those who rest all on experience. For they had no history, worthy to be called history, that went back a thousand years; but only fables and rumors of antiquity. And of the regions and districts of the world they knew but a small portion; giving indiscriminately the name of Scythians to all in the North, of Celts to all in the West; knowing nothing of Africa beyond the hither side of Ethiopia, of Asia beyond the Ganges; much less were they acquainted with the provinces of the New World, even by hearsay or any well-founded rumor; nay, a multitude of climates and zones, wherein innumerable nations breathe and live, were pronounced by them to be uninhabitable; and the travels of Democritus, Plato, and Pythagoras, which were rather suburban excursions than distant journeys, were talked of as something great. In our times on the other hand both many parts of the New World and the limits on every side of the Old World are known, and our stock of experience has increased to an infinite amount. Wherefore if (like astrologers) we draw signs from the season of their nativity or birth, nothing great can be predicted of those systems of philosophy.

LXXIII

Of all signs there is none more certain or more noble than that taken from fruits. For fruits and works are as it were sponsors and sureties for the truth of philosophies. Now, from all these systems of the Greeks, and their ramifications through particular sciences there can hardly after the lapse of so many years be adduced a single experiment which tends to relieve and benefit the condition of man, and which can with truth be referred to the speculations and theories of philosophy. And Celsus ingenuously and wisely owns as much, when he tells us that the experimental part of medicine was first discovered, and that afterwards men philosophized about it, and hunted for and assigned causes; and not by an inverse process that philosophy and the knowledge of causes led to the discovery and development of the experimental part. And therefore it was not strange that among the Egyptians, who rewarded inventors with divine honors and sacred rites, there were more images of brutes than of men; inasmuch as brutes by their natural instinct have produced many discoveries, whereas men by discussion and the conclusions of reason have given birth to few or none.

Some little has indeed been produced by the industry of chemists; but it has been produced accidentally and in passing, or else by a kind of variation of experiments, such as mechanics use; and not by any art or theory; for the theory which they have devised rather confuses the experiments than aids them. They too who have busied themselves with natural magic, as they call it, have but few discoveries to show, and those trifling and imposture-like. Wherefore, as in religion we are warned to show our faith by works, so in philosophy by the same rule the system should be judged of by its fruits, and pronounced frivolous if it be barren; more especially if, in place of fruits of grape and olive, it bear thorns and briars of dispute and contention.

LXXIV

Signs also are to be drawn from the increase and progress of systems and sciences. For what is founded on nature grows and increases; while what is founded on opinion varies but increases not. If therefore those doctrines had not plainly been like a plant torn up from its roots, but had remained attached to the womb of nature and continued to draw nourishment from her, that could never have come to pass which we have seen now for twice a thousand years; namely, that

the sciences stand where they did and remain almost in the
same condition; receiving no noticeable increase, but on the
contrary, thriving most under their first founder, and then
declining. Whereas in the mechanical arts, which are founded
on nature and the light of experience, we see the contrary
happen, for these (as long as they are popular) are continually
thriving and growing, as having in them a breath of life; at
first rude, then convenient, afterwards adorned, and at all
times advancing.

LXXV

There is still another sign remaining (if sign it can be
called, when it is rather testimony, nay, of all testimony the
most valid); I mean the confession of the very authorities
whom men now follow. For even they who lay down the law
on all things so confidently, do still in their more sober moods
fall to complaints of the subtlety of nature, the obscurity of
things, and the weakness of the human mind. Now if this were
all they did, some perhaps of a timid disposition might be
deterred from further search, while others of a more ardent
and hopeful spirit might be whetted and incited to go on
farther. But not content to speak for themselves, whatever
is beyond their own or their master's knowledge or reach they
set down as beyond the bounds of possibility, and pronounce,
as if on the authority of their art, that it cannot be known or
done; thus most presumptuously and invidiously turning the
weakness of their own discoveries into a calumny on nature
herself, and the despair of the rest of the world. Hence the
school of the New Academy, which held *Acatalepsia* as a
tenet and doomed men to perpetual darkness. Hence the
opinion that forms or true differences of things (which are
in fact laws of pure act) are past finding out and beyond the
reach of man. Hence too those opinions in the department of
action and operation; as that the heat of the sun and of fire
are quite different in kind,—lest men should imagine that by
the operations of fire anything like the works of nature can
be educed and formed. Hence the notion that composition
only is the work of man, and mixture of none but nature,—

lest men should expect from art some power of generating
or transforming natural bodies. By this sign, therefore, men
will easily take warning not to mix up their fortunes and
labors with dogmas not only despaired of but dedicated to
despair.

LXXVI

Neither is this other sign to be omitted;—that formerly
there existed among philosophers such great disagreement,
and such diversities in the schools themselves; a fact which
sufficiently shows that the road from the senses to the understanding was not skillfully laid out, when the same groundwork of philosophy (the nature of things to wit) was torn
and split up into such vague and multifarious errors. And
although in these times disagreements and diversities of opinion on first principles and entire systems are for the most
part extinguished, still on parts of philosophy there remain
innumerable questions and disputes, so that it plainly appears
that neither in the systems themselves nor in the modes of
demonstration is there anything certain or sound.

LXXVII

And as for the general opinion that in the philosophy of
Aristotle at any rate there is great agreement; since after its
publication the systems of older philosophers died away,
while in the times which followed nothing better was found;
so that it seems to have been so well laid and established as
to have drawn both ages in its train; I answer in the first
place, that the common notion of the falling off of the old
systems upon the publication of Aristotle's works is a false
one; for long afterwards, down even to the times of Cicero
and subsequent ages, the works of the old philosophers still
remained. But in the times which followed, when on the
inundation of barbarians into the Roman empire human
learning had suffered shipwreck, then the systems of Aristotle
and Plato, like planks of lighter and less solid material, floated
on the waves of time, and were preserved. Upon the point
of consent also men are deceived, if the matter be looked into

more keenly. For true consent is that which consists in the coincidence of free judgments, after due examination. But far the greater number of those who have assented to the philosophy of Aristotle have addicted themselves thereto from prejudgment and upon the authority of others; so that it is a following and going along together, rather than consent. But even if it had been a real and widespread consent, still so little ought consent to be deemed a sure and solid confirmation, that it is in fact a strong presumption the other way. For the worst of all auguries is from consent in matters intellectual (divinity excepted, and politics where there is right of vote). For nothing pleases the many unless it strikes the imagination, or binds the understanding with the bands of common notions, as I have already said. We may very well transfer therefore from moral to intellectual matters, the saying of Phocion, that if the multitude assent and applaud men ought immediately to examine themselves as to what blunder or fault they may have committed. This sign therefore is one of the most unfavorable. And so much for this point; namely, that the signs of truth and soundness in the received systems and sciences are not good; whether they be drawn from their origin, or from their fruits, or from their progress, or from the confessions of their founders, or from general consent.

LXXVIII

I now come to the *causes* of these errors, and of so long a continuance in them through so many ages; which are very many and very potent;—that all wonder how these considerations which I bring forward should have escaped men's notice till now, may cease; and the only wonder be, how now at last they should have entered into any man's head and become the subject of his thoughts; which truly I myself esteem as the result of some happy accident, rather than of any excellence of faculty in me; a birth of time rather than a birth of wit. Now, in the first place, those so many ages, if you weigh the case truly, shrink into a very small compass. For out of the five and twenty centuries over which the memory and

learning of men extends, you can hardly pick out six that
were fertile in sciences or favorable to their development.
In times no less than in regions there are wastes and deserts.
For only three revolutions and periods of learning can properly be reckoned; one among the Greeks, the second among
the Romans, and the last among us, that is to say, the nations
of Western Europe; and to each of these hardly two centuries can justly be assigned. The intervening ages of the
world, in respect of any rich or flourishing growth of the
sciences, were unprosperous. For neither the Arabians nor
the schoolmen need be mentioned; who in the intermediate
times rather crushed the sciences with a multitude of treatises,
than increased their weight. And therefore the first cause
of so meager a progress in the sciences is duly and orderly
referred to the narrow limits of the time that has been favorable to them.

LXXIX

In the second place there presents itself a cause of great
weight in all ways; namely, that during those very ages in
which the wits and learning of men have flourished most, or
indeed flourished at all, the least part of their diligence was
given to natural philosophy. Yet this very philosophy it is
that ought to be esteemed the great mother of the sciences.
For all arts and all sciences, if torn from this root, though
they may be polished and shaped and made fit for use, yet
they will hardly grow. Now it is well known that after the
Christian religion was received and grew strong, by far the
greater number of the best wits applied themselves to theology; that to this both the highest rewards were offered, and
helps of all kinds most abundantly supplied; and that this
devotion to theology chiefly occupied that third portion or
epoch of time among us Europeans of the West; and the
more so because about the same time both literature began
to flourish and religious controversies to spring up. In the
age before, on the other hand, during the continuance of
the second period among the Romans, the meditations and
labors of philosophers were principally employed and con-

sumed on moral philosophy, which to the heathen was as theology to us. Moreover in those times the greatest wits applied themselves very generally to public affairs; the magnitude of the Roman empire requiring the services of a great number of persons. Again, the age in which natural philosophy was seen to flourish most among the Greeks, was but a brief particle of time; for in early ages the Seven Wise Men, as they were called (all except Thales) applied themselves to morals and politics; and in later times, when Socrates had drawn down philosophy from heaven to earth, moral philosophy became more fashionable than ever, and diverted the minds of men from the philosophy of nature.

Nay, the very period itself in which inquiries concerning nature flourished, was by controversies and the ambitious display of new opinions corrupted and made useless. Seeing therefore that during those three periods natural philosophy was in a great degree either neglected or hindered, it is no wonder if men made but small advance in that to which they were not attending.

LXXX

To this it may be added that natural philosophy, even among those who have attended to it, has scarcely ever possessed, especially in these later times, a disengaged and whole man (unless it were some monk studying in his cell, or some gentleman in his country house), but that it has been made merely a passage and bridge to something else. And so this great mother of the sciences has with strange indignity been degraded to the offices of a servant; having to attend on the business of medicine or mathematics, and likewise to wash and imbue youthful and unripe wits with a sort of first dye, in order that they may be the fitter to receive another afterwards. Meanwhile let no man look for much progress in the sciences—especially in the practical part of them—unless natural philosophy be carried on and applied to particular sciences, and particular sciences be carried back again to natural philosophy. For want of this, astronomy, optics, music, a number of mechanical arts, medicine itself,—nay, what one might more wonder at, moral and political philosophy, and the logical sciences,—altogether lack profoundness, and merely glide along the surface and variety of things; because after these particular sciences have been once distributed and established, they are no more nourished by natural philosophy; which might have drawn out of the true contemplation of motions, rays, sounds, texture and configuration of bodies, affections, and intellectual perceptions, the means of imparting to them fresh strength and growth. And therefore it is nothing strange if the sciences grow not, seeing they are parted from their roots.

LXXXI

Again there is another great and powerful cause why the sciences have made but little progress; which is this. It is not possible to run a course aright when the goal itself has not been rightly placed. Now the true and lawful goal of the sciences is none other than this: that human life be endowed with new discoveries and powers. But of this the great majority have no feeling, but are merely hireling and professorial; except when it occasionally happens that some workman of acuter wit and covetous of honor applies himself to a new invention; which he mostly does at the expense of his fortunes. But in general, so far are men from proposing to themselves to augment the mass of arts and sciences, that from the mass already at hand they neither take nor look for anything more than what they may turn to use in their lectures, or to gain, or to reputation, or to some similar advantage. And if any one out of all the multitude court science with honest affection and for her own sake, yet even with him the object will be found to be rather the variety of contemplations and doctrines than the severe and rigid search after truth. And if by chance there be one who seeks after truth in earnest, yet even he will propose to himself such a kind of truth as shall yield satisfaction to the mind and understanding in rendering causes for things long since discovered, and not the truth which shall lead to new assurance of works and new light of axioms. If then the end of the sciences has

not yet been well placed, it is not strange that men have erred
as to the means.

And as men have misplaced the end and goal of the sciences; so again, even if they had placed it right, yet they have
chosen a way to it which is altogether erroneous and im-
passable. And an astonishing thing it is to one who rightly
considers the matter, that no mortal should have seriously
applied himself to the opening and laying out of a road for
the human understanding direct from the sense, by a course
of experiment orderly conducted and well built up; but that
all has been left either to the mist of tradition, or the whirl
and eddy of argument, or the fluctuations and mazes of
chance and of vague and ill-digested experience. Now let
any man soberly and diligently consider what the way is by
which men have been accustomed to proceed in the investigation and discovery of things; and in the first place he will
no doubt remark a method of discovery very simple and in-
artificial; which is the most ordinary method, and is no more
than this. When a man addresses himself to discover something, he first seeks out and sets before him all that has been
said about it by others; then he begins to meditate for himself; and so by much agitation and working of the wit solicits
and as it were evokes his own spirit to give him oracles:
which method has no foundation at all, but rests only upon
opinions and is carried about with them.

Another may perhaps call in logic to discover it for him;
but that has no relation to the matter except in name. For
logical invention does not discover principles and chief
axioms, of which arts are composed, but only such things as
appear to be consistent with them. For if you grow more
curious and importunate and busy, and question her of pro-
bations and invention of principles or primary axioms, her
answer is well known: she refers you to the faith you are
bound to give to the principles of each separate art.

There remains simple experience; which, if taken as it
comes, is called accident; if sought for, experiment. But this

kind of experience is no better than a broom without its band, as the saying is;—a mere groping, as of men in the dark, that feel all round them for the chance of finding their way; when they had much better wait for daylight, or light a candle, and then go. But the true method of experience on the contrary first lights the candle, and then by means of the candle shows the way; commencing as it does with experience duly ordered and digested, not bungling or erratic, and from it educing axioms, and from established axioms again new experiments; even as it was not without order and method that the divine word operated on the created mass. Let men therefore cease to wonder that the course of science is not yet wholly run, seeing that they have gone altogether astray; either leaving and abandoning experience entirely, or losing their way in it and wandering round and round as in a labyrinth; whereas a method rightly ordered leads by an unbroken route through the woods of experience to the open ground of axioms.

LXXXIII

This evil however has been strangely increased by an opinion or conceit, which though of long standing is vain and hurtful; namely, that the dignity of the human mind is impaired by long and close intercourse with experiments and particulars, subject to sense and bound in matter; especially as they are laborious to search, ignoble to meditate, harsh to deliver, illiberal to practice, infinite in number, and minute in subtlety. So that it has come at length to this, that the true way is not merely deserted, but shut out and stopped up; experience being, I do not say abandoned or badly managed, but rejected with disdain.

LXXXIV

Again, men have been kept back as by a kind of enchantment from progress in the sciences by reverence for antiquity, by the authority of men accounted great in philosophy, and then by general consent. Of the last I have spoken above.

As for antiquity, the opinion touching it which men entertain is quite a negligent one, and scarcely consonant with the word itself. For the old age of the world is to be accounted the true antiquity; and this is the attribute of our own times, not of that earlier age of the world in which the ancients lived; and which, though in respect of us it was the elder, yet in respect of the world it was the younger. And truly as we look for greater knowledge of human things and a riper judgment in the old man than in the young, because of his experience and of the number and variety of the things which he has seen and heard and thought of; so in like manner from our age, if it but knew its own strength and chose to essay and exert it, much more might fairly be expected than from the ancient times, inasmuch as it is a more advanced age of the world, and stored and stocked with infinite experiments and observations.

Nor must it go for nothing that by the distant voyages and travels which have become frequent in our times, many things in nature have been laid open and discovered which may let in new light upon philosophy. And surely it would be disgraceful if, while the regions of the material globe,—that is, of the earth, of the sea, and of the stars,—have been in our times laid widely open and revealed, the intellectual globe should remain shut up within the narrow limits of old discoveries.

And with regard to authority, it shows a feeble mind to grant so much to authors and yet deny time his rights, who is the author of authors, nay rather of all authority. For rightly is truth called the daughter of time, not of authority. It is no wonder therefore if those enchantments of antiquity and authority and consent have so bound up men's powers that they have been made impotent (like persons bewitched) to accompany with the nature of things.

LXXXV

Nor is it only the admiration of antiquity, authority, and consent, that has forced the industry of man to rest satisfied with the discoveries already made; but also an admiration for the works themselves of which the human race has long been in possession. For when a man looks at the variety and the beauty of the provision which the mechanical arts have brought together for men's use, he will certainly be more inclined to admire the wealth of man than to feel his wants: not considering that the original observations and operations of nature (which are the life and moving principle of all that variety) are not many nor deeply fetched, and that the rest is but patience, and the subtle and ruled motion of the hand and instruments;—as the making of clocks (for instance) is certainly a subtle and exact work: their wheels seem to imitate the celestial orbs, and their alternating and orderly motion, the pulse of animals: and yet all this depends on one or two axioms of nature.

Again, if you observe the refinement of the liberal arts, or even that which relates to the mechanical preparation of natural substances; and take notice of such things as the discovery in astronomy of the motions of the heavens, of harmony in music, of the letters of the alphabet (to this day not in use among the Chinese) in grammar: or again in things mechanical, the discovery of the works of Bacchus and Ceres —that is, of the arts of preparing wine and beer, and of making bread; the discovery once more of the delicacies of the table, of distillations and the like; and if you likewise bear in mind the long periods which it has taken to bring these things to their present degree of perfection (for they are all ancient except distillation), and again (as has been said of clocks) how little they owe to observations and axioms of nature, and how easily and obviously and as it were by casual suggestion they may have been discovered; you will easily cease from wondering, and on the contrary will pity the condition of mankind, seeing that in a course of so many ages there has been so great a dearth and barrenness of arts and inventions. And yet these very discoveries which we have just mentioned, are older than philosophy and intellectual arts. So that, if the truth must be spoken, when the rational and dogmatical sciences began the discovery of useful works came to an end.

And again, if a man turn from the workshop to the library,

and wonder at the immense variety of books he sees there, let him but examine and diligently inspect their matter and contents, and his wonder will assuredly be turned the other way; for after observing their endless repetitions, and how men are ever saying and doing what has been said and done before, he will pass from admiration of the variety to astonishment at the poverty and scantiness of the subjects which till now have occupied and possessed the minds of men.

And if again he descend to the consideration of those arts which are deemed curious rather than safe, and look more closely into the works of the alchemists or the magicians, he will be in doubt perhaps whether he ought rather to laugh over them or to weep. For the alchemist nurses eternal hope, and when the thing fails, lays the blame upon some error of his own; fearing either that he has not sufficiently understood the words of his art or of his authors (whereupon he turns to tradition and auricular whispers), or else that in his manipulations he has made some slip of a scruple in weight or a moment in time (whereupon he repeats his trials to infinity); and when meanwhile among the chances of experiment he lights upon some conclusions either in aspect new or for utility not contemptible, he takes these for earnest of what is to come, and feeds his mind upon them, and magnifies them to the most, and supplies the rest in hope. Not but that alchemists have made a good many discoveries, and presented men with useful inventions. But their case may be well compared to the fable of the old man, who bequeathed to his sons gold buried in a vineyard, pretending not to know the exact spot; whereupon the sons applied themselves diligently to the digging of the vineyard and though no gold was found there, yet the vintage by that digging was made more plentiful.

Again the students of natural magic, who explain everything by sympathies and antipathies, have in their idle and most slothful conjectures ascribed to substances wonderful virtues and operations; and if ever they have produced works, they have been such as aim rather at admiration and novelty than at utility and fruit.

In superstitious magic on the other hand (if of this also we must speak), it is especially to be observed that they are but subjects of a certain and definite kind wherein the curious and superstitious arts, in all nations and ages, and religions also, have worked or played. These therefore we may pass. Meanwhile it is nowise strange if opinion of plenty has been the cause of want.

LXXXVI

Further, this admiration of men for knowledges and arts, —an admiration in itself weak enough, and well-nigh childish,—has been increased by the craft and artifices of those who have handled and transmitted sciences. For they set them forth with such ambition and parade, and bring them into the view of the world so fashioned and masked, as if they were complete in all parts and finished. For if you look at the method of them and the divisions, they seem to embrace and comprise everything which can belong to the subject. And although these divisions are ill filled out and are but as empty cases, still to the common mind they present the form and plan of a perfect science. But the first and most ancient seekers after truth were wont, with better faith and better fortune too, to throw the knowledge which they gathered from the contemplation of things, and which they meant to store up for use, into aphorisms; that is, into short and scattered sentences, not linked together by an artificial method; and did not pretend or profess to embrace the entire art. But as the matter now is, it is nothing strange if men do not seek to advance in things delivered to them as long since perfect and complete.

LXXXVII

Moreover the ancient systems have received no slight accession of reputation and credit from the vanity and levity of those who have propounded new ones; especially in the active and practical department of natural philosophy. For there ⸺ not been wanting talkers and dreamers who, partly from ⸺ partly in imposture, have loaded mankind with promises, offering and announcing the prolongation of life, the retardation of age, the alleviation of pain, the repairing of natural defects, the deceiving of the senses; arts of binding and inciting the affections, of illuminating and exalting the intellectual faculties, of transmuting substances, of strengthening and multiplying motions at will, of making impressions and alterations in the air, of bringing down and procuring celestial influences; arts of divining things future, and bringing things distant near, and revealing things secret; and many more. But with regard to these lavish promisers, this judgment would not be far amiss; that there is as much difference in philosophy between their vanities and true arts, as there is in history between the exploits of Julius Caesar or Alexander the Great, and the exploits of Amadis of Gaul or Arthur of Britain. For it is true that those illustrious generals really did greater things than these shadowy heroes are even feigned to have done; but they did them by means and ways of action not fabulous or monstrous. Yet surely it is not fair that the credit of true history should be lessened because it has sometimes been injured and wronged by fables. Meanwhile it is not to be wondered at, if a great prejudice is raised against new propositions, especially when works are also mentioned, because of those impostors who have attempted the like; since their excess of vanity, and the disgust it has bred, have their effect still in the destruction of all greatness of mind in enterprises of this kind.

LXXXVIII

Far more however has knowledge suffered from littleness of spirit and the smallness and slightness of the tasks which human industry has proposed to itself. And what is worst of all, this very littleness of spirit comes with a certain air of arrogance and superiority.

For in the first place there is found in all arts one general device, which has now become familiar,—that the author lays the weakness of his art to the charge of nature: whatever his art cannot attain he sets down on the authority of the same art to be in nature impossible. And truly no art can be condemned if it be judge itself. Moreover the philosophy which is now in vogue embraces and cherishes certain tenets, the purpose of which (if it be diligently examined) is to persuade men that nothing difficult, nothing by which nature may be commanded and subdued, can be expected from art or human labor; as with respect to the doctrine that the heat of the sun and of fire differ in kind, and to that other concerning mixture, has been already observed. Which things, if they be noted accurately, tend wholly to the unfair circumscription of human power, and to a deliberate and factitious despair; which not only disturbs the auguries of hope, but also cuts the sinews and spur of industry, and throws away the chances of experience itself; and all for the sake of having their art thought perfect, and for the miserable vainglory of making it believed that whatever has not yet been discovered and comprehended can never be discovered or comprehended hereafter.

And even if a man apply himself fairly to facts, and endeavor to find out something new, yet he will confine his aim and intention to the investigation and working out of some one discovery and no more; such as the nature of the magnet, the ebb and flow of the sea, the system of the heavens, and things of this kind, which seem to be in some measure secret, and have hitherto been handled without much success. Whereas it is most unskillful to investigate the nature of any thing in the thing itself; seeing that the same nature which appears in some things to be latent and hidden is in others manifest and palpable; wherefore in the former it produces wonder, in the latter excites no attention; as we find it in the nature of consistency, which in wood or stone is not observed, but is passed over under the appellation of solidity, without further inquiry as to why separation or solution of continuity is avoided; while in the case of bubbles, which form themselves into certain pellicles, curiously shaped into hemispheres, so that the solution of continuity is avoided for a moment, it is thought a subtle matter. In fact what in some is accounted a secret has in others a manifest and well-nature, which will never be recognized as long as the experiments and thoughts of men are engaged on the former only.

But generally speaking, in mechanics old discoveries pass for new, if a man does but refine or embellish them, or unite several in one, or couple them better with their use, or make the work in greater or less volume than it was before, or the like.

Thus then it is no wonder if noble inventions and worthy of mankind have not been brought to light, when men have been contented and delighted with such trifling and puerile tasks, and have even fancied that in them they have been endeavoring after, if not accomplishing, some great matter.

LXXXIX

Neither is it to be forgotten that in every age natural philosophy has had a troublesome adversary and hard to deal with; namely, superstition, and the blind and immoderate zeal of religion. For we see among the Greeks that those who first proposed to men's then uninitiated ears the natural causes for thunder and for storms, were thereupon found guilty of impiety. Nor was much more forbearance shown by some of the ancient fathers of the Christian church to those who on most convincing grounds (such as no one in his senses would now think of contradicting) maintained that the earth was round, and of consequence asserted the existence of the antipodes.

Moreover, as things now are, to discourse of nature is made harder and more perilous by the summaries and systems of the schoolmen; who having reduced theology into regular order as well as they were able, and fashioned it into the shape of an art, ended in incorporating the contentious and thorny philosophy of Aristotle, more than was fit, with the body of religion.

To the same result, though in a different way, tend the speculations of those who have taken upon them to deduce the truth of the Christian religion from the principles of philosophers, and to confirm it by their authority; pompously solemnizing this union of the sense and faith as a lawful marriage, and entertaining men's minds with a pleasing variety

of matter, but all the while disparaging things divine by mingling them with things human. Now in such mixtures of theology with philosophy only the received doctrines of philosophy are included; while new ones, albeit changes for the
better, are all but expelled and exterminated.

Lastly, you will find that by the simpleness of certain di-
vines, access to any philosophy, however pure, is well nigh
closed. Some are weakly afraid lest a deeper search into nature should transgress the permitted limits of sober-minded-
ness; wrongfully wresting and transferring what is said in
holy writ against those who pry into sacred mysteries, to the
hidden things of nature, which are barred by no prohibition.
Others with more subtlety surmise and reflect that if second
causes are unknown everything can more readily be referred
to the divine hand and rod; a point in which they think religion greatly concerned; which is in fact nothing else but to
seek to gratify God with a lie. Others fear from past example
that movements and changes in philosophy will end in assaults on religion. And others again appear apprehensive that
in the investigation of nature something may be found to sub-
vert or at least shake the authority of religion, especially with
the unlearned. But these two last fears seem to me to savor
utterly of carnal wisdom; as if men in the recesses and secret
thoughts of their hearts doubted and distrusted the strength
of religion and the empire of faith over the sense, and therefore feared that the investigation of truth in nature might be
dangerous to them. But if the matter be truly considered, natural philosophy is after the word of God at once the surest
medicine against superstition, and the most approved nourishment for faith, and therefore she is rightly given to religion
as her most faithful handmaid, since the one displays the will
of God, the other his power. For he did not err who said "Ye
err in that ye know not the Scriptures and the power of
God," thus coupling and blending in an indissoluble bond information concerning his will and meditation concerning his
power. Meanwhile it is not surprising if the growth of natural philosophy is checked, when religion, the thing which
has most power over men's minds, has by the simpleness and

incautious zeal of certain persons been drawn to take part against her.

XC

Again, in the customs and institutions of schools, academies, colleges, and similar bodies destined for the abode of learned men and the cultivation of learning, everything is found adverse to the progress of science. For the lectures and exercises there are so ordered, that to think or speculate on anything out of the common way can hardly occur to any man. And if one or two have the boldness to use any liberty of judgment, they must undertake the task all by themselves; they can have no advantage from the company of others. And if they can endure this also, they will find their industry and largeness of mind no slight hindrance to their fortune. For the studies of men in these places are confined and as it were imprisoned in the writings of certain authors, from whom if any man dissent he is straightway arraigned as a turbulent person and an innovator. But surely there is a great distinction between matters of state and the arts; for the danger from new motion and from new light is not the same. In matters of state a change even for the better is distrusted, because it unsettles what is established; these things resting on authority, consent, fame and opinion, not on demonstration. But arts and sciences should be like mines, where the noise of new works and further advances is heard on every side. But though the matter be so according to right reason, it is not so acted on in practice; and the points above mentioned in the administration and government of learning put a severe restraint upon the advancement of the sciences.

XCI

Nay, even if that jealousy were to cease, still it is enough to check the growth of science, that efforts and labors in this field go unrewarded. For it does not rest with the same persons to cultivate sciences and to reward them. The growth of them comes from great wits; the prizes and rewards of them are in the hands of the people, or of great persons, who are

but in very few cases even moderately learned. Moreover this
kind of progress is not only unrewarded with prizes and substantial benefits; it has not even the advantage of popular
applause. For it is a greater matter than the generality of
men can take in, and is apt to be overwhelmed and extinguished by the gales of popular opinions. And it is nothing
strange if a thing not held in honor does not prosper.

XCII

But by far the greatest obstacle to the progress of science
and to the undertaking of new tasks and provinces therein,
is found in this—that men despair and think things impossible.
For wise and serious men are wont in these matters to be altogether distrustful; considering with themselves the obscurity of nature, the shortness of life, the deceitfulness of
the senses, the weakness of the judgment, the difficulty of
experiment and the like; and so supposing that in the revolution of time and of the ages of the world the sciences have
their ebbs and flows; that at one season they grow and flourish, at another wither and decay, yet in such sort that when
they have reached a certain point and condition they can advance no further. If therefore any one believes or promises
more, they think this comes of an ungoverned and unripened
mind, and that such attempts have prosperous beginnings, become difficult as they go on, and end in confusion. Now since
these are thoughts which naturally present themselves to
grave men and of great judgment, we must take good heed
that we be not led away by our love for a most fair and excellent object to relax or diminish the severity of our judgment; we must observe diligently what encouragement dawns
upon us and from what quarter; and, putting aside the lighter
breeze of hope, we must thoroughly sift and examine those
which promise greater steadiness and constancy. Nay, and
we must take state-prudence too into our counsels, whose
rule is to distrust, and to take the less favorable view of
human affairs. I am now therefore to speak touching *hope;*
especially as I am not a dealer in promises, and wish neither
to force nor to ensnare men's judgments, but to lead them by

the hand with their good will. And though the strongest means of inspiring hope will be to bring men to particulars; especially to particulars digested and arranged in my Tables of Discovery (the subject partly of the second, but much more of the fourth part of my *Instauration*), since this is not merely the promise of the thing but the thing itself: nevertheless that everything may be done with gentleness, I will proceed with my plan of preparing men's minds; of which preparation to give hope is no unimportant part. For without it the rest tends rather to make men sad (by giving them a worse and meaner opinion of things as they are than they now have, and making them more fully to feel and know the unhappiness of their own condition) than to induce any alacrity or to whet their industry in making trial. And therefore it is fit that I publish and set forth those conjectures of mine which make hope in this matter reasonable: just as Columbus did, before that wonderful voyage of his across the Atlantic, when he gave the reasons for his conviction that new lands and continents might be discovered besides those which were known before; which reasons, though rejected at first, were afterwards made good by experience, and were the causes and beginnings of great events.

XCIII

The beginning is from God: for the business which is in hand, having the character of good so strongly impressed upon it, appears manifestly to proceed from God, who is the Author of Good, and the Father of Lights. Now in divine operations even the smallest beginnings lead of a certainty to their end. And as it was said of spiritual things, "The kingdom of God cometh not with observation," so is it in all the greater works of Divine Providence; everything glides on smoothly and noiselessly, and the work is fairly going on before men are aware that it has begun. Nor should the prophecy of Daniel be forgotten, touching the last ages of the world:— "Many shall go to and fro, and knowledge shall be increased;" clearly intimating that the thorough passage of the world (which now by so many distant voyages seems to be accomplished, or in course of accomplishment), and the advancement of the sciences, are destined by fate, that is, by Divine Providence, to meet in the same age.

XCIV

Next comes a consideration of the greatest importance as an argument of hope; I mean that drawn from the errors of past time, and of the ways hitherto trodden. For most excellent was the censure once passed upon a government that had been unwisely administered. "That which is the worst thing in reference to the past, ought to be regarded as best for the future. For if you had done all that your duty demanded, and yet your affairs were no better, you would not have even a hope left you that further improvement is possible. But now, when your misfortunes are owing, not to the force of circumstances, but to your own errors, you may hope that by dismissing or correcting these errors, a great change may be made for the better." In like manner, if during so long a course of years men had kept the true road for discovering and cultivating sciences, and had yet been unable to make further progress therein, bold doubtless and rash would be the opinion that further progress is possible. But if the road itself has been mistaken, and men's labor spent on unfit objects, it follows that the difficulty has its rise not in things themselves, which are not in our power, but in the human understanding, and the use and application thereof, which admits of remedy and medicine. It will be of great use therefore to set forth what these errors are; for as many impediments as there have been in times past from this cause, so many arguments are there of hope for the time to come. And although they have been partly touched before, I think fit here also, in plain and simple words, to represent them.

XCV

Those who have handled sciences have been either men of experiment or men of dogmas. The men of experiment are like the ant; they only collect and use: the reasoners resemble spiders, who make cobwebs out of their own substance. But the bee takes a middle course, it gathers its material from the flowers of the garden and of the field, but transforms and digests it by a power of its own. Not unlike this is the true business of philosophy: for it neither relies solely or chiefly on the powers of the mind, nor does it take the matter which it gathers from natural history and mechanical experiments and lay it up in the memory whole, as it finds it; but lays it up in the understanding altered and digested. Therefore from a closer and purer league between these two faculties, the experimental and the rational, (such as has never yet been made) much may be hoped.

XCVI

We have as yet no natural philosophy that is pure; all is tainted and corrupted: in Aristotle's school by logic; in Plato's by natural theology; in the second school of Platonists, such as Proclus and others, by mathematics, which ought only to give definiteness to natural philosophy, not to generate or give it birth. From a natural philosophy pure and unmixed, better things are to be expected.

XCVII

No one has yet been found so firm of mind and purpose as resolutely to compel himself to sweep away all theories and common notions, and to apply the understanding, thus made fair and even, to a fresh examination of particulars. Thus it happens that human knowledge, as we have it, is a mere medley and ill-digested mass, made up of much credulity and much accident, and also of the childish notions which we at first imbibed.

Now if anyone of ripe age, unimpaired senses, and well-purged mind, apply himself anew to experience and particulars, better hopes may be entertained of that man. In which point I promise to myself a like fortune to that of Alexander the Great; and let no man tax me with vanity till he have heard the end; for the thing which I mean tends to the putting off of all vanity. For of Alexander and his deeds Aes-

chines spake thus: "Assuredly we do not live the life of
mortal men; but to this end were we born, that in after ages
wonders might be told of us;" as if what Alexander had done
seemed to him miraculous. But in the next age Titus Livius
took a better and a deeper view of the matter, saying in effect,
that Alexander "had done no more than take courage to de-
spise vain apprehensions." And a like judgment I suppose may
be passed on myself in future ages: that I did no great things,
but simply made less account of things that were accounted
great. In the meanwhile, as I have already said, there is no
hope except in a new birth of science; that is, in raising it
regularly up from experience and building it afresh; which
no one (I think) will say has yet been done or thought of.

XCVIII

Now for grounds of experience—since to experience we
must come—we have as yet had either none or very weak
ones; no search has been made to collect a store of particular
observations sufficient either in number, or in kind, or in
certainty, to inform the understanding, or in any way adequate. On the contrary, men of learning, but easy withal and
idle, have taken for the construction or for the confirmation
of their philosophy certain rumors and vague fames or airs
of experience, and allowed to these the weight of lawful evidence. And just as if some kingdom or state were to direct its
counsels and affairs, not by letters and reports from ambassa-
dors and trustworthy messengers, but by the gossip of the
streets; such exactly is the system of management introduced
into philosophy with relation to experience. Nothing duly
investigated, nothing verified, nothing counted, weighed, or
measured, is to be found in natural history: and what in observation is loose and vague, is in information deceptive and
treacherous. And if anyone thinks that this is a strange thing
to say, and something like an unjust complaint, seeing that
Aristotle, himself so great a man, and supported by the wealth
of so great a king, has composed so accurate a history of animals; and that others with greater diligence, though less pre-
tense, have made many additions; while others, again, have

compiled copious histories and descriptions of metals, plants, and fossils; it seems that he does not rightly apprehend what it is that we are now about. For a natural history which is composed for its own sake is not like one that is collected to supply the understanding with information for the building up of philosophy. They differ in many ways, but especially in this; that the former contains the variety of natural species only, and not experiments of the mechanical arts. For even as in the business of life a man's disposition and the secret workings of his mind and affections are better discovered when he is in trouble than at other times; so likewise the secrets of nature reveal themselves more readily under the vexations of art than when they go their own way. Good hopes may therefore be conceived of natural philosophy, when natural history, which is the basis and foundation of it, has been drawn up on a better plan; but not till then.

XCIX

Again, even in the great plenty of mechanical experiments, there is yet a great scarcity of those which are of most use for the information of the understanding. For the mechanic, not troubling himself with the investigation of truth, confines his attention to those things which bear upon his particular work, and will not either raise his mind or stretch out his hand for anything else. But then only will there be good ground of hope for the further advance of knowledge, when there shall be received and gathered together into natural history a variety of experiments, which are of no use in themselves, but simply serve to discover causes and axioms; which I call *experimenta lucifera*, experiments of *light*, to distinguish them from those which I call *fructifera*, experiments of *fruit*.

Now experiments of this kind have one admirable property and condition; they never miss or fail. For since they are applied, not for the purpose of producing any particular effect, but only of discovering the natural cause of some effect, they answer the end equally well whichever way they turn out; for they settle the question.

C

But not only is a greater abundance of experiments to be sought for and procured, and that too of a different kind from those hitherto tried; an entirely different method, order, and process for carrying on and advancing experience must also be introduced. For experience, when it wanders in its own track, is, as I have already remarked, mere groping in the dark, and confounds men rather than instructs them. But when it shall proceed in accordance with a fixed law, in regular order, and without interruption, then may better things be hoped of knowledge.

CI

But even after such a store of natural history and experience as is required for the work of the understanding, or of philosophy, shall be ready at hand, still the understanding is by no means competent to deal with it offhand and by memory alone; no more than if a man should hope by force of memory to retain and make himself master of the computation of an ephemeris. And yet hitherto more has been done in matter of invention by thinking than by writing; and experience has not yet learned her letters. Now no course of invention can be satisfactory unless it be carried on in writing. But when this is brought into use, and experience has been taught to read and write, better things may be hoped.

CII

Moreover, since there is so great a number and army of particulars, and that army so scattered and dispersed as to distract and confound the understanding, little is to be hoped for from the skirmishings and slight attacks and desultory movements of the intellect, unless all the particulars which pertain to the subject of inquiry shall, by means of Tables of Discovery, apt, well arranged, and as it were animate, be drawn up and marshaled; and the mind be set to work upon the helps duly prepared and digested which these tables supply.

CIII

But after this store of particulars has been set out duly and in order before our eyes, we are not to pass at once to the investigation and discovery of new particulars or works; or at any rate if we do so we must not stop there. For although I do not deny that when all the experiments of all the arts shall have been collected and digested, and brought within one man's knowledge and judgment, the mere transferring of the experiments of one art to others may lead, by means of that experience which I term *literate*, to the discovery of many new things of service to the life and state of man; yet it is no great matter that can be hoped from that: but from the new light of axioms, which having been educed from those particulars by a certain method and rule, shall in their turn point out the way again to new particulars, greater things may be looked for. For our road does not lie on a level, but ascends and descends; first ascending to axioms, then descending to works.

CIV

The understanding must not however be allowed to jump and fly from particulars to remote axioms and of almost the highest generality (such as the first principles, as they are called, of arts and things), and taking stand upon them as truths that cannot be shaken, proceed to prove and frame the middle axioms by reference to them: which has been the practice hitherto; the understanding being not only carried that way by a natural impulse, but also by the use of syllogistic demonstration trained and inured to it. But then, and then only, may we hope well of the sciences, when in a just scale of ascent, and by successive steps not interrupted or broken, we rise from particulars to lesser axioms; and then to middle axioms, one above the other; and last of all to the most general. For the lowest axioms differ but slightly from bare experience, while the highest and most general (which we now have) are notional and abstract and without solidity. But the middle are the true and solid and living axioms, on which depend the affairs and fortunes of men; and above them again, last of all, those which are indeed the most general,—such I mean as are not abstract, but of which those intermediate axioms are really limitations.

The understanding must not therefore be supplied with wings, but rather hung with weights, to keep it from leaping and flying. Now this has never yet been done; when it is done, we may entertain better hopes of the sciences.

CV

In establishing axioms, another form of induction must be devised than has hitherto been employed; and it must be used for proving and discovering not first principles (as they are called) only, but also the lesser axioms, and the middle, and indeed all. For the induction which proceeds by simple enumeration is childish; its conclusions are precarious, and exposed to peril from a contradictory instance; and it generally decides on too small a number of facts, and on those only which are at hand. But the induction which is to be available for the discovery and demonstration of sciences and arts, must analyze nature by proper rejections and exclusions; and then, after a sufficient number of negatives, come to a conclusion on the affirmative instances: which has not yet been done or even attempted, save only by Plato, who does indeed employ this form of induction to a certain extent for the purpose of discussing definitions and ideas. But in order to furnish this induction or demonstration well and duly for its work, very many things are to be provided which no mortal has yet thought of; insomuch that greater labor will have to be spent in it than has hitherto been spent on the syllogism. And this induction must be used not only to discover axioms, but also in the formation of notions. And it is in this induction that our chief hope lies.

CVI

But in establishing axioms by this kind of induction, we must also examine and try whether the axiom so established be framed to the measure of those particulars only from which it is derived, or whether it be larger and wider. And if it be larger and wider, we must observe whether by indicating to us new particulars it confirm that wideness and largeness as by a collateral security: that we may not either stick fast in things already known, or loosely grasp at shadows and abstract forms; not at things solid and realized in matter. And when this process shall have come into use, then at last shall we see the dawn of a solid hope.

CVII

And here also should be remembered what was said above concerning the extending of the range of natural philosophy to take in the particular sciences, and the referring or bringing back of the particular sciences to natural philosophy; that the branches of knowledge may not be severed and cut off from the stem. For without this the hope of progress will not be so good.

CVIII

So much then for the removing of despair and the raising of hope through the dismissal or rectification of the errors of past time. We must now see what else there is to ground hope upon. And this consideration occurs at once—that if many useful discoveries have been made by accident or upon occasion, when men were not seeking for them but were busy about other things; no one can doubt but that when they apply themselves to seek and make this their business, and that too by method and in order and not by desultory impulses, they will discover far more. For although it may happen once or twice that a man shall stumble on a thing by accident which, when taking great pains to search for it, he could not find; yet upon the whole it unquestionably falls out the other way. And therefore far better things, and more of them, and at shorter intervals, are to be expected from man's reason and industry and direction and fixed application, than from accident and animal instinct and the like, in which inventions have hitherto had their origin.

CIX

Another argument of hope may be drawn from this—that some of the inventions already known are such as before they were discovered it could hardly have entered any man's head to think of; they would have been simply set aside as impossible. For in conjecturing what may be men set before them the example of what has been, and divine of the new with an imagination preoccupied and colored by the old; which way of forming opinions is very fallacious; for streams that are drawn from the springheads of nature do not always run in the old channels.

If, for instance, before the invention of ordnance, a man had described the thing by its effects, and said that there was a new invention, by means of which the strongest towers and walls could be shaken and thrown down at a great distance; men would doubtless have begun to think over all the ways of multiplying the force of catapults and mechanical engines by weights and wheels and such machinery for ramming and projecting: but the notion of a fiery blast suddenly and violently expanding and exploding would hardly have entered into any man's imagination or fancy; being a thing to which nothing immediately analogous had been seen, except perhaps in an earthquake or in lightning, which as *magnalia* or marvels of nature, and by man not imitable, would have been immediately rejected.

In the same way, if before the discovery of silk, anyone had said that there was a kind of thread discovered for the purposes of dress and furniture, which far surpassed the thread of linen or of wool in fineness and at the same time in strength, and also in beauty and softness; men would have begun immediately to think of some silky kind of vegetable, or of the finer hair of some animal, or of the feathers and down of birds; but of a web woven by a tiny worm, and that in such abundance, and renewing itself yearly, they would assuredly never have thought. Nay, if anyone had said anything about a worm, he would no doubt have been laughed at as dreaming of a new kind of cobwebs.

So again, if before the discovery of the magnet, any one had said that a certain instrument had been invented by means of which the quarters and points of the heavens could be taken and distinguished with exactness; men would have been carried by their imagination to a variety of conjectures concerning the more exquisite construction of astronomical instruments; but that anything could be discovered agreeing so well in its movements with the heavenly bodies, and yet not a heavenly body itself, but simply a substance of metal or stone, would have been judged altogether incredible. Yet these things and others like them lay for so many ages of the world concealed from men, nor was it by philosophy or the rational arts that they were found out at last, but by accident and occasion: being indeed, as I said, altogether different in kind and as remote as possible from anything that was known before; so that no preconceived notion could possibly have led to the discovery of them.

There is therefore much ground for hoping that there are still laid up in the womb of nature many secrets of excellent use, having no affinity or parallelism with anything that is now known, but lying entirely out of the beat of the imagination, which have not yet been found out. They too no doubt will some time or other, in the course and revolution of many ages, come to light of themselves, just as the others did; only by the method of which we are now treating they can be speedily and suddenly and simultaneously presented and anticipated.

CX

But we have also discoveries to show of another kind, which prove that noble inventions may be lying at our very feet, and yet mankind may step over without seeing them. For however the discovery of gunpowder, of silk, of the magnet, of sugar, of paper, or the like, may seem to depend on certain properties of things themselves and nature, there is at any rate nothing in the art of printing which is not plain and obvious. Nevertheless for want of observing that although it is more difficult to arrange types of letters than to write letters by the motion of the hand, there is yet this difference between the two, that types once arranged serve for innumerable impressions, but letters written with the hand for a single copy only; or perhaps again for want of observing that ink can be so thickened as to color without running (particularly when the letters face upwards and the impression is made from above)—for want, I say, of observing these things, men went for so many ages without this most beautiful discovery, which is of so much service in the propagation of knowledge.

But such is the infelicity and unhappy disposition of the human mind in this course of invention, that it first distrusts and then despises itself: first will not believe that any such thing can be found out; and when it is found out, cannot understand how the world should have missed it so long. And this very thing may be justly taken as an argument of hope; namely, that there is a great mass of inventions still remaining, which not only by means of operations that are yet to be discovered, but also through the transferring, comparing, and applying of those already known, by the help of that learned experience of which I spoke, may be deduced and brought to light.

CXI

There is another ground of hope that must not be omitted. Let men but think over their infinite expenditure of understanding, time, and means on matters and pursuits of far less use and value; whereof if but a small part were directed to sound and solid studies, there is no difficulty that might not be overcome. This I thought good to add, because I plainly confess that a collection of history natural and experimental, such as I conceive it and as it ought to be, is a great, I may say a royal work, and of much labor and expense.

CXII

Meantime, let no man be alarmed at the multitude of particulars, but let this rather encourage him to hope. For the particular phenomena of art and nature are but a handful to the inventions of the wit, when disjoined and separated from the evidence of things. Moreover this road has an issue in the open ground and not far off; the other has no issue at all, but endless entanglement. For men hitherto have made but short stay with experience, but passing her lightly by, have wasted an infinity of time on meditations and glosses of the wit. But if someone were by that could answer our questions and tell us in each case what the fact in nature is, the discovery of all causes and sciences would be but the work of a few years.

CXIII

Moreover I think that men may take some hope from my own example. And this I say not by way of boasting, but because it is useful to say it. If there be any that despond, let them look at me, that being of all men of my time the most busied in affairs of state, and a man of health not very strong (whereby much time is lost), and in this course altogether a pioneer, following in no man's track, nor sharing these counsels with anyone, have nevertheless by resolutely entering on the true road, and submitting my mind to *things*, advanced these matters, as I suppose, some little way. And then let them consider what may be expected (after the way has been thus indicated) from men abounding in leisure, and from association of labors, and from successions of ages: the rather because it is not a way over which only one man can pass at a time (as is the case with that of reasoning), but one in which the labors and industries of men (especially as regards the collecting of experience) may with the best effect be first distributed and then combined. For then only will men begin to know their strength, when instead of great numbers doing all the same things, one shall take charge of one thing and another of another.

CXIV

Lastly, even if the breath of hope which blows on us from that new continent were fainter than it is and harder to perceive; yet the trial (if we would not bear a spirit altogether abject) must by all means be made. For there is no comparison between that which we may lose by not trying and by not succeeding; since by not trying we throw away the chance of an immense good; by not succeeding we only incur the loss of a little human labor. But as it is, it appears to me from what has been said, and also from what has been left unsaid, that there is hope enough and to spare, not only to make a bold man try, but also to make a sober-minded and wise man believe.

CXV

Concerning the grounds then for putting away despair, which has been one of the most powerful causes of delay and hindrance to the progress of knowledge, I have now spoken. And this also concludes what I had to say touching the *signs* and *causes* of the errors, sluggishness, and ignorance which have prevailed; especially since the more subtle causes, which do not fall under popular judgment and observation, must be referred to what has been said on the idols of the human mind.

And here likewise should close that part of my *Instauration*, which is devoted to pulling down: which part is performed by three refutations; first, by the refutation of the *natural human reason*, left to itself; secondly, by the refutation of the *demonstrations;* and thirdly, by the refutation of the *theories*, or the received systems of philosophy and doctrine. And the refutation of these has been such, as alone it could be; that is to say, by signs and the evidence of causes; since no other kind of confutation was open to me, differing as I do from others both on first principles and on rules of demonstration.

It is time therefore to proceed to the art itself and rule of interpreting nature; still however there remains something to be premised. For whereas in this first book of aphorisms I proposed to prepare men's minds as well for understanding as for receiving what is to follow; now that I have purged and swept and leveled the floor of the mind, it remains that I place the mind in a good position and as it were in a favorable aspect towards what I have to lay before it. For in a new matter, it is not only the strong preoccupation of some old opinion that tends to create a prejudice, but also a false preconception or prefiguration of the new thing which is presented.

I will endeavor therefore to impart sound and true opinions as to the things I propose, although they are to serve only for the time and by way of interest (so to speak), till the thing itself, which is the principal, be fully known.

CXVI

First, then, I must request men not to suppose that after the fashion of ancient Greeks, and of certain moderns, as Telesius, Patricius, Severinus, I wish to found a new sect in philosophy. For this is not what I am about; nor do I think that it matters much to the fortunes of men what abstract notions one may entertain concerning nature and the principles of things; and no doubt many old theories of this kind can be revived and many new ones introduced; just as many theories of the heavens may be supposed, which agree well enough with the phenomena and yet differ with each other.

But for my part I do not trouble myself with any such speculative and withal unprofitable matters. My purpose, on the contrary, is to try whether I cannot in very fact lay more firmly the foundations, and extend more widely the limits, of the power and greatness of man. And although on some special subjects and in an incomplete form I am in possession of results which I take to be far more true and more certain and withal more fruitful than those now received, (and these I have collected into the fifth part of my Instauration,) yet I have no entire or universal theory to propound. For it does not seem that the time is come for such an attempt. Neither can I hope to live to complete the sixth part of the Instauration (which is destined for the philosophy discovered by the legitimate interpretation of nature), but hold it enough if in the intermediate business I bear myself soberly and profitably, sowing in the meantime for future ages the seeds of a purer truth, and performing my part towards the commencement of the great undertaking.

CXVII

And as I do not seek to found a school, so neither do I hold out offers or promises of particular works. It may be thought indeed, that I who make such frequent mention of works and

refer everything to that end, should produce some myself by
way of earnest. But my course and method, as I have often
clearly stated and would wish to state again, is this—not to
extract works from works or experiments from experiments
(as an empiric), but from works and experiments to extract
causes and axioms, and again from those causes and axioms
new works and experiments, as a legitimate interpreter of
nature. And although in my tables of discovery (which compose the fourth part of the Instauration), and also in the examples of particulars (which I have adduced in the second
part), and moreover in my observations on the history (which
I have drawn out in the third part), any reader of even
moderate sagacity and intelligence will everywhere observe
indications and outlines of many noble works; still I candidly
confess that the natural history which I now have, whether
collected from books or from my own investigations, is
neither sufficiently copious nor verified with sufficient accuracy to serve the purposes of legitimate interpretation.

Accordingly, if there be anyone more apt and better prepared for mechanical pursuits, and sagacious in hunting out
works by the mere dealing with experiment, let him by all
means use his industry to gather from my history and tables
many things by the way, and apply them to the production of
works, which may serve as interest until the principal be
forthcoming. But for myself, aiming as I do at greater things,
I condemn all unseasonable and premature tarrying over such
things as these: being (as I often say) like Atalanta's balls. For
I do not run off like a child after golden apples, but stake all
on the victory of art over nature in the race; nor do I make
haste to mow down the moss or the corn in blade, but wait
for the harvest in its due season.

CXVIII

There will be found no doubt, when my history and tables
of discovery are read, some things in the experiments themselves that are not quite certain, or perhaps that are quite
false; which may make a man think that the foundations and
principles upon which my discoveries rest are false and doubt-

ful. But this is of no consequence; for such things must needs happen at first. It is only like the occurrence in a written or printed page of a letter or two mistaken or misplaced; which does not much hinder the reader, because such errors are easily corrected by the sense. So likewise may there occur in my natural history many experiments which are mistaken and falsely set down, and yet they will presently by the discovery of causes and axioms be easily expunged and rejected. It is nevertheless true that if the mistakes in natural history and experiments are important, frequent, and continual, they cannot possibly be corrected or amended by any felicity of wit or art. And therefore, if in my natural history, which has been collected and tested with so much diligence, severity, and I may say religious care, there still lurk at intervals certain falsities or errors in the particulars—what is to be said of common natural history, which in comparison with mine is so negligent and inexact? and what of the philosophy and sciences built on such a sand (or rather quicksand)? Let no man therefore trouble himself for this.

CXIX

There will be met with also in my history and experiments many things which are trivial and commonly known; many which are mean and low; many, lastly, which are too subtle and merely speculative, and that seem to be of no use; which kind of things may possibly avert and alienate men's interest.

And first for those things which seem common; let men bear in mind that hitherto they have been accustomed to do no more than refer and adapt the causes of things which rarely happen to such as happen frequently; while of those which happen frequently they never ask the cause, but take them as they are for granted. And therefore they do not investigate the causes of weight, of the rotation of heavenly bodies, of heat, cold, light, hardness, softness, rarity, density, liquidity, solidity, animation, inanimation, similarity, dissimilarity, organization, and the like; but admitting these as self-evident and obvious, they dispute and decide on other things of less frequent and familiar occurrence.

But I, who am well aware that no judgment can be passed on uncommon or remarkable things, much less anything new brought to light, unless the causes of common things, and the causes of those causes, be first duly examined and found out, am of necessity compelled to admit the commonest things into my history. Nay, in my judgment philosophy has been hindered by nothing more than this—that things of familiar and frequent occurrence do not arrest and detain the thoughts of men, but are received in passing without any inquiry into their causes; insomuch that information concerning things which are not known is not oftener wanted than attention concerning things which are.

CXX

And for things that are mean or even filthy—things which (as Pliny says) must be introduced with an apology—such things, no less than the most splendid and costly, must be admitted into natural history. Nor is natural history polluted thereby; for the sun enters the sewer no less than the palace, yet takes no pollution. And for myself, I am not raising a capitol or pyramid to the pride of man, but laying a foundation in the human understanding for a holy temple after the model of the world. That model therefore I follow. For whatever deserves to exist deserves also to be known, for knowledge is the image of existence; and things mean and splendid exist alike. Moreover as from certain putrid substances—musk, for instance, and civet—the sweetest odors are sometimes generated, so too from mean and sordid instances there sometimes emanates excellent light and information. But enough and more than enough of this; such fastidiousness being merely childish and effeminate.

CXXI

But there is another objection which must be more carefully looked to: namely, that there are many things in this history which to common apprehension, or indeed to any understanding accustomed to the present system, will seem to be curiously and unprofitably subtle. Upon this point therefore above all I must say again what I have said already —that at first and for a time I am seeking for experiments of light, not for experiments of fruit; following therein, as I have often said, the example of the divine creation; which on the first day produced light only, and assigned to it alone one entire day, nor mixed up with it on that day any material work.

To suppose therefore that things like these are of no use is the same as to suppose that light is of no use, because it is not a thing solid or material. And the truth is that the knowledge of simple natures well examined and defined is as light; it gives entrance to all the secrets of nature's workshop, and virtually includes and draws after it whole bands and troops of works, and opens to us the sources of the noblest axioms; and yet in itself it is of no great use. So also the letters of the alphabet in themselves and apart have no use or meaning, yet they are the subject-matter for the composition and apparatus of all discourse. So again the seeds of things are of much latent virtue, and yet of no use except in their development. And the scattered rays of light itself, until they are made to converge, can impart none of their benefit.

But if objection be taken to speculative subtleties, what is to be said of the schoolmen, who have indulged in subtleties to such excess? in subtleties too that were spent on words, or at any rate on popular notions (which is much the same thing), not on facts or nature; and such as were useless not only in their origin but also in their consequences; and not like those I speak of, useless indeed for the present, but promising infinite utility hereafter. But let men be assured of this, that all subtlety of disputation and discourse, if not applied till after axioms are discovered, is out of season and preposterous; and that the true and proper or at any rate the chief time for subtlety is in weighing experience and in founding axioms thereon; for that other subtlety, though it grasps and snatches at nature, yet can never take hold of her. Certainly what is said of opportunity or fortune is most true of nature; she has a lock in front, but is bald behind.

Lastly, concerning the disdain to receive into natural history things either common, or mean, or over-subtle and in their original condition useless, the answer of the poor woman to the haughty prince, who had rejected her petition as an unworthy thing and beneath his dignity, may be taken for an oracle,—"Then leave off being king." For most certain it is that he who will not attend to things like these, as being too paltry and minute, can neither win the kingdom of nature nor govern it.

CXXII

It may be thought also a strange and a harsh thing that we should at once and with one blow set aside all sciences and all authors; and that too without calling in any of the ancients to our aid and support, but relying on our own strength.

And I know that if I had chosen to deal less sincerely, I might easily have found authority for my suggestions by referring them either to the old times before the Greeks (when natural science was perhaps more flourishing, though it made less noise, not having yet passed into the pipes and trumpets of the Greeks), or even, in part at least, to some of the Greeks themselves; and so gained for them both support and honor; as men of no family devise for themselves by the good help of genealogies the nobility of a descent from some ancient stock. But for my part, relying on the evidence and truth of things, I reject all forms of fiction and imposture; nor do I think that it matters any more to the business in hand, whether the discoveries that shall now be made were long ago known to the ancients, and have their settings and their risings according to the vicissitude of things and course of ages, than it matters to mankind whether the new world be that island of Atlantis with which the ancients were acquainted, or now discovered for the first time. For new discoveries must be sought from the light of nature, not fetched back out of the darkness of antiquity.

And as for the universality of the censure, certainly if the matter be truly considered, such a censure is not only more probable but more modest too, than a partial one would be.

For if the errors had not been rooted in primary notions, there must have been some true discoveries to correct the false. But the errors being fundamental, and not so much of false judgment as of inattention and oversight, it is no wonder that men have not obtained what they have not tried for, nor reached a mark which they never set up, nor finished a course which they never entered on or kept.

And as for the presumption implied in it; certainly if a man undertakes by steadiness of hand and power of eye to describe a straighter line or more perfect circle than anyone else, he challenges a comparison of abilities; but if he only says that he with the help of a rule or a pair of compasses can draw a straighter line or a more perfect circle than anyone else can by eye and hand alone, he makes no great boast. And this remark, be it observed, applies not merely to this first and inceptive attempt of mine, but to all that shall take the work in hand hereafter. For my way of discovering sciences goes far to level men's wits, and leaves but little to individual excellence; because it performs everything by the surest rules and demonstrations. And therefore I attribute my part in all this, as I have often said, rather to good luck than to ability, and account it a birth of time rather than of wit. For certainly chance has something to do with men's thoughts, as well as with their works and deeds.

CXXIII

I may say then of myself that which one said in jest (since it marks the distinction so truly), "It cannot be that we should think alike, when one drinks water and the other drinks wine." Now other men, as well in ancient as in modern times, have in the matter of sciences drunk a crude liquor like water, either flowing spontaneously from the understanding, or drawn up by logic, as by wheels from a well. Whereas I pledge mankind in liquor strained from countless grapes, from grapes ripe and fully seasoned, collected in clusters, and gathered, and then squeezed in the press, and finally purified and clarified in the vat. And therefore it is no wonder if they and I do not think alike.

CXXIV

Again, it will be thought, no doubt, that the goal and mark of knowledge which I myself set up (the very point which I object to in others) is not the true or the best; for that the contemplation of truth is a thing worthier and loftier than all utility and magnitude of works; and that this long and anxious dwelling with experience and matter and the fluctuations of individual things, drags down the mind to earth, or rather sinks it to a very Tartarus of turmoil and confusion; removing and withdrawing it from the serene tranquillity of abstract wisdom, a condition far more heavenly. Now to this I readily assent; and indeed this which they point at as so much to be preferred, is the very thing of all others which I am about. For I am building in the human understanding a true model of the world, such as it is in fact, not such as a man's own reason would have it to be; a thing which cannot be done without a very diligent dissection and anatomy of the world. But I say that those foolish and apish images of world which the fancies of men have created in philosophical systems, must be utterly scattered to the winds. Be it known then how vast a difference there is (as I said above) between the idols of the human mind and the ideas of the divine. The former are nothing more than arbitrary abstractions; the latter are the creator's own stamp upon creation, impressed and defined in matter by true and exquisite lines. Truth therefore and utility are here the very same things: and works themselves are of greater value as pledges of truth than as contributing to the comforts of life.

CXXV

It may be thought again that I am but doing what has been done before; that the ancients themselves took the same course which I am now taking; and that it is likely therefore that I too, after all this stir and striving, shall come at last to some one of those systems which prevailed in ancient times. For the ancients too, it will be said, provided at the outset of their speculations a great store and abundance of examples and particulars, digested the same into notebooks

under heads and titles, from them completed their systems
and arts, and afterwards, when they understood the matter,
published them to the world,—adding a few examples here
and there for proof and illustration; but thought it superfluous and inconvenient to publish their notes and minutes and
digests of particulars; and therefore did as builders do,—after
the house was built they removed the scaffolding and ladders
out of sight. And so no doubt they did. But this objection (or
scruple rather) will be easily answered by anyone who has
not quite forgotten what I have said above. For the form of
inquiry and discovery that was in use among the ancients is
by themselves professed, and appears on the very face of their
writings. And that form was simply this. From a few examples
and particulars (with the addition of common notions and
perhaps of some portion of the received opinions which have
been most popular) they flew at once to the most general
conclusions, or first principles of science: taking the truth
of these as fixed and immovable, they proceeded by means of
intermediate propositions to educe and prove from them the
inferior conclusions; and out of these they framed the art.
After that, if any new particulars and examples repugnant
to their dogmas were mooted and adduced, either they subtly
molded them into their system by distinctions or explanations
of their rules, or else coarsely got rid of them by exceptions;
while to such particulars as were not repugnant they labored
to assign causes in conformity with those their principles. But
this was not the natural history and experience that was
wanted; far from it; and besides, that flying off to the highest
generalities ruined all.

CXXVI

It will also be thought that by forbidding men to pronounce
and to set down principles as established until they have duly
arrived through the intermediate steps at the highest generalities, I maintain a sort of suspension of the judgment, and
bring it to what the Greeks call *Acatalepsia*,—a denial of the
capacity of the mind to comprehend truth. But in reality, that
which I meditate and propound is not *Acatalepsia*, but *Eu-*

catalepsia; not denial of the capacity to understand, but provision for understanding truly; for I do not take away authority from the senses, but supply them with helps; I do not slight the understanding, but govern it. And better surely it is that we should know all we need to know, and yet think our knowledge imperfect, than that we should think our knowledge perfect, and yet not know anything we need to know.

CXXVII

It may also be asked (in the way of doubt rather than objection) whether I speak of natural philosophy only, or whether I mean that the other sciences, logic, ethics, and politics, should be carried on by this method. Now I certainly mean what I have said to be understood of them all; and as the common logic, which governs by the syllogism, extends not only to natural but to all sciences; so does mine also, which proceeds by induction, embrace everything. For I form a history and tables of discovery for anger, fear, shame, and the like; for matters political; and again for the mental operations of memory, composition and division, judgment and the rest; not less than for heat and cold, or light, or vegetation, or the like. But nevertheless since my method of interpretation, after the history has been prepared and duly arranged, regards not the working and discourse of the mind only (as the common logic does) but the nature of things also, I supply the mind with such rules and guidance that it may in every case apply itself aptly to the nature of things. And therefore I deliver many and diverse precepts in the doctrine of Interpretation, which in some measure modify the method of invention according to the quality and condition of the subject of the inquiry.

CXXVIII

On one point not even a doubt ought to be entertained; namely, whether I desire to pull down and destroy the philosophy and arts and sciences which are at present in use. So far from that, I am most glad to see them used, cultivated, and honored. There is no reason why the arts which are now in fashion should not continue to supply matter for disputation and ornaments for discourse, to be employed for the convenience of professors and men of business; to be in short like current coin, which passes among men by consent. Nay I frankly declare that what I am introducing will be but little fitted for such purposes as these, since it cannot be brought down to common apprehension, save by effects and works only. But how sincere I am in my professions of affection and good will towards the received sciences, my published writings, especially the books on the Advancement of Learning, sufficiently show; and therefore I will not attempt to prove it further by words. Meanwhile I give constant and distinct warning that by the methods now in use neither can any great progress be made in the doctrines and contemplative part of sciences, nor can they be carried out to any magnitude of works.

CXXIX

It remains for me to say a few words touching the excellency of the end in view. Had they been uttered earlier, they might have seemed like idle wishes; but now that hopes have been raised and unfair prejudices removed, they may perhaps have greater weight. Also, if I had finished all myself, and had no occasion to call in others to help and take part in the work, I should even now have abstained from such language, lest it might be taken as a proclamation of my own deserts. But since I want to quicken the industry and rouse and kindle the zeal of others, it is fitting that I put men in mind of some things.

In the first place then, the introduction of famous discoveries appears to hold by far the first place among human actions; and this was the judgment of the former ages. For to the authors of inventions they awarded divine honors; while to those who did good service in the state (such as founders of cities and empires, legislators, saviors of their country from long enduring evils, quellers of tyrannies, and the like) they decreed no higher honors than heroic. And certainly if a man rightly compare the two, he will find that this judgment of antiquity was just. For the benefits of discoveries may extend to the whole race of man, civil benefits only to particular places; the latter last not beyond a few ages, the former through all time. Moreover the reformation of a state in civil matters is seldom brought in without violence and confusion; but discoveries carry blessings with them, and confer benefits without causing harm or sorrow to any.

Again, discoveries are as it were new creations, and imitations of God's works; as well sang the poet:—

> To man's frail race great Athens long ago
> First gave the seed whence waving harvests grow,
> And *re-created* all our life below.

And it appears worthy of remark in Solomon, that though mighty in empire and in gold; in the magnificence of his works, his court, his household, and his fleet; in the luster of his name and the worship of mankind: yet he took none of these to glory in, but pronounced that "The glory of God is to conceal a thing; the glory of the king to search it out."

Again, let a man only consider what a difference there is between the life of men in the most civilized province of Europe, and in the wildest and most barbarous districts of New India; he will feel it be great enough to justify the saying that "man is a god to man," not only in regard of aid and benefit, but also by a comparison of condition. And this difference comes not from soil, not from climate, not from race, but from the arts.

Again, it is well to observe the force and virtue and consequences of discoveries; and these are to be seen nowhere more conspicuously than in those three which were unknown to the ancients, and of which the origin, though recent, is obscure and inglorious; namely, printing, gunpowder, and the magnet. For these three have changed the whole face and state of things throughout the world; the first in literature, the second in warfare, the third in navigation; whence have followed innumerable changes; insomuch that no empire, no sect, no star seems to have exerted greater power and influence in human affairs than these mechanical discoveries.

Further, it will not be amiss to distinguish the three kinds and as it were grades of ambition in mankind. The first is of those who desire to extend their own power in their native country; which kind is vulgar and degenerate. The second is of those who labor to extend the power of their country and its dominion among men. This certainly has more dignity, though not less covetousness. But if a man endeavor to establish and extend the power and dominion of the human race itself over the universe, his ambition (if ambition it can be called) is without doubt both a more wholesome thing and a more noble than the other two. Now the empire of man over things depends wholly on the arts and sciences. For we cannot command nature except by obeying her.

Again, if men have thought so much of some one particular discovery as to regard him as more than man who has been able by some benefit to make the whole human race his debtor, how much higher a thing to discover that by means of which all things else shall be discovered with ease! And yet (to speak the whole truth), as the uses of light are infinite, in enabling us to walk, to ply our arts, to read, to recognize one another; and nevertheless the very beholding of the light is itself a more excellent and a fairer thing than all the uses of it;—so assuredly the very contemplation of things, as they are, without superstition or imposture, error or confusion, is in itself more worthy than all the fruit of inventions.

Lastly, if the debasement of arts and sciences to purposes of wickedness, luxury, and the like, be made a ground of objection, let no one be moved thereby. For the same may be said of all earthly goods; of wit, courage, strength, beauty, wealth, light itself, and the rest. Only let the human race recover the right over nature which belongs to it by divine bequest, and let power be given it; the exercise thereof will be governed by sound reason and true religion.

CXXX

And now it is time for me to propound the art itself of interpreting nature; in which, although I conceive that I have given true and most useful precepts, yet I do not say either that it is absolutely necessary (as if nothing could be done without it) or that it is perfect. For I am of opinion that if men had ready at hand a just history of nature and experience, and labored diligently thereon; and if they could bind themselves to two rules,—the first, to lay aside received opinions and notions; and the second, to refrain the mind for a time from the highest generalizations, and those next to them, —they would be able by the native and genuine force of the mind, without any other art, to fall into my form of interpretation. For interpretation is the true and natural work of the mind when freed from impediments. It is true however that by my precepts everything will be in more readiness, and much more sure.

Nor again do I mean to say that no improvement can be made upon these. On the contrary, I that regard the mind not only in its own faculties but in its connection with things, must needs hold that the art of discovery may advance as discoveries advance.

René Descartes

DISCOURSE ON THE
METHOD OF RIGHTLY
CONDUCTING THE REASON,
AND SEEKING TRUTH
IN THE SCIENCES

René Descartes
[1596–1650]

Modern science, it can be said, began with Descartes. Like Francis Bacon he strove to create a new methodology, but his was based more on deduction than experience. A mathematician who extended his inquiries to embrace the general principles of all knowledge, Descartes commenced by subjecting everything, including doubt itself, to the test of doubt. His frequently quoted *Cogito, ergo sum*—I think, therefore I am —is offered by him as a certainty and becomes the foundation on which he builds an edifice spacious enough to contain consideration of the principles of science and proof of the existence of God. From the time he left France at twenty-two, Descartes lived almost all the rest of his life in Holland. There his first studies in mathematics projected him into philosophy, physics, psychology, physiology and cosmology. In each he was a pioneer whose influence has been dominant for three centuries, especially in the field of the philosophy of science. *Discourse on Method*, given here in its entirety, remains his most noteworthy essay.

PREFATORY NOTE

BY THE AUTHOR

If this Discourse appear too long to be read at once, it may be divided into six parts: and, in the first, will be found various considerations touching the Sciences; in the second, the principal rules of the Method which the Author has discovered; in the third, certain of the rules of Morals which he has deduced from this Method; in the fourth, the reasonings by which he establishes the existence of God and of the Human Soul, which are the foundations of his Metaphysic; in the fifth, the order of the Physical questions which he has investigated, and, in particular, the explication of the motion of the heart and of some other difficulties pertaining to Medicine, as also the difference between the soul of man and that of the brutes; and, in the last, what the Author believes to be required in order to greater advancement in the investigation of Nature than has yet been made, with the reasons that have induced him to write.

DISCOURSE ON METHOD

RENÉ DESCARTES

PART I

Good sense is, of all things among men, the most equally distributed; for every one thinks himself so abundantly provided with it, that those even who are the most difficult to satisfy in everything else, do not usually desire a larger measure of this quality than they already possess. And in this it is not likely that all are mistaken: the conviction is rather to be held as testifying that the power of judging aright and of distinguishing truth from error, which is properly what is called good sense or reason, is by nature equal in all men; and that the diversity of our opinions, consequently, does not arise from some being endowed with a larger share of reason than others, but solely from this, that we conduct our thoughts along different ways, and do not fix our attention on the same objects. For to be possessed of a vigorous mind is not enough; the prime requisite is rightly to apply it. The greatest minds, as they are capable of the highest excellences, are open likewise to the greatest aberrations; and those who travel very slowly may yet make far greater progress, provided they keep always to the straight road, than those who, while they run, forsake it.

For myself, I have never fancied my mind to be in any respect more perfect than those of the generality; on the contrary, I have often wished that I were equal to some others in promptitude of thought, or in clearness and distinctness of imagination, or in fullness and readiness of memory. And besides these, I know of no other qualities that contribute to the perfection of the mind; for as to the reason or sense, inasmuch as it is that alone which constitutes us men, and distinguishes us from the brutes, I am disposed to believe that it is to be found complete in each individual; and on this point to adopt the common opinion of philosophers, who say that the difference of greater and less holds only among the *accidents*, and not among the *forms* or *natures* of *individuals* of the same *species*.

I will not hesitate, however, to avow my belief that it has been my singular good fortune to have very early in life fallen in with certain tracks which have conducted me to considerations and maxims, of which I have formed a method that gives me the means, as I think, of gradually augmenting my knowledge, and of raising it by little and little to the highest point which the mediocrity of my talents and the brief duration of my life will permit me to reach. For I have already reaped from it such fruits that, although I have been accustomed to think lowly enough of myself, and although when I look with the eye of a philosopher at the varied courses and pursuits of mankind at large, I find scarcely one which does not appear vain and useless, I nevertheless derive the highest satisfaction from the progress I conceive myself to have already made in the search after truth, and cannot help entertaining such expectations of the future as to believe that if, among the occupations of men as men, there is any one really excellent and important, it is that which I have chosen.

After all, it is possible I may be mistaken; and it is but a little copper and glass, perhaps, that I take for gold and diamonds. I know how very liable we are to delusion in what relates to ourselves, and also how much the judgments of our friends are to be suspected when given in our favour. But I shall endeavour in this discourse to describe the paths I have followed, and to delineate my life as in a picture, in order that each one may be able to judge of them for himself, and that in the general opinion entertained of them, as gathered from current report, I myself may have a new help towards instruction to be added to those I have been in the habit of employing.

My present design, then, is not to teach the method which each ought to follow for the right conduct of his reason, but solely to describe the way in which I have endeavoured to conduct my own. They who set themselves to give precepts must of course regard themselves as possessed of greater skill than those to whom they prescribe; and if they err in the slightest particular, they subject themselves to censure. But as this tract is put forth merely as a history, or, if you will, as a tale, in which, amid some examples worthy of imitation, there will be found, perhaps, as many more which it were advisable not to follow, I hope it will prove useful to some without being hurtful to any, and that my openness will find some favour with all.

From my childhood, I have been familiar with letters; and as I was given to believe that by their help a clear and certain knowledge of all that is useful in life might be acquired, I was ardently desirous of instruction. But as soon as I had finished the entire course of study, at the close of which it is customary to be admitted into the order of the learned, I completely changed my opinion. For I found myself involved in so many doubts and errors, that I was convinced I had advanced no farther in all my attempts at learning, than the discovery at every turn of my own ignorance. And yet I was studying in one of the most celebrated schools in Europe, in which I thought there must be learned men, if such were anywhere to be found. I had been taught all that others learned there; and not contented with the sciences actually taught us, I had, in addition, read all the books that had fallen into my hands, treating of such branches as are esteemed the most curious and rare. I knew the judgment which others had formed of me; and I did not find that I was considered inferior to my fellows, although there were among them some who were already marked out to fill the places of our instructors. And, in fine, our age appeared to me as flourishing, and as fertile in powerful minds as any preceding one. I was thus led to take the liberty of judging of all other men by myself, and of concluding that there was no science in existence that was of such a nature as I had previously been given to believe.

I still continued, however, to hold in esteem the studies of the schools. I was aware that the languages taught in them are necessary to the understanding of the writings of the ancients; that the grace of fable stirs the mind; that the memorable deeds of history elevate it; and, if read with discretion, aid in forming the judgment; that the perusal of all excellent books is, as it were, to interview with the noblest men of past ages, who have written them, and even a studied interview, in which are discovered to us only their choicest thoughts; that eloquence has incomparable force and beauty; that poesy has its ravishing graces and delights; that in the mathematics there are many refined discoveries eminently suited to gratify the inquisitive, as well as further all the arts and lessen the labour of man; that numerous highly useful precepts and exhortations to virtue are contained in treatises on morals; that theology points out the path to heaven; that philosophy affords the means of discoursing with an appearance of truth on all matters, and commands the admiration of the more simple; that jurisprudence, medicine, and the other sciences, secure for their cultivators honours and riches; and, in fine, that it is useful to bestow some attention upon all, even upon those abounding the most in superstition and error, that we may be in a position to determine their real value, and guard against being deceived.

But I believed that I had already given sufficient time to languages, and likewise to the reading of the writings of the ancients, to their histories and fables. For to hold converse with those of other ages and to travel, are almost the same thing. It is useful to know something of the manners of different nations, that we may be enabled to form a more correct judgment regarding our own, and be prevented from thinking that everything contrary to our customs is ridiculous and irrational,—a conclusion usually come to by those whose experience has been limited to their own country. On the other hand, when too much time is occupied in traveling, we become strangers to our native country; and the over curious in the customs of the past are generally ignorant of those of the present. Besides, fictitious narratives lead us to imagine the possibility of many events that are impossible; and even the most faithful histories, if they do not wholly misrepresent matters, or exaggerate their importance to render the account of them more worthy of perusal, omit, at least, almost always the meanest and least striking of the attendant circumstances; hence it happens that the remainder does not represent the truth, and that such as regulate their conduct by examples drawn from this source, are apt to fall into the extravagances of the knight-errants of romance, and to entertain projects that exceed their powers.

I esteemed eloquence highly, and was in raptures with poesy; but I thought that both were gifts of nature rather than fruits of study. Those in whom the faculty of reason is predominant, and who most skilfully dispose their thoughts with a view to render them clear and intelligible, are always the best able to persuade others of the truth of what they lay down, though they should speak only in the language of Lower Britanny, and be wholly ignorant of the rules of rhetoric; and those whose minds are stored with the most agreeable fancies, and who can give expression to them with the greatest embellishment and harmony, are still the best poets, though unacquainted with the art of poetry.

I was especially delighted with the mathematics, on account of the certitude and evidence of their reasonings; but I had not as yet a precise knowledge of their true use; and thinking that they but contributed to the advancement of the mechanical arts, I was astonished that foundations, so strong and solid, should have had no loftier superstructure reared on them. On the other hand, I compared the disquisitions of the ancient moralists to very towering and magnificent palaces with no better foundation than sand and mud: they laud the virtues very highly, and exhibit them as estimable far above anything on earth; but they give us no adequate criterion of virtue, and frequently that which they designate with so fine a name is but apathy, or pride, or despair, or parricide.

I revered our theology, and aspired as much as any one to reach heaven: but being given assuredly to understand that the way is not less open to the most ignorant than to the most learned, and that the revealed truths which lead to heaven are above our comprehension, I did not presume to subject them to the impotency of my reason; and I thought that in order competently to undertake their examination, there was need of some special help from heaven, and of being more than man.

Of philosophy I will say nothing, except that when I saw that it had been cultivated for many ages by the most distinguished men, and that yet there is not a single matter within its sphere which is not still in dispute, and nothing, therefore, which is above doubt, I did not presume to anticipate that my success would be greater in it than that of others; and further, when I considered the number of conflicting opinions touching a single matter that may be upheld by learned men, while there can be but one true, I reckoned as well-nigh false all that was only probable.

As to the other sciences, inasmuch as these borrow their principles from philosophy, I judged that no solid superstructures could be reared on foundations so infirm; and neither the honour nor the gain held out by them was sufficient to determine me to their cultivation: for I was not, thank Heaven, in a condition which compelled me to make merchandise of science for the bettering of my fortune; and thought I might not profess to scorn glory as a cynic, I yet made very slight account of that honour which I hoped to acquire only through fictitious titles. And, in fine, of false sciences I thought I knew the worth sufficiently to escape being deceived by the professions of an alchemist, the predictions of an astrologer, the impostures of a magician, or by the artifices and boasting of any of those who profess to know things of which they are ignorant.

For these reasons, as soon as my age permitted me to pass

from under the control of my instructors, I entirely abandoned the study of letters, and resolved no longer to seek any other science than the knowledge of myself, or of the great book of the world. I spent the remainder of my youth in travelling, in visiting courts and armies, in holding intercourse with men of different dispositions and ranks, in collecting varied experience, in proving myself in the different situations into which fortune threw me, and, above all, in making such reflection on the matter of my experience as to secure my improvement. For it occurred to me that I should find much more truth in the reasonings of each individual with reference to the affairs in which he is personally interested, and the issue of which must presently punish him if he has judged amiss, than in those conducted by a man of letters in his study, regarding speculative matters that are of no practical moment, and followed by no consequences to himself, farther, perhaps, than that they foster his vanity the better the more remote they are from common sense; requiring, as they must in this case, the exercise of greater ingenuity and art to render them probable. In addition, I had always a most earnest desire to know how to distinguish the true from the false, in order that I might be able clearly to discriminate the right path in life, and proceed in it with confidence.

It is true that, while busied only in considering the manners of other men, I found here, too, scarce any ground for settled conviction, and remarked hardly less contradiction among them than in the opinions of the philosophers. So that the greatest advantage I derived from the study consisted in this, that, observing many things which, however extravagant and ridiculous to our apprehension, are yet by common consent received and approved by other great nations, I learned to entertain too decided a belief in regard to nothing of the truth of which I had been persuaded merely by example and custom; and thus I gradually extricated myself from many errors powerful enough to darken our natural intelligence, and incapacitate us in great measure from listening to reason. But after I had been occupied several years in thus studying the book of the world, and in essaying to gather some experience, I at length resolved to make myself an object of study, and to employ all the powers of my mind in choosing the paths I ought to follow, an undertaking which was accompanied with greater success than it would have been had I never quitted my country or my books.

PART II

I was then in Germany, attracted thither by the wars in that country, which have not yet been brought to a termination; and as I was returning to the army from the coronation of the emperor, the setting in of winter arrested me in a locality where, as I found no society to interest me, and was besides fortunately undisturbed by any cares or passions, I remained the whole day in seclusion,[1] with full opportunity to occupy my attention with my own thoughts. Of these one of the very first that occurred to me was, that there is seldom so much perfection in works composed of many separate parts, upon which different hands had been employed, as in those completed by a single master. Thus it is observable that the buildings which a single architect has planned and executed, are generally more elegant and commodious than those which several have attempted to improve, by making old walls serve for purposes for which they were not originally built. Thus also, those ancient cities which, from being at first only villages, have become, in course of time, large towns, are usually but ill laid out compared with the regularly constructed towns which a professional architect has freely planned on an open plain; so that although the several buildings of the former may often equal or surpass in beauty those of the latter, yet when one observes their indiscriminate juxtaposition, there a large one and here a small, and the consequent crookedness and irregularity of the streets, one is disposed to allege that chance rather than any human will guided by reason must have led to such an arrangement. And

---

[1] Literally, in a room heated by means of a stove.

if we consider that nevertheless there have been at all times certain officers whose duty it was to see that private buildings contributed to public ornament, the difficulty of reaching high perfection with but the materials of others to operate on, will be readily acknowledged. In the same way I fancied that those nations which, starting from a semi-barbarous state and advancing to civilisation by slow degrees, have had their laws successively determined, and, as it were, forced upon them simply by experience of the hurtfulness of particular crimes and disputes, would by this process come to be possessed of less perfect institutions than those which, from the commencement of their association as communities, have followed the appointments of some wise legislator. It is thus quite certain that the constitution of the true religion, the ordinances of which are derived from God, must be incomparably superior to that of every other. And, to speak of human affairs, I believe that the past pre-eminence of Sparta was due not to the goodness of each of its laws in particular, for many of these were very strange, and even opposed to good morals, but to the circumstance that, originated by a single individual, they all tended to a single end. In the same way I thought that the sciences contained in books (such of them at least as are made up of probable reasonings, without demonstrations), composed as they are of the opinions of many different individuals massed together, are farther removed from truth than the simple inferences which a man of good sense using his natural and unprejudiced judgment draws respecting the matters of his experience. And because we have all to pass through a state of infancy to manhood, and have been of necessity, for a length of time, governed by our desires and preceptors (whose dictates were frequently conflicting, while neither perhaps always counselled us for the best), I farther concluded that it is almost impossible that our judgments can be so correct or solid as they would have been, had our reason been mature from the moment of our birth, and had we always been guided by it alone.

It is true, however, that it is not customary to pull down

all the houses of a town with the single design of rebuilding them differently, and thereby rendering the streets more handsome; but it often happens that a private individual takes down his own with the view of erecting it anew, and that people are even sometimes constrained to this when their houses are in danger of falling from age, or when the foundations are insecure. With this before me by way of example, I was persuaded that it would indeed be preposterous for a private individual to think of reforming a state by fundamentally changing it throughout, and overturning it in order to set it up amended; and the same I thought was true of any similar project for reforming the body of the sciences, or the order of teaching them established in the schools: but as for the opinions which up to that time I had embraced, I thought that I could not do better than resolve at once to sweep them wholly away, that I might afterwards be in a position to admit either others more correct, or even perhaps the same when they had undergone the scrutiny of reason. I firmly believed that in this way I should much better succeed in the conduct of my life, than if I built only upon old foundations, and leant upon principles which, in my youth, I had taken upon trust. For although I recognised various difficulties in this undertaking, these were not, however, without remedy, nor once to be compared with such as attend the slightest reformation in public affairs. Large bodies, if once overthrown, are with great difficulty set up again, or even kept erect when once seriously shaken, and the fall of such is always disastrous. Then if there are any imperfections in the constitutions of states (and that many such exist the diversity of constitutions is alone sufficient to assure us), custom has without doubt materially smoothed their inconveniences, and has even managed to steer altogether clear of, or insensibly corrected a number which sagacity could not have provided against with equal effect; and, in fine, the defects are almost always more tolerable than the change necessary for their removal; in the same manner that highways which wind among mountains, by being much frequented, become gradually so smooth and commodious, that it is much better to follow them than to seek a straighter path by climbing over the tops of rocks and descending to the bottoms of precipices.

Hence it is that I cannot in any degree approve of those restless and busy meddlers who, called neither by birth nor fortune to take part in the management of public affairs, are yet always projecting reforms; and if I thought that this tract contained aught which might justify the suspicion that I was a victim of such folly, I would by no means permit its publication. I have never contemplated anything higher than the reformation of my own opinions, and basing them on a foundation wholly my own. And although my own satisfaction with my work has led me to present here a draft of it, I do not by any means therefore recommend to every one else to make a similar attempt. Those whom God has endowed with a larger measure of genius will entertain, perhaps, designs still more exalted; but for the many I am much afraid lest even the present undertaking be more than they can safely venture to imitate. The single design to strip one's self of all past beliefs is one that ought not to be taken by every one. The majority of men is composed of two classes, for neither of which would this be at all a befitting resolution: in the *first* place, of those who with more than a due confidence in their own powers, are precipitate in their judgments and want the patience requisite for orderly and circumspect thinking; whence it happens, that if men of this class once take the liberty to doubt of their accustomed opinions, and quit the beaten highway, they will never be able to thread the byway that would lead them by a shorter course, and will lose themselves and continue to wander for life; in the *second* place, of those who, possessed of sufficient sense or modesty to determine that there are others who excel them in the power of discriminating between truth and error, and by whom they may be instructed, ought rather to content themselves with the opinions of such than trust for more correct to their own reason.

For my own part, I should doubtless have belonged to the latter class, had I received instruction from but one master, or had I never known the diversities of opinion that from time immemorial have prevailed among men of the greatest learning. But I had become aware, even so early as during my college life, that no opinion, however absurd and incredible, can be imagined, which has not been maintained by some one of the philosophers; and afterwards in the course of my travels I remarked that all those whose opinions are decidedly repugnant to ours are not on that account barbarians and savages, but on the contrary that many of these nations make an equally good, if not a better, use of their reason than we do. I took into account also the very different character which a person brought up from infancy in France or Germany exhibits, from that which, with the same mind originally, this individual would have possessed had he lived always among the Chinese or with savages, and the circumstance that in dress itself the fashion which pleased us ten years ago, and which may again, perhaps, be received into favour before ten years have gone, appears to us at this moment extravagant and ridiculous. I was thus led to infer that the ground of our opinions is far more custom and example than any certain knowledge. And, finally, although such be the ground of our opinions, I remarked that a plurality of suffrages is no guarantee of truth where it is at all of difficult discovery, as in such cases it is much more likely that it will be found by one than by many. I could, however, select from the crowd no one whose opinions seemed worthy of preference, and thus I found myself constrained, as it were, to use my own reason in the conduct of my life.

But like one walking alone and in the dark, I resolved to proceed so slowly and with such circumspection, that if I did not advance far, I would at least guard against falling. I did not even choose to dismiss summarily any of the opinions that had crept into my belief without having been introduced by reason, but first of all took sufficient time carefully to satisfy myself of the general nature of the task I was setting myself, and ascertain the true method by which to arrive at the knowledge of whatever lay within the compass of my powers.

Among the branches of philosophy, I had, at an earlier

period, given some attention to logic, and among those of the mathematics to geometrical analysis and algebra,—three arts or sciences which ought, as I conceived, to contribute something to my design. But, on examination, I found that, as for logic, its syllogisms and the majority of its other precepts are of avail rather in the communication of what we already know, or even as the art of Lully, in speaking without judgment of things of which we are ignorant, than in the investigation of the unknown; and although this science contains indeed a number of correct and very excellent precepts, there are, nevertheless, so many others, and these either injurious or superfluous, mingled with the former, that it is almost quite as difficult to effect a severance of the true from the false as it is to extract a Diana or a Minerva from a rough block of marble. Then as to the analysis of the ancients and the algebra of the moderns, besides that they embrace only matters highly abstract, and, to appearance, of no use, the former is so exclusively restricted to the consideration of figures, that it can exercise the understanding only on condition of greatly fatiguing the imagination; and, in the latter, there is so complete a subjection to certain rules and formulas, that there results an art full of confusion and obscurity calculated to embarrass, instead of a science fitted to cultivate the mind. By these considerations I was induced to seek some other method which would comprise the advantages of the three and be exempt from their defects. And as a multitude of laws often only hampers justice, so that a state is best governed when, with few laws, these are rigidly administered; in like manner, instead of the great number of precepts of which logic is composed, I believed that the four following would prove perfectly sufficient for me, provided I took the firm and unwavering resolution never in a single instance to fail in observing them.

The *first* was never to accept anything for true which I did not clearly know to be such; that is to say, carefully to avoid precipitancy and prejudice, and to comprise nothing more in my judgment than what was presented to my mind so clearly and distinctly as to exclude all ground of doubt.

The *second*, to divide each of the difficulties under examination into as many parts as possible, and as might be necessary for its adequate solution.

The *third*, to conduct my thoughts in such order that, by commencing with objects the simplest and easiest to know, I might ascend by little and little, and, as it were, step by step, to the knowledge of the more complex, assigning in thought a certain order even to those objects which in their own nature do not stand in a relation of antecedence and sequence.

And the *last*, in every case to make enumerations so complete, and reviews so general, that I might be assured that nothing was omitted.

The long chains of simple and easy reasonings by means of which geometers are accustomed to reach the conclusions of their most difficult demonstrations, had led me to imagine that all things, to the knowledge of which man is competent, are mutually connected in the same way, and that there is nothing so far removed from us as to be beyond our reach, or so hidden that we cannot discover it, provided only we abstain from accepting the false for the true, and always preserve in our thoughts the order necessary for the deduction of one truth from another. And I had little difficulty in determining the objects with which it was necessary to commence, for I was already persuaded that it must be with the simplest and easiest to know, and, considering that of all those who have hitherto sought truth in the sciences, the mathematicians alone have been able to find any demonstrations, that is, any certain and evident reasons, I did not doubt but that such must have been the rule of their investigations. I resolved to commence, therefore, with the examination of the simplest objects, not anticipating, however, from this any other advantage than that to be found in accustoming my mind to the love and nourishment of truth, and to a distaste for all such reasonings as were unsound. But I had no intention on that account of attempting to master all the particular sciences commonly denominated mathematics: but observing that, however different their objects, they all agree in considering only the various relations or proportions subsisting among those objects, I thought it best for my purpose to consider these proportions in the most general form possible, without referring them to any objects in particular, except such as would most facilitate the knowledge of them, and without by any means restricting them to these, that afterwards I might thus be the better able to apply them to every other class of objects to which they are legitimately applicable. Perceiving further, that in order to understand these relations I should sometimes have to consider them one by one, and sometimes only to bear them in mind, or embrace them in the aggregate, I thought that, in order the better to consider them individually, I should view them as subsisting between straight lines, than which I could find no objects more simple, or capable of being more distinctly represented to my imagination and senses; and on the other hand, that in order to retain them in the memory, or embrace an aggregate of many, I should express them by certain characters the briefest possible. In this way I believed that I could borrow all that was best both in geometrical analysis and in algebra, and correct all the defects of the one by help of the other.

And, in point of fact, the accurate observance of these few precepts gave me, I take the liberty of saying, such ease in unravelling all the questions embraced in these two sciences, that in the two or three months I devoted to their examination, not only did I reach solutions of questions I had formerly deemed exceedingly difficult, but even as regards questions of the solution of which I continued ignorant, I was enabled, as it appeared to me, to determine the means whereby, and the extent to which, a solution was possible; results attributable to the circumstance that I commenced with the simplest and most general truths, and that thus each truth discovered was a rule available in the discovery of subsequent ones. Nor in this perhaps shall I appear too vain, if it be considered that, as the truth on any particular point is one, whoever apprehends the truth, knows all that on that point can be known. The child, for example, who has been instructed in the elements of arithmetic, and has made a particular addition, according to rule, may be assured that he has found, with respect to the sum of the numbers before him, all that in this instance is within the reach of human genius. Now, in conclusion, the method which teaches adherence to the true order, and an exact enumeration of all the conditions of the thing sought includes all that gives certitude to the rules of arithmetic.

But the chief ground of my satisfaction with this method, was the assurance I had of thereby exercising my reason in all matters, if not with absolute perfection, at least with the greatest attainable by me: besides, I was conscious that by its use my mind was becoming gradually habituated to clearer and more distinct conceptions of its objects; and I hoped also, from not having restricted this method to any particular matter, to apply it to the difficulties of the other sciences, with not less success than to those of algebra. I should not, however, on this account have ventured at once on the examination of all the difficulties of the sciences which presented themselves to me, for this would have been contrary to the order prescribed in the method, but observing that the knowledge of such is dependent on principles borrowed from philosophy, in which I found nothing certain, I thought it necessary first of all to endeavour to establish its principles. And because I observed, besides, that an inquiry of this kind was of all others of the greatest moment, and one in which precipitancy and anticipation in judgment were most to be dreaded, I thought that I ought not to approach it till I had reached a more mature age (being at that time but twenty-three), and had first of all employed much of my time in preparation for the work, as well by eradicating from my mind all the erroneous opinions I had up to that moment accepted, as by amassing variety of experience to afford materials for my reasonings, and by continually exercising myself in my chosen method with a view to increased skill in its application.

PART III

And, finally, as it is not enough, before commencing to rebuild the house in which we live, that it be pulled down, and materials and builders provided, or that we engage in the work ourselves, according to a plan which we have beforehand carefully drawn out, but as it is likewise necessary that we be furnished with some other house in which we may live commodiously during the operations, so that I might not remain irresolute in my actions, while my reason compelled me to suspend my judgment, and that I might not be prevented from living thenceforward in the greatest possible felicity, I formed a provisory code of morals, composed of three or four maxims, with which I am desirous to make you acquainted.

The *first* was to obey the laws and customs of my country, adhering firmly to the faith in which, by the grace of God, I had been educated from my childhood, and regulating my conduct in every other matter according to the most moderate opinions, and the farthest removed from extremes, which should happen to be adopted in practice with general consent of the most judicious of those among whom I might be living. For, as I had from that time begun to hold my own opinions for nought because I wished to subject them all to examination, I was convinced that I could not do better than follow in the meantime the opinions of the most judicious; and although there are some perhaps among the Persians and Chinese as judicious as among ourselves, expediency seemed to dictate that I should regulate my practice conformably to the opinions of those with whom I should have to live; and it appeared to me that, in order to ascertain the real opinions of such, I ought rather to take cognisance of what they practised than of what they said, not only because, in the corruption of our manners, there are few disposed to speak exactly as they believe, but also because very many are not aware of what it is that they really believe; for, as the act of mind by which a thing is believed is different from that by which we know that we believe it, the one act is often found without the other. Also, amid many opinions held in equal repute, I chose always the most moderate, as much for the reason that these are always the most convenient for practice, and probably the best (for all excess is generally vicious), as that, in the event of my falling into error, I might be at less distance from the truth than if, having chosen one of the extremes, it should turn out to be the other which I ought to have adopted. And I placed in the class of extremes especially all promises by which somewhat of our freedom is abridged; not that I disapproved of the laws which, to provide against the instability of men of feeble resolution, when what is sought to be accomplished is some good, permit engagements by vows and contracts binding the parties to persevere in it, or even, for the security of commerce, sanction similar engagements where the purpose sought to be realised is indifferent: but because I did not find anything on earth which was wholly superior to change, and because, for myself in particular, I hoped gradually to perfect my judgments, and not to suffer them to deteriorate, I would have deemed it a grave sin against good sense, if, for the reason that I approved of something at a particular time, I therefore bound myself to hold it for good at a subsequent time, when perhaps it had ceased to be so, or I had ceased to esteem it such.

My *second* maxim was to be as firm and resolute in my actions as I was able, and not to adhere less steadfastly to the most doubtful opinions, when once adopted, than if they had been highly certain; imitating in this the example of travellers who, when they have lost their way in a forest, ought not to wander from side to side, far less remain in one place, but proceed constantly towards the same side in as straight a line as possible, without changing their direction for slight reasons, although perhaps it might be chance alone which at first determined the selection; for in this way, if they do not exactly reach the point they desire, they will come at least in the end to some place that will probably be preferable to the middle of a forest. In the same way, since in action it frequently happens that no delay is permissible, it is very certain that, when it is not in our power to determine what is true, we ought to act according to what is most probable; and even although we should not remark a greater probability in one opinion than in another, we ought notwithstanding to choose one or the other, and afterwards consider it, in so far as it relates to practice, as no longer dubious, but manifestly true and certain, since the reason by which our choice has been determined is itself possessed of these qualities. This principle was sufficient thenceforward to rid me of all those repentings and pangs of remorse that usually disturb the consciences of such feeble and uncertain minds as, destitute of any clear and determinate principle of choice, allow themselves one day to adopt a course of action as the best, which they abandon the next, as the opposite.

My *third* maxim was to endeavour always to conquer myself rather than fortune, and change my desires rather than the order of the world, and in general, accustom myself to the persuasion that, except our own thoughts, there is nothing absolutely in our power; so that when we have done our best in respect of things external to us, all wherein we fail of success is to be held, as regards us, absolutely impossible: and this single principle seemed to me sufficient to prevent me from desiring for the future anything which I could not obtain, and thus render me contented; for since our will naturally seeks those objects alone which the understanding represents as in some way possible of attainment, it is plain, that if we consider all external goods as equally beyond our power, we shall no more regret the absence of such goods as seem due to our birth, when deprived of them without any fault of ours, than our not possessing the kingdoms of China or Mexico; and thus making, so to speak, a virtue of necessity, we shall no more desire health in disease, or freedom in imprisonment, than we now do bodies incorruptible as diamonds, or the wings of birds to fly with. But I confess there is need of prolonged discipline and frequently repeated meditation to accustom the mind to view all objects in this light; and I believe that in this chiefly consisted the secret of the power of such philosophers as in former times were enabled to rise superior to the influence of fortune, and, amid suffering and poverty, enjoy a happiness which their gods might have envied. For, occupied incessantly with the consideration of the limits prescribed to their power by nature, they became so entirely convinced that nothing was at their disposal except their own thoughts, that this conviction was of itself sufficient to prevent their entertaining any desire of other objects; and over their thoughts they acquired a sway so absolute, that they had some ground on this account for esteeming themselves more rich and more powerful, more free and more happy, than other men who, whatever be the favours heaped on them by nature and fortune, if destitute of this philosophy, can never command the realisation of all their desires.

In fine, to conclude this code of morals, I thought of reviewing the different occupations of men in this life, with the view of making choice of the best. And, without wishing to offer any remarks on the employments of others, I may state that it was my conviction that I could not do better than continue in that in which I was engaged, viz., in devoting my whole life to the culture of my reason, and in making the greatest progress I was able in the knowledge of truth, on the principles of the method which I had prescribed to myself. This method, from the time I had begun to apply it, had been to me the source of satisfaction so intense as to lead me to believe that more perfect or more innocent could not be enjoyed in this life; and as by its means I daily discovered truths that appeared to me of some importance, and of which other men were generally ignorant, the gratification thence arising so occupied my mind that I was wholly indifferent to every other object. Besides, the three preceding maxims were founded singly on the design of continuing the work of self-instruction. For since God has endowed each of us with some light of reason by which to distinguish truth from error, I could not have believed that I ought for a single moment to rest satisfied with the opinions of another, unless I had resolved to exercise my own judgment in examining these whenever I should be duly qualified for the task. Nor could I have proceeded on such opinions without scruple, had I supposed that I should thereby forfeit any advantage for attaining still more accurate, should such exist. And, in fine, I could not have restrained my desires, nor remained satisfied, had I not followed a path in which I thought myself certain of attaining all the knowledge to the acquisition of which I was competent, as well as the largest amount of what is truly good which I could ever hope to secure. Inasmuch as we neither seek nor shun any object except in so far as our understanding represents it as good or bad, all that is necessary to right action is right judgment, and to the best action the most correct judgment,—that is, to the acquisition of all the virtues with all else that is truly valuable and within our reach; and the assurance of such an acquisition cannot fail to render us contented.

Having thus provided myself with these maxims, and having placed them in reserve along with the truths of faith, which have ever occupied the first place in my belief, I came to the conclusion that I might with freedom set about ridding myself of what remained of my opinions. And, inasmuch as I hoped to be better able successfully to accomplish this work by holding intercourse with mankind, than by remaining longer shut up in the retirement where these thoughts had occurred to me, I betook me again to travelling before the winter was well ended. And, during the nine subsequent years, I did nothing but roam from one place to another, desirous of being a spectator rather than an actor in the plays exhibited on the theatre of the world; and, as I made it my business in each matter to reflect particularly upon what might fairly be doubted and prove a source of error, I gradually rooted out from my mind all the errors which had hitherto crept into it. Not that in this I imitated the sceptics who doubt only that they may doubt, and seek nothing beyond uncertainty itself; for, on the contrary, my design was singly to find ground of assurance, and cast aside the loose earth and sand, that I might reach the rock or the clay. In this, as appears to me, I was successful enough; for, since I endeavoured to discover the falsehood or incertitude of the propositions I examined, not by feeble conjectures, but by clear and certain reasonings, I met with nothing so doubtful as not to yield some conclusion of adequate certainty, although this were merely the inference, that the matter in question contained nothing certain. And, just as in pulling down an old house, we usually reserve the ruins to contribute towards the erection, so, in destroying such of my opinions as I judged to be ill-founded, I made a variety of observations and acquired an amount of experience of which I availed myself in the establishment of more certain. And further, I continued to exercise myself in the method I had prescribed; for, besides taking care in general to conduct all my thoughts according to its rules, I reserved some hours from time to time which I expressly devoted to the employment of the method in the solution of mathematical difficulties, or even in the solution likewise of some questions belonging to other sciences, but which, by my having detached them from such principles of these sciences as were of inadequate certainty, were rendered almost mathematical: the truth of this will be manifest from the numerous examples contained in this volume.[2] And thus, without in appearance living otherwise than those who, with no other occupation than that of spending their lives agreeably and innocently, study to sever pleasure from vice, and who, that they may enjoy their leisure without ennui, have recourse to such pursuits as are honourable, I was nevertheless prosecuting my design, and making greater progress in the knowledge of truth, than I might, perhaps, have made had I been engaged in the perusal of books merely, or in holding converse with men of letters.

These nine years passed away, however, before I had come to any determinate judgment respecting the difficulties which form matter of dispute among the learned, or had commenced to seek the principles of any philosophy more certain than the vulgar. And the examples of many men of the highest genius, who had, in former times, engaged in this inquiry, but, as appeared to me, without success, led me to imagine it to be a work of so much difficulty, that I would not perhaps have ventured on it so soon had I not heard it currently rumoured that I had already completed the inquiry. I know not what were the grounds of this opinion; and, if my conversation contributed in any measure to its rise, this must have happened

---

[2] The "Discourse on Method" was originally published along with the "Dioptrics," the "Meteorics," and the "Geometry."

rather from my having confessed my ignorance with greater freedom than those are accustomed to do who have studied a little, and expounded, perhaps, the reasons that led me to doubt of many of those things that by others are esteemed certain, than from my having boasted of any system of philosophy. But, as I am of a disposition that makes me unwilling to be esteemed different from what I really am, I thought it necessary to endeavour by all means to render myself worthy of the reputation accorded to me; and it is now exactly eight years since this desire constrained me to remove from all those places where interruption from any of my acquaintances was possible, and betake myself to this country,[3] in which the long duration of the war has led to the establishment of such discipline, that the armies maintained seem to be of use only in enabling the inhabitants to enjoy more securely the blessings of peace; and where, in the midst of a great crowd actively engaged in business, and more careful of their own affairs than curious about those of others, I have been enabled to live without being deprived of any of the conveniences to be had in the most populous cities, and yet as solitary and as retired as in the midst of the most remote deserts.

PART IV

I am in doubt as to the propriety of making my first meditations in the place above mentioned matter of discourse; for these are so metaphysical, and so uncommon, as not, perhaps, to be acceptable to every one. And yet, that it may be determined whether the foundations that I have laid are sufficiently secure, I find myself in a measure constrained to advert to them. I had long before remarked that, in relation to practice, it is sometimes necessary to adopt, as if above doubt, opinions which we discern to be highly uncertain, as has been already said; but as I then desired to give my attention solely to the search after truth, I thought that a procedure exactly the opposite was called for, and that I ought to reject as abso-

---

[3] Holland; to which country he withdrew in 1629.

lutely false all opinions in regard to which I could suppose the least ground for doubt, in order to ascertain whether after that there remained aught in my belief that was wholly indubitable. Accordingly, seeing that our senses sometimes deceive us, I was willing to suppose that there existed nothing really such as they presented to us; and because some men err in reasoning, and fall into paralogisms, even on the simplest matters of geometry, I, convinced that I was as open to error as any other, rejected as false all the reasonings I had hitherto taken for demonstrations; and finally, when I considered that the very same thoughts (presentations) which we experience when awake may also be experienced when we are asleep, while there is at that time not one of them true, I supposed that all the objects (presentations) that had ever entered into my mind when awake, had in them no more truth than the illusions of my dreams. But immediately upon this I observed that, whilst I thus wished to think that all was false, it was absolutely necessary that I, who thus thought, should be somewhat; and as I observed that this truth, *I think, hence I am*, was so certain and of such evidence, that no ground of doubt, however extravagant, could be alleged by the sceptics capable of shaking it, I concluded that I might, without scruple, accept it as the first principle of the philosophy of which I was in search.

In the next place, I attentively examined what I was, and as I observed that I could suppose that I had no body, and that there was no world nor any place in which I might be; but that I could not therefore suppose that I was not; and that, on the contrary, from the very circumstance that I thought to doubt of the truth of other things, it most clearly and certainly followed that I was; while, on the other hand, if I had only ceased to think, although all the other objects which I had ever imagined had been in reality existent, I would have had no reason to believe that I existed; I thence concluded that I was a substance whose whole essence or nature consists only in thinking, and which, that it may exist, has need of no place, nor is dependent on any material thing; so that "I," that is to say, the mind by which I am what I am, is wholly distinct from the body, and is even more easily known than the latter, and is such, that although the latter were not, it would still continue to be all that it is.

After this I inquired in general into what is essential to the truth and certainty of a proposition; for since I had discovered one which I knew to be true, I thought that I must likewise be able to discover the ground of this certitude. And as I observed that in the words *I think, hence I am,* there is nothing at all which gives me assurance of their truth beyond this, that I see very clearly that in order to think it is necessary to exist, I concluded that I might take, as a general rule, the principle, that all the things which we very clearly and distinctly conceive are true, only observing, however, that there is some difficulty in rightly determining the objects which we distinctly conceive.

In the next place, from reflecting on the circumstance that I doubted, and that consequently my being was not wholly perfect (for I clearly saw that it was a greater perfection to know than to doubt), I was led to inquire whence I had learned to think of something more perfect than myself; and I clearly recognised that I must hold this notion from some nature which in reality was more perfect. As for the thoughts of many other objects external to me, as of the sky, the earth, light, heat, and a thousand more, I was less at a loss to know whence these came; for since I remarked in them nothing which seemed to render them superior to myself, I could believe that, if these were true, they were dependencies on my own nature, in so far as it possessed a certain perfection, and, if they were false, that I held them from nothing, that is to say, that they were in me because of a certain imperfection of my nature. But this could not be the case with the idea of a nature more perfect than myself; for to receive it from nothing was a thing manifestly impossible; and, because it is not less repugnant that the more perfect should be an effect of, and dependence on the less perfect, than that something should proceed from nothing, it was equally impossible that I could hold it from myself: accordingly, it but remained that it had been placed in me by a nature which was in reality more perfect than mine, and which even possessed within itself all the perfections of which I could form any idea; that is to say, in a single word, which was God. And to this I added that, since I knew some perfections which I did not possess, I was not the only being in existence (I will here, with your permission, freely use the terms of the schools); but, on the contrary, that there was of necessity some other more perfect Being upon whom I was dependent, and from whom I had received all that I possessed; for if I had existed alone, and independently of every other being, so as to have had from myself all the perfection, however little, which I actually possessed, I should have been able, for the same reason, to have had from myself the whole remainder of perfection, of the want of which I was conscious, and thus could of myself have become infinite, eternal, immutable, omniscient, all-powerful, and, in fine, have possessed all the perfections which I could recognise in God. For in order to know the nature of God (whose existence has been established by the preceding reasonings), as far as my own nature permitted, I had only to consider in reference to all the properties of which I found in my mind some idea, whether their possession was a mark of perfection; and I was assured that no one which indicated any imperfection was in him, and that none of the rest was awanting. Thus I perceived that doubt, inconstancy, sadness, and such like, could not be found in God, since I myself would have been happy to be free from them. Besides, I had ideas of many sensible and corporeal things; for although I might suppose that I was dreaming, and that all which I saw or imagined was false, I could not, nevertheless, deny that the ideas were in reality in my thoughts. But, because I had already very clearly recognised in myself that the intelligent nature is distinct from the corporeal, and as I observed that all composition is an evidence of dependency, and that a state of dependency is manifestly a state of imperfection, I therefore determined that it could not be a perfection in God to be compounded of these two natures, and that consequently he was not so compounded; but that if there were any bodies in the world, or even any intelligences, or other natures that were not wholly perfect, their existence depended on his power in such a way that they could not subsist without him for a single moment.

I was disposed straightway to search for other truths; and when I had represented to myself the object of the geometers, which I conceived to be a continuous body, or a space indefinitely extended in length, breadth, and height or depth, divisible into divers parts which admit of different figures and sizes, and of being moved or transposed in all manner of ways (for all this the geometers suppose to be in the object they contemplate), I went over some of their simplest demonstrations. And, in the first place, I observed, that the great certitude which by common consent is accorded to these demonstrations, is founded solely upon this, that they are clearly conceived in accordance with the rules I have already laid down. In the next place, I perceived that there was nothing at all in these demonstrations which could assure me of the existence of their object: thus, for example, supposing a triangle to be given, I distinctly perceived that its three angles were necessarily equal to two right angles, but I did not on that account perceive anything which could assure me that any triangle existed: while, on the contrary, recurring to the examination of the idea of a Perfect Being, I found that the existence of the Being was comprised in the idea in the same way that the equality of its three angles to two right angles is comprised in the idea of a triangle, or as in the idea of a sphere, the equidistance of all points on its surface from the centre, or even still more clearly; and that consequently it is at least as certain that God, who is this Perfect Being, is, or exists, as any demonstration of geometry can be.

But the reason which leads many to persuade themselves that there is a difficulty in knowing this truth, and even also in knowing what their mind really is, is that they never raise their thoughts above sensible objects, and are so accustomed to consider nothing except by way of imagination, which is a mode of thinking limited to material objects, that all that is not imaginable seems to them not intelligible. The truth of this is sufficiently manifest from the single circumstance, that the philosophers of the schools accept as a maxim that there is nothing in the understanding which was not previously in the senses, in which however it is certain that the ideas of God and of the soul have never been; and it appears to me that they who make use of their imagination to comprehend these ideas do exactly the same thing as if, in order to hear sounds or smell odours, they strove to avail themselves of their eyes; unless indeed that there is this difference, that the sense of sight does not afford us an inferior assurance to those of smell or hearing; in place of which, neither our imagination nor our senses can give us assurance of anything unless our understanding intervene.

Finally, if there be still persons who are not sufficiently persuaded of the existence of God and of the soul, by the reasons I have adduced, I am desirous that they should know that all the other propositions, of the truth of which they deem themselves perhaps more assured, as that we have a body, and that there exist stars and an earth, and such like, are less certain; for, although we have a moral assurance of these things, which is so strong that there is an appearance of extravagance in doubting of their existence, yet at the same time no one, unless his intellect is impaired, can deny, when the question relates to a metaphysical certitude, that there is sufficient reason to exclude entire assurance, in the observation that when asleep we can in the same way imagine ourselves possessed of another body and that we see other stars and another earth, when there is nothing of the kind. For how do we know that the thoughts which occur in dreaming are false rather than those other which we experience when awake, since the former are often not less vivid and distinct than the latter? And though men of the highest genius study this question as long as they please, I do not believe that they will be able to give any reason which can be sufficient to remove this doubt, unless they presuppose the existence of God. For, in the first place, even the principle which I have already taken as a rule, viz., that all the things which we clearly and distinctly conceive are true, is certain only because God is or exists and because he is a Perfect Being, and because all that we possess is derived from him: whence it follows that our ideas or notions, which to the extent of their clearness and distinctness are real, and proceed from God, must to that extent be true. Accordingly, whereas we not unfrequently have ideas or notions in which some falsity is contained, this can only be the case with such as are to some extent confused and obscure, and in this proceed from nothing (participate of negation), that is, exist in us thus confused because we are not wholly perfect. And it is evident that it is not less repugnant that falsity or imperfection, in so far as it is imperfection, should proceed from God, than that truth or perfection should proceed from nothing. But if we did not know that all which we possess of real and true proceeds from a Perfect and Infinite Being, however clear and distinct our ideas might be, we should have no ground on that account for the assurance that they possessed the perfection of being true.

But after the knowledge of God and of the soul has rendered us certain of this rule, we can easily understand that the truth of the thoughts we experience when awake, ought not in the slightest degree to be called in question on account of the illusions of our dreams. For if it happened that an individual, even when asleep, had some very distinct idea, as, for example, if a geometer should discover some new demonstration, the circumstance of his being asleep would not militate against its truth; and as for the most ordinary error of our dreams, which consists in their representing to us various objects in the same way as our external senses, this is not prejudicial, since it leads us very properly to suspect the truth of the ideas of sense; for we are not unfrequently deceived in the same manner when awake; as when persons in the jaundice see all objects yellow, or when the stars or bodies at a great distance appear to us much smaller than they are. For, in fine, whether awake or asleep, we ought never to allow ourselves to be persuaded of the truth of anything unless on the evidence of our reason. And it must be noted that I say of our *reason*, and not of our imagination or of our senses: thus, for example, although we very clearly see the sun, we ought not therefore to determine that it is only of the size

which our sense of sight presents; and we may very distinctly
imagine the head of a lion joined to the body of a goat, without being therefore shut up to the conclusion that a chimæra
exists; for it is not a dictate of reason that what we thus see
or imagine is in reality existent; but it plainly tells us that all
our ideas or notions contain in them some truth; for otherwise
it could not be that God, who is wholly perfect and veracious,
should have placed them in us. And because our reasonings
are never so clear or so complete during sleep as when we
are awake, although sometimes the acts of our imagination
are then as lively and distinct, if not more so than in our waking moments, reason further dictates that, since all our
thoughts cannot be true because of our partial imperfection,
those possessing truth must infallibly be found in the experience of our waking moments rather than in that of our
dreams.

PART V

I would here willingly have proceeded to exhibit the whole
chain of truths which I deduced from these primary; but as
with a view to this it would have been necessary now to treat
of many questions in dispute among the learned, with whom
I do not wish to be embroiled, I believe that it will be better
for me to refrain from this exposition, and only mention in
general what these truths are, that the more judicious may be
able to determine whether a more special account of them
would conduce to the public advantage. I have ever remained
firm in my original resolution to suppose no other principle
than that of which I have recently availed myself in demon-
strating the existence of God and of the soul, and to accept
as true nothing that did not appear to me more clear and certain than the demonstrations of the geometers had formerly
appeared; and yet I venture to state that not only have I
found means to satisfy myself in a short time on all the principal difficulties which are usually treated of in philosophy,
but I have also observed certain laws established in nature by
God in such a manner, and of which he has impressed on our

minds such notions, that after we have reflected sufficiently upon these, we cannot doubt that they are accurately observed in all that exists or takes place in the world: and farther, by considering the concatenation of these laws, it appears to me that I have discovered many truths more useful and more important than all I had before learned, or even had expected to learn.

But because I have essayed to expound the chief of these discoveries in a treatise which certain considerations prevent me from publishing, I cannot make the results known more conveniently than by here giving a summary of the contents of this treatise. It was my design to comprise in it all that, before I set myself to write it, I thought I knew of the nature of material objects. But like the painters who, finding themselves unable to represent equally well on a plain surface all the different faces of a solid body, select one of the chief, on which alone they make the light fall, and throwing the rest into the shade, allow them to appear only in so far as they can be seen while looking at the principal one; so, fearing lest I should not be able to comprise in my discourse all that was in my mind, I resolved to expound singly, though at considerable length, my opinions regarding light; then to take the opportunity of adding something on the sun and the fixed stars, since light almost wholly proceeds from them; on the heavens since they transmit it; on the planets, comets, and earth, since they reflect it; and particularly on all the bodies that are upon the earth, since they are either coloured, or transparent, or luminous; and finally on man, since he is the spectator of these objects. Further, to enable me to cast this variety of subjects somewhat into the shade, and to express my judgment regarding them with greater freedom, without being necessitated to adopt or refute the opinions of the learned, I resolved to leave all the people here to their disputes, and to speak only of what would happen in a new world, if God were now to create somewhere in the imaginary spaces matter sufficient to compose one, and were to agitate variously and confusedly the different parts of this matter, so that there resulted a chaos as disordered as the poets ever feigned, and after that did nothing more than lend his ordinary concurrence to nature, and allow her to act in accordance with the laws which he had established. On this supposition, I, in the first place, described this matter, and essayed to represent it in such a manner that to my mind there can be nothing clearer and more intelligible, except what has been recently said regarding God and the soul; for I even expressly supposed that it possessed none of those forms or qualities which are so debated in the schools, nor in general anything the knowledge of which is not so natural to our minds that no one can so much as imagine himself ignorant of it. Besides, I have pointed out what are the laws of nature; and, with no other principle upon which to found my reasonings except the infinite perfection of God, I endeavoured to demonstrate all those about which there could be any room for doubt, and to prove that they are such, that even if God had created more worlds, there could have been none in which these laws were not observed. Thereafter I showed how the greatest part of the matter of this chaos must, in accordance with these laws, dispose and arrange itself in such a way as to present the appearance of heavens; how in the meantime some of its parts must compose an earth and some planets and comets, and others a sun and fixed stars. And, making a digression at this stage on the subject of light, I expounded at considerable length what the nature of that light must be which is found in the sun and the stars, and how thence in an instant of time it traverses the immense spaces of the heavens, and how from the planets and comets it is reflected towards the earth. To this I likewise added much respecting the substance, the situation, the motions, and all the different qualities of these heavens and stars; so that I thought I had said enough respecting them to show that there is nothing observable in the heavens or stars of our system that must not, or at least may not appear precisely alike in those of the system which I described. I came next to speak of the earth in particular, and to show how, even though I had expressly supposed that God had given no weight to the matter of which it is composed, this should not prevent all its parts from tending exactly to its centre; how with water and air on its surface, the disposition of the heavens and heavenly bodies, more especially of the moon, must cause a flow and ebb, like in all its circumstances to that observed in our seas, as also a certain current both of water and air from east to west, such as is likewise observed between the tropics; how the mountains, seas, fountains, and rivers might naturally be formed in it, and the metals produced in the mines, and the plants grow in the fields; and in general, how all the bodies which are commonly denominated mixed or composite might be generated: and, among other things in the discoveries alluded to, inasmuch as besides the stars, I knew nothing except fire which produces light, I spared no pains to set forth all that pertains to its nature,—the manner of its production and support, and to explain how heat is sometimes found without light, and light without heat; to show how it can induce various colours upon different bodies and other diverse qualities; how it reduces some to a liquid state and hardens others; how it can consume almost all bodies, or convert them into ashes and smoke; and finally, how from these ashes, by the mere intensity of its action, it forms glass: for as this transmutation of ashes into glass appeared to me as wonderful as any other in nature, I took a special pleasure in describing it.

I was not, however, disposed, from these circumstances, to conclude that this world had been created in the manner I described; for it is much more likely that God made it at the first such as it was to be. But this is certain, and an opinion commonly received among theologians, that the action by which he now sustains it is the same with that by which he originally created it; so that even although he had from the beginning given it no other form than that of chaos, provided only he had established certain laws of nature, and had lent it his concurrence to enable it to act as it is wont to do, it may be believed, without discredit to the miracle of creation, that, in this way alone, things purely material might, in course of time, have become such as we observe them at present; and their nature is much more easily conceived when they are beheld coming in this manner gradually into existence, than when they are only considered as produced at once in a finished and perfect state.

From the description of inanimate bodies and plants, I passed to animals, and particularly to man. But since I had not as yet sufficient knowledge to enable me to treat of these in the same manner as of the rest, that is to say, by deducing effects from their causes, and by showing from what elements and in what manner nature must produce them, I remained satisfied with the supposition that God formed the body of man wholly like to one of ours, as well in the external shape of the members as in the internal conformation of the organs, of the same matter with that I had described, and at first placed in it no rational soul, nor any other principle, in room of the vegetative or sensitive soul, beyond kindling in the heart one of those fires without light, such as I had already described, and which I thought was not different from the heat in hay that has been heaped together before it is dry, or that which causes fermentation in new wines before they are run clear of the fruit. For, when I examined the kind of functions which might, as consequences of this supposition, exist in this body, I found precisely all those which may exist in us independently of all power of thinking, and consequently without being in any measure owing to the soul; in other words, to that part of us which is distinct from the body, and of which it has been said above that the nature distinctively consists in thinking,—functions in which the animals void of reason may be said wholly to resemble us; but among which I could not discover any of those that, as dependent on thought alone, belong to us as men, while, on the other hand, I did afterwards discover these as soon as I supposed God to have created a rational soul, and to have annexed it to this body in a particular manner which I described.

But, in order to show how I there handled this matter, I mean here to give the explication of the motion of the heart and arteries, which, as the first and most general motion observed in animals, will afford the means of readily determining what should be thought of all the rest. And that there may be less difficulty in understanding what I am about to say on this subject, I advise those who are not versed in anatomy, before they commence the perusal of these observations, to take the trouble of getting dissected in their presence the heart of some large animal possessed of lungs (for this is throughout sufficiently like the human), and to have shown to them its two ventricles or cavities: in the first place, that in the right side, with which correspond two very ample tubes, viz., the hollow vein (*vena cava*), which is the principal receptacle of the blood, and the trunk of the tree, as it were, of which all the other veins in the body are branches; and the arterial vein (*vena arteriosa*), inappropriately so denominated, since it is in truth only an artery, which, taking its rise in the heart, is divided, after passing out from it, into many branches which presently disperse themselves all over the lungs; in the second place, the cavity in the left side, with which correspond in the same manner two canals in size equal to or larger than the preceding, viz., the venous artery (*arteria venosa*), likewise inappropriately thus designated, because it is simply a vein which comes from the lungs, where it is divided into many branches, interlaced with those of the arterial vein, and those of the tube called the windpipe, through which the air we breathe enters; and the great artery which, issuing from the heart, sends its branches all over the body. I should wish also that such persons were carefully shown the eleven pellicles which, like so many small valves, open and shut the four orifices that are in these two cavities, viz., three at the entrance of the hollow vein, where they are disposed in such a manner as by no means to prevent the blood which it contains from flowing into the right ventricle of the heart, and yet exactly to prevent its flowing out; three at the entrance to the arterial vein, which, arranged in a manner exactly the opposite of the former, readily permit the blood contained in this cavity to pass into the lungs, but hinder that contained in the lungs from returning to this cavity; and, in like manner, two others at the mouth of the venous artery, which allow the blood from the lungs to flow into the left cavity of the heart, but preclude its return; and three at the mouth of the great artery, which suffer the blood to flow from the heart, but prevent its reflux. Nor do we need to seek any other reason for the number of these pellicles beyond this that the orifice of the venous artery being on an oval shape from the nature of its situation, can be adequately closed with two, whereas the others being round are more conveniently closed with three. Besides, I wish such persons to observe that the grand artery and the arterial vein are of much harder and firmer texture than the venous artery and the hollow vein; and that the two last expand before entering the heart, and there form, as it were, two pouches denominated the auricles of the heart, which are composed of a substance similar to that of the heart itself; and that there is always more warmth in the heart than in any other part of the body; and, finally, that this heat is capable of causing any drop of blood that passes into the cavities rapidly to expand and dilate, just as all liquors do when allowed to fall drop by drop into a highly heated vessel.

For, after these things, it is not necessary for me to say anything more with a view to explain the motion of the heart, except that when its cavities are not full of blood, into these the blood of necessity flows,—from the hollow vein into the right, and from the venous artery into the left; because these two vessels are always full of blood, and their orifices, which are turned towards the heart, cannot then be closed. But as soon as two drops of blood have thus passed, one into each of the cavities, these drops which cannot but be very large, because the orifices through which they pass are wide, and the vessels from which they come full of blood, are immediately rarefied, and dilated by the heat they meet with. In this way they cause the whole heart to expand, and at the same time press home and shut the five small valves that are at the entrances of the two vessels from which they flow, and thus prevent any more blood from coming down into the heart, and becoming more and more rarefied, they push open the six small valves that are in the orifices of the other two vessels, through which they pass out, causing in this way all the branches of the arterial vein and of the grand artery to expand almost simultaneously with the heart—which immediately thereafter begins to contract, as do also the arteries, because the blood that has entered them has cooled, and the six small valves close, and the five of the hollow vein and of the venous artery open anew and allow a passage to other two drops of blood, which cause the heart and the arteries again to expand as before. And, because the blood which thus enters into the heart passes through these two pouches called auricles, it thence happens that their motion is the contrary of that of the heart, and that when it expands they contract. But lest those who are ignorant of the force of mathematical demonstrations, and who are not accustomed to distinguish true reasons from mere verisimilitudes, should venture, without examination, to deny what has been said, I wish it to be considered that the motion which I have now explained follows as necessarily from the very arrangement of the parts, which may be observed in the heart by the eye alone, and from the heat which may be felt with the fingers, and from the nature of the blood as learned from experience, as does the motion of a clock from the power, the situation, and shape of its counterweights and wheels.

But if it be asked how it happens that the blood in the veins, flowing in this way continually into the heart, is not exhausted, and why the arteries do not become too full, since all the blood which passes through the heart flows into them, I need only mention in reply what has been written by a physician [4] of England, who has the honour of having broken the ice on this subject, and of having been the first to teach that there are many small passages at the extremities of the arteries, through which the blood received by them from the heart passes into the small branches of the veins, whence it again returns to the heart; so that its course amounts precisely to a perpetual circulation. Of this we have abundant proof in the ordinary experience of surgeons, who, by binding the arm with a tie of moderate straitness above the part where they open the vein, cause the blood to flow more copiously than it would have done without any ligature; whereas quite the

---

[4] Harvey—*Lat. Tr.*

contrary would happen were they to bind it below; that is, between the hand and the opening, or were to make the ligature above the opening very tight. For it is manifest that the tie, moderately straitened, while adequate to hinder the blood already in the arm from returning towards the heart by the veins, cannot on that account prevent new blood from coming forward through the arteries, because these are situated below the veins, and their coverings, from their greater consistency, are more difficult to compress; and also that the blood which comes from the heart tends to pass through them to the hand with greater force than it does to return from the hand to the heart through the veins. And since the latter current escapes from the arm by the opening made in one of the veins, there must of necessity be certain passages below the ligature, that is, towards the extremities of the arm through which it can come thither from the arteries. This physician likewise abundantly establishes what he has advanced respecting the motion of the blood, from the existence of certain pellicles, so disposed in various places along the course of the veins, in the manner of small valves, as not to permit the blood to pass from the middle of the body towards the extremities, but only to return from the extremities to the heart; and farther, from experience which shows that all the blood which is in the body may flow out of it in a very short time through a single artery that has been cut, even although this had been closely tied in the immediate neighbourhood of the heart, and cut between the heart and the ligature, so as to prevent the supposition that the blood flowing out of it could come from any other quarter than the heart.

But there are many other circumstances which evince that what I have alleged is the true cause of the motion of the blood: thus, in the first place, the difference that is observed between the blood which flows from the veins, and that from the arteries, can only arise from this, that being rarefied, and, as it were, distilled by passing through the heart, it is thinner, and more vivid, and warmer immediately after leaving the heart, in other words, when in the arteries, than it was a short time before passing into either, in other words, when it was in the veins; and if attention be given, it will be found that this difference is very marked only in the neighbourhood of the heart; and is not so evident in parts more remote from it. In the next place, the consistency of the coats of which the arterial vein and the great artery are composed, sufficiently shows that the blood is impelled against them with more force than against the veins. And why should the left cavity of the heart and the great artery be wider and larger than the right cavity and the arterial vein, were it not that the blood of the venous artery, having only been in the lungs after it has passed through the heart, is thinner, and rarefies more readily, and in a higher degree, than the blood which proceeds immediately from the hollow vein? And what can physicians conjecture from feeling the pulse unless they know that according as the blood changes its nature it can be rarefied by the warmth of the heart, in a higher or lower degree, and more or less quickly than before? And if it be inquired how this heat is communicated to the other members, must it not be admitted that this is effected by means of the blood, which, passing through the heart, is there heated anew, and thence diffused over all the body? Whence it happens, that if the blood be withdrawn from any part, the heat is likewise withdrawn by the same means; and although the heart were as hot as glowing iron, it would not be capable of warming the feet and hands as at present, unless it continually sent thither new blood. We likewise perceive from this, that the true use of respiration is to bring sufficient fresh air into the lungs, to cause the blood which flows into them from the right ventricle of the heart, where it has been rarefied and, as it were, changed into vapours, to become thick, and to convert it anew into blood, before it flows into the left cavity, without which process it would be unfit for the nourishment of the fire that is there. This receives confirmation from the circumstance, that it is observed of animals destitute of lungs that they have also but one cavity in the heart, and that in children who cannot use them while in the womb, there is a hole through which the blood flows from the hollow vein into the left cavity of the heart, and a tube through which it passes from the arterial vein into the grand artery without passing through the lung. In the next place, how could digestion be carried on in the stomach unless the heart communicated heat to it through the arteries, and along with this certain of the more fluid parts of the blood, which assist in the dissolution of the food that has been taken in? Is not also the operation which converts the juice of food into blood easily comprehended, when it is considered that it is distilled by passing and repassing through the heart perhaps more than one or two hundred times in a day? And what more need be adduced to explain nutrition, and the production of the different humours of the body, beyond saying, that the force with which the blood, in being rarefied, passes from the heart towards the extremities of the arteries, causes certain of its parts to remain in the members at which they arrive, and there occupy the place of some others expelled by them; and that according to the situation, shape, or smallness of the pores with which they meet, some rather than others flow into certain parts, in the same way that some sieves are observed to act, which, by being variously perforated, serve to separate different species of grain? And, in the last place, what above all is here worthy of observation, is the generation of the animal spirits, which are like a very subtle wind, or rather a very pure and vivid flame which, continually ascending in great abundance from the heart to the brain, thence penetrates through the nerves into the muscles, and gives motion to all the members; so that to account for other parts of the blood which, as most agitated and penetrating, are the fittest to compose these spirits, proceeding towards the brain, it is not necessary to suppose any other cause, than simply, that the arteries which carry them thither proceed from the heart in the most direct lines, and that, according to the rules of mechanics, which are the same with those of nature, when many objects tend at once to the same point where there is not sufficient room for all (as is the case with the parts of the blood which flow forth from the left cavity of the heart and tend towards the brain), the weaker and less agitated parts must necessarily be driven aside from that point by the stronger which alone in this way reach it.

I had expounded all these matters with sufficient minuteness in the treatise which I formerly thought of publishing. And after these, I had shown what must be the fabric of the nerves and muscles of the human body to give the animal spirits contained in it the power to move the members, as when we see heads shortly after they have been struck off still move and bite the earth, although no longer animated; what changes must take place in the brain to produce waking, sleep, and dreams; how light, sounds, odours, tastes, heat, and all the other qualities of external objects impress it with different ideas by means of the senses; how hunger, thirst, and the other internal affections can likewise impress upon it diverse ideas; what must be understood by the common sense (*sensus communis*) in which these ideas are received, by the memory which retains them, by the fantasy which can change them in various ways, and out of them compose new ideas, and which, by the same means, distributing the animal spirits through the muscles, can cause the members of such a body to move in as many different ways, and in a manner as suited, whether to the objects that are presented to its senses or to its internal affections, as can take place in our own case apart from the guidance of the will. Nor will this appear at all strange to those who are acquainted with the variety of movements performed by the different automata, or moving machines fabricated by human industry, and that with help of but few pieces compared with the great multitude of bones, muscles, nerves, arteries, veins, and other parts that are found in the body of each animal. Such persons will look upon this body as a machine made by the hands of God, which is incomparably better arranged, and adequate to movements more admirable than is any machine of human invention. And here I specially stayed to show that, were there such machines exactly resembling in organs and outward form an ape or any other irrational animal, we could have no means of knowing that they were in any respect of a different nature from these animals; but if there were machines bearing the image of our bodies, and capable of imitating our actions as far as it is morally possible, there would still remain two most certain tests whereby to know that they were not therefore really men. Of these the first is that they could never use words or other signs arranged in such a manner as is competent to us in order to declare our thoughts to others: for we may easily conceive a machine to be so constructed that it emits vocables, and even that it emits some correspondent to the action upon it of external objects which cause a change in its organs; for example, if touched in a particular place it may demand what we wish to say to it; if in another it may cry out that it is hurt, and such like; but not that it should arrange them variously so as appositely to reply to what is said in its presence, as men of the lowest grade of intellect can do. The second test is, that although such machines might execute many things with equal or perhaps greater perfection than any of us, they would, without doubt, fail in certain others from which it could be discovered that they did not act from knowledge, but solely from the disposition of their organs: for while reason is an universal instrument that is alike available on every occasion, these organs, on the contrary, need a particular arrangement for each particular action; whence it must be morally impossible that there should exist in any machine a diversity of organs sufficient to enable it to act in all the occurrences of life, in the way in which our reason enables us to act. Again, by means of these two tests we may likewise know the difference between men and brutes. For it is highly deserving of remark, that there are no men so dull and stupid, not even idiots, as to be incapable of joining together different words, and thereby constructing a declaration by which to make their thoughts understood; and that on the other hand, there is no other animal, however perfect or happily circumstanced, which can do the like. Nor does this inability arise from want of organs: for we observe that magpies and parrots can utter words like ourselves, and are yet unable to speak as we do, that is, so as to show that they understand what they say; in place of which men born deaf and dumb, and thus not less, but rather more than the brutes, destitute of the organs which others use in speaking, are in the habit of spontaneously inventing certain signs by which they discover their thoughts to those who, being usually in their company, have leisure to learn their language. And this proves not only that the brutes have less reason than man, but that they have none at all: for we see that very little is required to enable a person to speak; and since a certain inequality of capacity is observable among animals of the same species, as well as among men, and since some are more capable of being instructed than others, it is incredible that the most perfect ape or parrot of its species, should not in this be equal to the most stupid infant of its kind, or at least to one that was crack-brained, unless the soul of brutes were of a nature wholly different from ours. And we ought not to confound speech with the natural movements which indicate the passions, and can be imitated by machines as well as manifested by animals; nor must it be thought with certain of the ancients, that the brutes speak, although we do not understand their language. For if such were the case, since they are endowed with many organs analogous to ours, they could as easily communicate their thoughts to us as to their fellows. It is also very worthy of remark, that, though there are many animals which manifest more industry than we in certain of their actions, the same animals are yet observed to show none at all in many others: so that the circumstance that they do better than we does not prove that they are endowed with mind, for it would thence follow that they possessed greater reason than any of us, and could surpass us in all things; on the contrary, it rather proves that they are destitute of reason, and that it is nature which acts in them according to the disposition of their organs: thus it is seen, that a clock composed only of wheels and weights can number the hours and measure time more exactly than we with all our skill.

I had after this described the reasonable soul, and shown that it could by no means be educed from the power of matter, as the other things of which I had spoken, but that it must be expressly created; and that it is not sufficient that it be lodged in the human body exactly like a pilot in a ship, unless perhaps to move its members, but that it is necessary for it to be joined and united more closely to the body, in order to have sensations and appetites similar to ours, and thus constitute a real man. I here entered, in conclusion, upon the subject of the soul at considerable length, because it is of the greatest moment: for after the error of those who deny the existence of God, an error which I think I have already sufficiently refuted, there is none that is more powerful in leading feeble minds astray from the straight path of virtue than the supposition that the soul of the brutes is of the same nature with our own; and consequently that after this life we have nothing to hope for or fear, more than flies and ants; in place of which, when we know how far they differ we much better comprehend the reasons which establish that the soul is of a nature wholly independent of the body, and that consequently it is not liable to die with the latter; and, finally, because no other causes are observed capable of destroying it, we are naturally led thence to judge that it is immortal.

PART VI

Three years have now elapsed since I finished the treatise containing all these matters; and I was beginning to revise it, with the view to put it into the hands of a printer, when I learned that persons to whom I greatly defer, and whose authority over my actions is hardly less influential than is my own reason over my thoughts, had condemned a certain doctrine in physics, published a short time previously by another individual,[5] to which I will not say that I adhered, but only that, previously to their censure, I had observed in it nothing which I could imagine to be prejudicial either to religion or to the state, and nothing therefore which would have prevented me from giving expression to it in writing, if reason had persuaded me of its truth; and this led me to fear lest among my own doctrines likewise some one might be found in which I had departed from the truth, notwithstanding the great care I have always taken not to accord belief to new opinions of which I had not the most certain demonstrations, and not to give expression to aught that might tend to the

---

[5] Galileo.

hurt of any one. This has been sufficient to make me alter my purpose of publishing them; for although the reasons by which I had been induced to take this resolution were very strong, yet my inclination, which has always been hostile to writing books, enabled me immediately to discover other considerations sufficient to excuse me for not undertaking the task. And these reasons, on one side and the other, are such, that not only is it in some measure my interest here to state them, but that of the public, perhaps, to know them.

I have never made much account of what has proceeded from my own mind; and so long as I gathered no other advantage from the method I employ beyond satisfying myself on some difficulties belonging to the speculative sciences, or endeavouring to regulate my actions according to the principles it taught me, I never thought myself bound to publish anything respecting it. For in what regards manners, every one is so full of his own wisdom, that there might be found as many reformers as heads, if any were allowed to take upon themselves the task of mending them, except those whom God has constituted the supreme rulers of his people, or to whom he has given sufficient grace and zeal to be prophets; and although my speculations greatly pleased myself, I believed that others had theirs, which perhaps pleased them still more. But as soon as I had acquired some general notions respecting physics, and beginning to make trial of them in various particular difficulties, had observed how far they can carry us, and how much they differ from the principles that have been employed up to the present time, I believed that I could not keep them concealed without sinning grievously against the law by which we are bound to promote, as far as in us lies, the general good of mankind. For by them I perceived it to be possible to arrive at knowledge highly useful in life; and in room of the speculative philosophy usually taught in the schools, to discover a practical, by means of which, knowing the force and action of fire, water, air, the stars, the heavens, and all the other bodies that surround us, as distinctly as we know the various crafts of our artisans, we might also apply them in the same way to all the uses to which they are adapted, and thus render ourselves the lords and possessors of nature. And this is a result to be desired, not only in order to the invention of an infinity of arts, by which we might be enabled to enjoy without any trouble the fruits of the earth, and all its comforts, but also and especially for the preservation of health, which is without doubt, of all the blessings of this life, the first and fundamental one; for the mind is so intimately dependent upon the condition and relation of the organs of the body, that if any means can ever be found to render men wiser and more ingenious than hitherto, I believe that it is in medicine they must be sought for. It is true that the science of medicine, as it now exists, contains few things whose utility is very remarkable: but without any wish to depreciate it, I am confident that there is no one, even among those whose profession it is, who does not admit that all at present known in it is almost nothing in comparison of what remains to be discovered; and that we could free ourselves from an infinity of maladies of body as well as of mind, and perhaps also even from the debility of age, if we had sufficiently ample knowledge of their causes, and of all the remedies provided for us by nature. But since I designed to employ my whole life in the search after so necessary a science, and since I had fallen in with a path which seems to me such, that if any one follow it he must inevitably reach the end desired, unless he be hindered either by the shortness of life or the want of experiments, I judged that there could be no more effectual provision against these two impediments than if I were faithfully to communicate to the public all the little I might myself have found, and incite men of superior genius to strive to proceed farther, by contributing, each according to his inclination and ability, to the experiments which it would be necessary to make, and also by informing the public of all they might discover, so that, by the last beginning where those before them had left off, and thus connecting the lives and labours of many, we might collectively proceed much farther than each by himself could do.

I remarked, moreover, with respect to experiments, that they become always more necessary the more one is advanced in knowledge; for, at the commencement, it is better to make use only of what is spontaneously presented to our senses, and of which we cannot remain ignorant, provided we bestow on it any reflection, however slight, than to concern ourselves about more uncommon and recondite phenomena: the reason of which is, that the more uncommon often only mislead us so long as the causes of the more ordinary are still unknown; and the circumstances upon which they depend are almost always so special and minute as to be highly difficult to detect. But in this I have adopted the following order: first, I have essayed to find in general the principles, or first causes of all that is or can be in the world, without taking into consideration for this end anything but God himself who has created it, and without educing them from any other source than from certain germs of truths naturally existing in our minds. In the second place, I examined what were the first and most ordinary effects that could be deduced from these causes; and it appears to me that, in this way, I have found heavens, stars, an earth, and even on the earth, water, air, fire, minerals, and some other things of this kind, which of all others are the most common and simple, and hence the easiest to know. Afterwards, when I wished to descend to the more particular, so many diverse objects presented themselves to me, that I believed it to be impossible for the human mind to distinguish the forms or species of bodies that are upon the earth, from an infinity of others which might have been, if it had pleased God to place them there, or consequently to apply them to our use, unless we rise to causes through their effects, and avail ourselves of many particular experiments. Thereupon, turning over in my mind all the objects that had ever been presented to my senses, I freely venture to state that I have never observed any which I could not satisfactorily explain by the principles I had discovered. But it is necessary also to confess that the power of nature is so ample and vast, and these principles so simple and general, that I have hardly observed a single particular effect which I cannot at once recognise as capable of being deduced in many different modes from the principles, and that my greatest difficulty usually is to discover in which of these modes the effect is dependent upon them; for out of this difficulty I cannot otherwise extricate myself than by again seeking certain experiments, which may be such that their result is not the same, if it is in the one of these modes that we must explain it, as it would be if it were to be explained in the other. As to what remains, I am now in a position to discern, as I think, with sufficient clearness what course must be taken to make the majority of those experiments which may conduce to this end: but I perceive likewise that they are such and so numerous, that neither my hands nor my income, though it were a thousand times larger than it is, would be sufficient for them all; so that, according as henceforward I shall have the means of making more or fewer experiments, I shall in the same proportion make greater or less progress in the knowledge of nature. This was what I had hoped to make known by the treatise I had written, and so clearly to exhibit the advantage that would thence accrue to the public, as to induce all who have the common good of man at heart, that is, all who are virtuous in truth, and not merely in appearance, or according to opinion, as well to communicate to me the experiments they had already made, as to assist me in those that remain to be made.

But since that time other reasons have occurred to me, by which I have been led to change my opinion, and to think that I ought indeed to go on committing to writing all the results which I deemed of any moment, as soon as I should have tested their truth, and to bestow the same care upon them as I would have done had it been my design to publish them. This course commended itself to me, as well because I thus afforded myself more ample inducement to examine them thoroughly, for doubtless that is always more narrowly scrutinised which we believe will be read by many, than that which is written merely for our private use (and frequently what has seemed to me true when I first conceived it, has appeared false when I have set about committing it to writing), as because I thus lost no opportunity of advancing the interests of the public, as far as in me lay, and since thus likewise, if my writings possess any value, those into whose hands they may fall after my death may be able to put them to what use they deem proper. But I resolved by no means to consent to their publication during my lifetime, lest either the oppositions or the controversies to which they might give rise, or even the reputation, such as it might be, which they would acquire for me, should be any occasion of my losing the time that I had set apart for my own improvement. For though it be true that every one is bound to promote to the extent of his ability the good of others, and that to be useful to no one is really to be worthless, yet it is likewise true that our cares ought to extend beyond the present; and it is good to omit doing what might perhaps bring some profit to the living, when we have in view the accomplishment of other ends that will be of much greater advantage to posterity. And in truth, I am quite willing it should be known that the little I have hitherto learned is almost nothing in comparison with that of which I am ignorant, and to the knowledge of which I do not despair of being able to attain; for it is much the same with those who gradually discover truth in the sciences, as with those who when growing rich find less difficulty in making great acquisitions, than they formerly experienced when poor in making acquisitions of much smaller amount. Or they may be compared to the commanders of armies, whose forces usually increase in proportion to their victories, and who need greater prudence to keep together the residue of their troops after a defeat than after a victory to take towns and provinces. For he truly engages in battle who endeavours to surmount all the difficulties and errors which prevent him from reaching the knowledge of truth, and he is overcome in fight who admits a false opinion touching a matter of any generality and importance, and he requires thereafter much more skill to recover his former position than to make great advances when once in possession of thoroughly ascertained principles. As for myself, if I have succeeded in discovering any truths in the sciences (and I trust that what is contained in this volume will show that I have found some), I can declare that they are but the consequences and results of five or six principal difficulties which I have surmounted, and my encounters with which I reckoned as battles in which victory declared for me. I will not hesitate even to avow my belief that nothing further is wanting to enable me fully to realise my designs than to gain two or three similar victories; and that I am not so far advanced in years but that, according to the ordinary course of nature, I may still have sufficient leisure for this end. But I conceive myself the more bound to husband the time that remains the greater my expectation of being able to employ it aright, and I should doubtless have much to rob me of it, were I to publish the principles of my physics: for although they are almost all so evident that to assent to them no more is needed than simply to understand them, and although there is not one of them of which I do not expect to be able to give demonstration, yet, as it is impossible that they can be in accordance with all the diverse opinions of others, I foresee that I should frequently be turned aside from my grand design, on occasion of the opposition which they would be sure to awaken.

It may be said, that these oppositions would be useful both in making me aware of my errors, and, if my speculations contain anything of value, in bringing others to a fuller understanding of it; and still farther, as many can see better than one, in leading others who are now beginning to avail themselves of my principles, to assist me in turn with their discoveries. But though I recognise my extreme liability to error, and scarce ever trust to the first thoughts which occur to me, yet the experience I have had of possible objections to my views prevents me from anticipating any profit from them. For I have already had frequent proof of the judgments, as well of those I esteemed friends, as of some others to whom I thought I was an object of indifference, and even of some whose malignity and envy would, I knew, determine them to endeavour to discover what partiality concealed from the eyes of my friends. But it has rarely happened that anything has been objected to me which I had myself altogether overlooked, unless it were something far removed from the subject: so that I have never met with a single critic of my opinions who did not appear to me either less rigorous or less equitable than myself. And further, I have never observed that any truth before unknown has been brought to light by the disputations that are practised in the schools; for while each strives for the victory, each is much more occupied in making the best of mere verisimilitude, than in weighing the reasons on both sides of the question; and those who have been long good advocates are not afterwards on that account the better judges.

As for the advantage that others would derive from the communication of my thoughts, it could not be very great; because I have not yet so far prosecuted them as that much does not remain to be added before they can be applied to practice. And I think I may say without vanity, that if there is any one who can carry them out that length, it must be myself rather than another: not that there may not be in the world many minds incomparably superior to mine, but because one cannot so well seize a thing and make it one's own, when it has been learned from another, as when one has himself discovered it. And so true is this of the present subject that, though I have often explained some of my opinions to persons of much acuteness, who, whilst I was speaking, appeared to understand them very distinctly, yet, when they repeated them, I have observed that they almost always changed them to such an extent that I could no longer acknowledge them as mine. I am glad, by the way, to take this opportunity of requesting posterity never to believe on hearsay that anything has proceeded from me which has not been published by myself; and I am not at all astonished at the extravagances attributed to those ancient philosophers whose own writings we do not possess; whose thoughts, however, I do not on that account suppose to have been really absurd, seeing they were among the ablest men of their times, but only that these have been falsely represented to us. It is observable, accordingly, that scarcely in a single instance has any one of their disciples surpassed them; and I am quite sure that the most devoted of the present followers of Aristotle would think themselves happy if they had as much knowledge of nature as he possessed, were it even under the condition that they should never afterwards attain to higher. In this respect they are like the ivy which never strives to rise above the tree that sustains it, and which frequently even returns downwards when it has reached the top; for it seems to me that they also sink, in other words, render themselves less wise than they would be if they gave up study, who, not contented with knowing all that is intelligibly explained in their author, desire in addition to find in him the solution of many difficulties of which he says not a word, and never perhaps so much as thought. Their fashion of philosophising, however, is well suited to persons whose abilities fall below mediocrity; for the obscurity of the distinctions and principles of which they make use enables them to speak of all things with as much confidence as if they really knew them, and to defend all that they say on any subject against the most subtle and skilful, without its being possible for any one to convict them of error. In this they seem to me to be like a blind man, who, in order to fight on equal terms with a person that sees, should have made him descend to the bottom of an intensely dark cave: and I may say that such persons have an interest in my refraining from publishing the principles of the philosophy of which I make use; for, since these are of a kind the simplest and most evident, I should, by publishing them, do much the same as if I were to throw open the windows, and allow the light of day to enter the cave into which the combatants had descended. But even superior men have no reason for any great anxiety to know these principles, for if what they desire is to be able to speak of all things, and to acquire a reputation for learning, they will gain their end more easily by remaining satisfied with the appearance of truth, which can be found without much difficulty in all sorts of matters, than by seeking the truth itself which unfolds itself but slowly and that only in some departments, while it obliges us, when we have to speak of others, freely to confess our ignorance. If, however, they prefer the knowledge of some few truths to the vanity of appearing ignorant of none, as such knowledge is undoubtedly much to be preferred, and, if they choose to follow a course similar to mine, they do not require for this that I should say anything more than I have already said in this discourse. For if they are capable of making greater advancement than I have made, they will much more be able of themselves to discover all that I believe myself to have found; since as I have never examined aught except in order, it is certain that what yet remains to be discovered is in itself more difficult and recondite, than that which I have already been enabled to find, and the gratification would be much less in learning it from me than in discovering it for themselves. Besides this, the habit which they will acquire, by seeking first what is easy, and then passing onward slowly and step by step to the more difficult, will benefit them more than all my instructions. Thus, in my own case, I am persuaded that if I had been taught from my youth all the truths of which I have since sought out demonstrations, and had thus learned them without labour, I should never, perhaps, have known any beyond these; at least, I should never have acquired the habit and the facility which I think I possess in always discovering new truths in proportion as I give myself to the search. And, in a single word, if there is any work in the world which cannot be so well finished by another as by him who has commenced it, it is that at which I labour.

It is true, indeed, as regards the experiments which may conduce to this end, that one man is not equal to the task of making them all; but yet he can advantageously avail himself, in this work, of no hands besides his own, unless those of artisans, or parties of the same kind, whom he could pay, and whom the hope of gain (a means of great efficacy) might stimulate to accuracy in the performance of what was prescribed to them. For as to those who, through curiosity or a desire of learning, of their own accord, perhaps, offer him their services, besides that in general their promises exceed their performance, and that they sketch out fine designs of which not one is ever realised, they will, without doubt, expect to be compensated for their trouble by the explication of some difficulties, or, at least, by compliments and useless speeches, in which he cannot spend any portion of his time without loss to himself. And as for the experiments that others have already made, even although these parties should be willing of themselves to communicate them to him (which is what those who esteem them secrets will never do), the experiments are, for the most part, accompanied with so many circumstances and superfluous elements, as to make it exceedingly difficult to disentangle the truth from its adjuncts; besides, he will find almost all of them so ill described, or even so false (because those who made them have wished to see in them only such facts as they deemed conformable to their principles), that, if in the entire number there should be some of a nature suited to his purpose, still their value could not compensate for the time what would be necessary to make the selection. So that if there existed any one whom we assuredly knew to be capable of making discoveries of the highest kind, and of the greatest possible utility to the public; and if all other men were therefore eager by all means to assist him in successfully prosecuting his designs, I do not see that they could do aught else for him beyond contributing to defray the expenses of the experiments that might be necessary; and for the rest, prevent his being deprived of his leisure by the unseasonable interruptions of any one. But besides that I neither have so high an opinion of myself as to be willing to make promise of anything extraordinary, nor feed on imaginations so vain as to fancy that the public must be much interested in my designs; I do not, on the other hand, own a soul so mean as to be capable of accepting from any one a favour of which it could be supposed that I was unworthy.

These considerations taken together were the reason why, for the last three years, I have been unwilling to publish the treatise I had on hand, and why I even resolved to give publicity during my life to no other that was so general, or by which the principles of my physics might be understood. But since then, two other reasons have come into operation that have determined me here to subjoin some particular specimens, and give the public some account of my doings and designs. Of these considerations, the first is, that if I failed to do so, many who were cognisant of my previous intention to publish some writings, might have imagined that the reasons which induced me to refrain from so doing, were less to my credit than they really are; for although I am not immoderately desirous of glory, or even, if I may venture so to say, although I am averse from it in so far as I deem it hostile to repose which I hold in greater account than aught else, yet, at the same time, I have never sought to conceal my actions as if they were crimes, nor made use of many precautions that I might remain unknown; and this partly because I should have thought such a course of conduct a wrong against myself, and partly because it would have occasioned me some sort of uneasiness which would again have been contrary to the perfect mental tranquillity which I court. And forasmuch as, while thus indifferent to the thought alike of fame or of forgetfulness, I have yet been unable to prevent myself from acquiring some sort of reputation, I have thought it incumbent on me to do my best to save myself at least from being ill-spoken of. The other reason that has determined me to commit to writing these specimens of philosophy is, that I am becoming daily more and more alive to the delay which my design of self-instruction suffers, for want of the infinity of experiments I require, and which it is impossible for me to make without the assistance of others: and, without flattering myself so much as to expect the public to take a large share in my interests, I am yet unwilling to be found so far wanting in the duty I owe to myself, as to give occasion to those who shall survive me to make it matter of reproach against me some day, that I might have left them many things in a much more perfect state than I have done, had I not too much neglected to make them aware of the ways in which they could have promoted the accomplishment of my designs.

And I thought that it was easy for me to select some matters which should neither be obnoxious to much controversy, nor should compel me to expound more of my principles than I desired, and which should yet be sufficient clearly to exhibit what I can or cannot accomplish in the sciences. Whether or not I have succeeded in this it is not for me to say; and I do not wish to forestall the judgments of others by speaking myself of my writings; but it will gratify me if they be examined, and, to afford the greater inducement to this, I request all who may have any objections to make to them, to take the trouble of forwarding these to my publisher, who will give me notice of them, that I may endeavour to subjoin at the same time my reply; and in this way readers seeing both at once will more easily determine where the truth lies; for I do not engage in any case to make prolix replies, but only with perfect frankness to avow my errors if I am convinced of them, or if I cannot perceive them, simply to state what I think is required for defence of the matters I have written, adding thereto no explication of any new matter that it may not be necessary to pass without end from one thing to another.

If some of the matters of which I have spoken in the beginning of the "Dioptrics" and "Meteorics" should offend at first sight, because I call them hypotheses and seem indifferent about giving proof of them, I request a patient and attentive reading of the whole, from which I hope those hesitating will derive satisfaction; for it appears to me that the reasonings are so mutually connected in these treatises, that, as the last are demonstrated by the first which are their causes, the first are in their turn demonstrated by the last which are their effects. Nor must it be imagined that I here commit the fallacy which the logicians call a circle; for since experience renders the majority of these effects most certain, the causes from which I deduce them do not serve so much to establish their reality as to explain their existence; but on the contrary, the reality of the causes is established by the reality of the effects. Nor have I called them hypotheses with any other end in view except that it may be known that I think I am able to deduce them from those first truths which I have already expounded; and yet that I have expressly determined not to do so, to prevent a certain class of minds from thence taking occasion to build some extravagant philosophy upon what they may take to be my principles, and my being blamed for it. I refer to those who imagine that they can master in a day all that another has taken twenty years to think out, as soon as he has spoken two or three words to them on the subject; or who are the more liable to error and the less capable of perceiving truth in very proportion as they are more subtle and lively. As to the opinions which are truly and wholly mine, I offer no apology for them as new,—persuaded as I am that if their reasons be well considered they will be found to be so simple and so conformed to common sense as to appear less extraordinary and less paradoxical than any others which can be held on the same subjects; nor do I even boast of being the earliest discoverer of any of them, but only of having adopted them, neither because they had nor because they had not been held by others, but solely because reason has convinced me of their truth.

Though artisans may not be able at once to execute the invention which is explained in the "Dioptrics," I do not think that any one on that account is entitled to condemn it; for since address and practice are required in order so to make and adjust the machines described by me as not to overlook the smallest particular, I should not be less astonished if they succeeded on the first attempt than if a person were in one day to become an accomplished performer on the guitar, by merely having excellent sheets of music set up before him. And if I write in French, which is the language of my country, in preference to Latin, which is that of my preceptors, it is because I expect that those who make use of their unprejudiced natural reason will be better judges of my opinions than those who give heed to the writings of the ancients only; and as for those who unite good sense with habits of study, whom alone I desire for judges, they will not, I feel assured, be so partial to Latin as to refuse to listen to my reasonings merely because I expound them in the vulgar tongue.

In conclusion, I am unwilling here to say anything very specific of the progress which I expect to make for the future in the sciences, or to bind myself to the public by any promise which I am not certain of being able to fulfil; but this only will I say, that I have resolved to devote what time I may still have to live to no other occupation than that of endeavouring to acquire some knowledge of Nature, which shall be of such a kind as to enable us therefrom to deduce rules in medicine of greater certainty than those at present in use; and that my inclination is so much opposed to all other pursuits, especially to such as cannot be useful to some without being hurtful to others, that if, by any circumstances, I had been constrained to engage in such, I do not believe that I should have been able to succeed. Of this I here make a public declaration, though well aware that it cannot serve to procure for me any consideration in the world, which, however, I do not in the least affect; and I shall always hold myself more obliged to those through whose favour I am permitted to enjoy my retirement without interruption than to any who might offer me the highest earthly preferments.

Auguste Comte

THE POSITIVE PHILOSOPHY

Auguste Comte
[1798–1857]

Science was the means by which Auguste Comte, the founder of Positivism, studied the organism of society. The laws of mathematics, astronomy, physics, chemistry and biology existed for him as mere contributions to the establishment of a science of society whose ultimate goal was to be service to humanity. Comte's chief emphasis was on the laws of natural phenomena rather than on causes, and all ideas were valid by the test of usefulness in the physical and social world. Before he arrived at the formulation of his Religion of Humanity, the French philosopher subjected each field of inquiry to what he called the "Law of Three Stages," which were, in the order of the importance attached to them by Comte, theological, metaphysical and positive. The first was an explanation of facts and events by supernatural means; the second, by the abstract, and the third, by explicable cause and effect. Influential in the nineteenth century, Positivism attracted men like John Stuart Mill and Herbert Spencer, and today, even if it is not recognized with high favor by specialists in science, it remains a designation for a kind of faith in the co-ordinated sciences as an effective social instrument.

THE POSITIVE PHILOSOPHY

AUGUSTE COMTE

A general statement of any system of philosophy may be either a sketch of a doctrine to be established, or a summary of a doctrine already established. If greater value belongs to the last, the first is still important, as characterizing from its origin the subject to be treated. In a case like the present, where the proposed study is vast and hitherto indeterminate, it is especially important that the field of research should be marked out with all possible accuracy. For this purpose, I will glance at the considerations which have originated this work, and which will be fully elaborated in the course of it.

In order to understand the true value and character of the Positive Philosophy, we must take a brief general view of the progressive course of the human mind, regarded as a whole; for no conception can be understood otherwise than through its history.

From the study of the development of human intelligence, in all directions, and through all times, the discovery arises of a great fundamental law, to which it is necessarily subject, and which has a solid foundation of proof, both in the facts of our organization and in our historical experience. The law is this:—that each of our leading conceptions,—each branch of our knowledge,—passes successively through three different theoretical conditions: the Theological, or fictitious; the Metaphysical, or abstract; and the Scientific, or positive. In other words, the human mind, by its nature, employs in its progress three methods of philosophizing, the character of which is essentially different, and even radically opposed: viz., the theological method, the metaphysical, and the positive. Hence arise three philosophies, or general systems of conceptions on the aggregate of phenomena, each of which excludes the others. The first is the necessary point of departure of the human understanding; and the third is its fixed and definitive state. The second is merely a state of transition.

In the theological state, the human mind, seeking the essential nature of beings, the first and final causes (the origin and purpose) of all effects,—in short, Absolute knowledge,—supposes all phenomena to be produced by the immediate action of supernatural beings.

In the metaphysical state, which is only a modification of the first, the mind supposes, instead of supernatural beings, abstract forces, veritable entities (that is, personified abstractions) inherent in all beings, and capable of producing all phenomena. What is called the explanation of phenomena is, in this stage, a mere reference of each to its proper entity.

In the final, the positive state, the mind has given over the vain search after Absolute notions, the origin and destination of the universe, and the causes of phenomena, and applies itself to the study of their laws,—that is, their invariable relations of succession and resemblance. Reasoning and observation, duly combined, are the means of this knowledge. What is now understood when we speak of an explanation of facts is simply the establishment of a connection between single phenomena and some general facts, the number of which continually diminishes with the progress of science.

The Theological system arrived at the highest perfection of which it is capable when it substituted the providential action of a single Being for the varied operations of the numerous divinities which had been before imagined. In the same way, in the last stage of the Metaphysical system, men substitute one great entity (Nature) as the cause of all phenomena, instead of the multitude of entities at first supposed. In the same way, again, the ultimate perfection of the Positive system would be (if such perfection could be hoped for) to represent all phenomena as particular aspects of a single general fact;—such as Gravitation, for instance.

The importance of the working of this general law will be established hereafter. At present, it must suffice to point out some of the grounds of it.

There is no science which, having attained the positive stage, does not bear marks of having passed through the others. Some time since it was (whatever it might be) composed, as we can now perceive, of metaphysical abstractions; and, further back in the course of time, it took its form from theological conceptions. We shall have only too much occasion to see, as we proceed, that our most advanced sciences still bear very evident marks of the two earlier periods through which they have passed.

The progress of the individual mind is not only an illustration, but an indirect evidence of that of the general mind. The point of departure of the individual and of the race being the same, the phases of the mind of a man correspond to the epochs of the mind of the race. Now, each of us is aware, if he looks back upon his own history, that he was a theologian in his childhood, a metaphysician in his youth, and a natural philosopher in his manhood. All men who are up to their age can verify this for themselves.

Besides the observation of facts, we have theoretical reasons in support of this law.

The most important of these reasons arises from the necessity that always exists for some theory to which to refer our facts, combined with the clear impossibility that, at the outset of human knowledge, men could have formed theories out of the observation of facts. All good intellects have repeated, since Bacon's time, that there can be no real knowledge but that which is based on observed facts. This is incontestable, in our present advanced stage; but, if we look back to the primitive stage of human knowledge, we shall see that it must have been otherwise then. If it is true that every theory must be based upon observed facts, it is equally true that facts cannot be observed without the guidance of some theory. Without such guidance, our facts would be desultory and fruitless; we could not retain them: for the most part we could not even perceive them.

Thus, between the necessity of observing facts in order to form a theory, and having a theory in order to observe facts, the human mind would have been entangled in a vicious circle, but for the natural opening afforded by Theological conceptions. This is the fundamental reason for the theological character of the primitive philosophy. This necessity is confirmed by the perfect suitability of the theological philosophy to the earliest researches of the human mind. It is remarkable that the most inaccessible questions,—those of the nature of beings, and the origin and purpose of phenomena,—should be the first to occur in a primitive state, while those which are really within our reach are regarded as almost unworthy of serious study. The reason is evident enough:—that experience alone can teach us the measure of our powers; and if men had not begun by an exaggerated estimate of what they can do, they would never have done all that they are capable of. Our organization requires this. At such a period there could have been no reception of a positive philosophy, whose function is to discover the laws of phenomena, and whose leading characteristic it is to regard as interdicted to human reason those sublime mysteries which theology explains, even to their minutest details, with the most attractive facility. It is just so under a practical view of the nature of the researches with which men first occupied themselves. Such inquiries offered the powerful charm of unlimited empire over the external world,—a world destined wholly for our use, and involved in every way with our existence. The theological philosophy, presenting this view, administered exactly the stimulus necessary to incite the human mind to the irksome labour without which it could make no progress. We can now scarcely conceive of such a state of things, our reason having become sufficiently mature to enter upon laborious scientific researches, without needing any such stimulus as wrought upon the imaginations of astrologers and alchemists. We have motive enough in the hope of discovering the laws of phenomena, with a view to the confirmation or rejection of a theory. But it could not be so in the earliest days; and it is to the chimeras of astrology and alchemy that we owe the long series of observations and experiments on which our positive science is based. Kepler felt this on behalf of astronomy, and Berthollet on behalf of chemistry. Thus was a spontaneous philosophy, the theological, the only possible beginning, method, and provisional system, out of which the Positive philosophy could grow. It is easy, after this, to perceive how Metaphysical methods and doctrines must have afforded the means of transition from the one to the other.

The human understanding, slow in its advance, could not step at once from the theological into the positive philosophy. The two are so radically opposed, that an intermediate system of conceptions has been necessary to render the transition possible. It is only in doing this, that Metaphysical conceptions have any utility whatever. In contemplating phenomena, men substitute for supernatural direction a corresponding entity. This entity may have been supposed to be derived from the supernatural action: but it is more easily lost sight of, leaving attention free for the facts themselves, till, at length, metaphysical agents have ceased to be anything more than the abstract names of phenomena. It is not easy to say by what other process than this our minds could have passed from supernatural considerations to natural; from the theological system to the positive.

The Law of human development being thus established, let us consider what is the proper nature of the Positive Philosophy.

As we have seen, the first characteristic of the Positive Philosophy is that it regards all phenomena as subjected to invariable natural *Laws*. Our business is,—seeing how vain is any research into what are called *Causes*, whether first or final,—to pursue an accurate discovery of these Laws, with a view to reducing them to the smallest possible number. By speculating upon causes, we could solve no difficulty about origin and purpose. Our real business is to analyse accurately the circumstances of phenomena, and to connect them by the natural relations of succession and resemblance. The best illustration of this is in the case of the doctrine of Gravitation. We say that the general phenomena of the universe are *explained* by it, because it connects under one head the whole immense variety of astronomical facts; exhibiting the constant tendency of atoms towards each other in direct proportion to their masses, and in inverse proportion to the squares of their distances; whilst the general fact itself is a mere extension of one which is perfectly familiar to us, and which we therefore say that we know;— the weight of bodies on the surface of the earth. As to what weight and attraction are, we have nothing to do with that, for it is not a matter of knowledge at all. Theologians and metaphysicians may imagine and refine about such questions; but positive philosophy rejects them. When any attempt has been made to explain them, it has ended only in saying that attraction is universal weight, and that weight is terrestrial attraction: that is, that the two orders of phenomena are identical; which is the point from which the question set out. Again, M. Fourier, in his fine series of researches on Heat, has given us all the most important and precise laws of the phenomena of heat, and many large and new truths, without once inquiring into its nature, as his predecessors had done when they disputed about calorific matter and the action of an universal ether. In treating his subject in the Positive method, he finds inexhaustible material for all his activity of research, without betaking himself to insoluble questions.

Before ascertaining the stage which the Positive Philosophy has reached, we must bear in mind that the different kinds of our knowledge have passed through the three stages of progress at different rates, and have not therefore arrived at the same time. The rate of advance depends on the nature of the knowledge in question, so distinctly that, as we shall see hereafter, this consideration constitutes an accessory to the fundamental law of progress. Any kind of knowledge reaches the positive stage early in proportion to its generality, simplicity, and independence of other departments. Astronomical science, which is above all made up of facts that are general, simple, and independent of other sciences, arrived first; then terrestrial Physics; then Chemistry; and, at length, Physiology.

It is difficult to assign any precise date to this revolution in science. It may be said, like everything else, to have been always going on; and especially since the labours of Aristotle and the school of Alexandria; and then from the introduction of natural science into the West of Europe by the Arabs. But, if we must fix upon some marked period, to serve as a rallying point, it must be that,—about two centuries ago,—when the human mind was astir under the precepts of Bacon, the conceptions of Descartes, and the discoveries of Galileo. Then it was that the spirit of the Positive philosophy rose up in opposition to that of the superstitious and scholastic systems which had hitherto obscured the true character of all science. Since that date, the progress of the Positive philosophy, and the decline of the other two, have been so marked that no rational mind now doubts that the revolution is destined to go on to its completion,—every branch of knowledge being, sooner or later, brought within the operation of Positive philosophy. This is not yet the case. Some are still lying outside: and not till they are brought in will the Positive philosophy possess that character of universality which is necessary to its definitive constitution.

In mentioning just now the four principal categories of phenomena,—astronomical, physical, chemical, and physiological,—there was an omission which will have been noticed. Nothing was said of Social phenomena. Though involved with the physiological, Social phenomena demand a distinct classification, both on account of their importance and of their difficulty. They are the most individual, the most complicated, the most dependent on all others; and therefore they must be the latest,—even if they had no special obstacle to encounter. This branch of science has not hitherto entered into the domain of Positive philosophy. Theological and metaphysical methods, exploded in other departments, are as yet exclusively applied, both in the way of inquiry and discussion, in all treatment of Social subjects, though the best minds are heartily weary of eternal disputes about divine right and the sovereignty of the people. This is the great, while it is evidently the only gap which has to be filled, to constitute, solid and entire, the Positive Philosophy. Now that the human mind has grasped celestial and terrestrial physics,—mechanical and chemical; organic physics, both vegetable and animal,—there remains one science, to fill up the series of sciences of observation,—Social physics. This is what men have now most need of: and this it is the principal aim of the present work to establish.

It would be absurd to pretend to offer this new science at once in a complete state. Others, less new, are in very unequal conditions of forwardness. But the same character of positivity which is impressed on all the others will be shown to belong to this. This once done, the philosophical system of the moderns will be in fact complete, as there will then be no phenomenon which does not naturally enter into some one of the five great categories. All our fundamental conceptions having become homogeneous, the Positive state will be fully established. It can never again change its character, though it will be for ever in course of development by additions of new knowledge. Having acquired the character of universality which has hitherto been the only advantage resting with the two preceding systems, it will supersede them by its natural superiority, and leave to them only an historical existence.

We have stated the special aim of this work. Its secondary and general aim is this:—to review what has been effected in the Sciences, in order to show that they are not radically separate, but all branches from the same trunk. If we had confined ourselves to the first and special object of the work, we should have produced merely a study of Social physics: whereas, in introducing the second and general we offer a study of Positive philosophy, passing in review all the positive sciences already formed.

The purpose of this work is not to give an account of the Natural Sciences. Besides that it would be endless, and that it would require a scientific preparation such as no one man possesses, it would be apart from our object, which is to go through a course of not Positive Science, but Positive Philosophy. We have only to consider each fundamental science in its relation to the whole positive system, and to the spirit which characterizes it; that is, with regard to its methods and its chief results.

The two aims, though distinct, are inseparable; for, on the one hand, there can be no positive philosophy without a basis of social science, without which it could not be all-comprehensive; and, on the other hand, we could not pursue Social science without having been prepared by the study of phenomena less complicated than those of society, and furnished with a knowledge of laws and anterior facts which have a bearing upon social science. Though the fundamental sciences are not all equally interesting to ordinary minds, there is no one of them that can be neglected in an inquiry like the present; and, in the eye of philosophy, all are of equal value to human welfare. Even those which appear the least interesting have their own value, either on account of the perfection of their methods, or as being the necessary basis of all the others.

Lest it should be supposed that our course will lead us into a wilderness of such special studies as are at present the bane of a true positive philosophy, we will briefly advert to the existing prevalence of such special pursuit. In the primitive state of human knowledge there is no regular division of intellectual labour. Every student cultivates all the sciences. As knowledge accrues, the sciences part off; and students devote themselves each to some one branch. It is owing to this division of employment, and concentration of whole minds upon a single department, that science has made so prodigious an advance in modern times; and the perfection of this division is one of the most important characteristics of the Positive philosophy. But, while admitting all the merits of this change, we cannot be blind to the eminent disadvantages which arise from the limitation of minds to a particular study. It is inevitable that each should be possessed with exclusive notions, and be therefore incapable of the general superiority of ancient students, who actually owed that general superiority to the inferiority of their knowledge. We must consider whether the evil can be avoided without losing the good of the modern arrangement; for the evil is becoming urgent. We all acknowledge that the divisions established for the convenience of scientific pursuit are radically artificial; and yet there are very few who can embrace in idea the whole of any one science: each science moreover being itself only a part of a great whole. Almost every one is busy about his own particular section, without much thought about its relation to the general system of positive knowledge. We must not be blind to the evil, nor slow in seeking a remedy. We must not forget that this is the weak side of the positive philosophy, by which it may yet be attacked, with some hope of success, by the adherents of the theological and metaphysical systems. As to the remedy, it certainly does not lie in a return to the ancient confusion of pursuits, which would be mere retrogression, if it were possible, which it is not. It lies in perfecting the division of employments itself,—in carrying it one degree higher,—in constituting one more speciality from the study of scientific generalities. Let us have a new class of students, suitably prepared, whose business it shall be to take the respective sciences as they are, determine the spirit of each, ascertain their relations and mutual connection, and reduce their respective principles to the smallest number of general principles, in conformity with the fundamental rules of the Positive Method. At the same time, let other students be prepared for their special pursuit by an education which recognizes the whole scope of positive science, so as to profit by the labours of the students of generalities, and so as to correct reciprocally, under that guidance, the results obtained by each. We see some approach already to this arrangement. Once established, there would be nothing to apprehend from any extent of division of employments. When we once have a class of learned men, at the disposal of all others, whose business it shall be to connect each new discovery with the general system, we may dismiss all fear of the great whole being lost sight of in the pursuit of the details of knowledge. The organization of scientific research will then be complete; and it will henceforth have occasion only to extend its development, and not to change its character. After all, the formation of such a new class as is proposed would be merely an extension of the principle which has created all the classes we have. While science was narrow, there was only one class: as it expanded, more were instituted. With a further advance a fresh need arises, and this new class will be the result.

The general spirit of a course of Positive Philosophy having been thus set forth, we must now glance at the chief advantages which may be derived, on behalf of human progression, from the study of it. Of these advantages, four may be especially pointed out.

I. The study of the Positive Philosophy affords the only rational means of exhibiting the logical laws of the human mind, which have hitherto been sought by unfit methods. To explain what is meant by this, we may refer to a saying of M. de Blainville, in his work on Comparative Anatomy, that every active, and especially every living being, may be regarded under two relations—the Statical and the Dynamical; that is, under conditions or in action. It is clear that all considerations range themselves under the one or the other of these heads. Let us apply this classification to the intellectual functions.

If we regard these functions under their Statical aspect—that is, if we consider the conditions under which they exist—we must determine the organic circumstances of the case, which inquiry involves it with anatomy and physiology. If we look at the Dynamic aspect, we have to study simply the exercise and results of the intellectual powers of the human race, which is neither more nor less than the general object of the Positive Philosophy. In short, looking at all scientific theories as so many great logical facts, it is only by the thorough observation of these facts that we can arrive at the knowledge of logical laws. These being the only means of knowledge of intellectual phenomena, the illusory psychology, which is the last phase of theology, is excluded. It pretends to accomplish the discovery of the laws of the human mind by contemplating it in itself; that is, by separating it from causes and effects. Such an attempt, made in defiance of the physiological study of our intellectual organs, and of the observation of rational methods of procedure, cannot succeed at this time of day.

The Positive Philosophy, which has been rising since the time of Bacon, has now secured such a preponderance, that the metaphysicians themselves profess to ground their pretended science on an observation of facts. They talk of external and internal facts, and say that their business is with the latter. This is much like saying that vision is explained by luminous objects painting their images upon the retina. To this the physiologists reply that another eye would be needed to see the image. In the same manner, the mind may observe all phenomena but its own. It may be said that a man's intellect may observe his passions, the seat of the reason being somewhat apart from that of the emotions in the brain; but there can be nothing like scientific observation of the passions, except from without, as the stir of the emotions disturbs the observing faculties more or less. It is yet more out of the question to make an intellectual observation of intellectual processes. The observing and observed organs are here the same, and its action cannot be pure and natural. In order to observe, your intellect must pause from activity; yet it is this very activity that you want to observe. If you cannot effect the pause, you cannot observe: if you do effect it, there is nothing to observe. The results of such a method are in proportion to its absurdity. After two thousand years of psychological pursuit, no one proposition is established to the satisfaction of its followers. They are divided, to this day, into a multitude of schools, still disputing about the very elements of their doctrine. This interior observation gives birth to almost as many theories as there are observers. We ask in vain for any one discovery, great or small, which has been made under this method. The psychologists have done some good in keeping up the activity of our understandings, when there was no better work for our faculties to do; and they may have added something to our stock of knowledge. If they have done so, it is by practising the Positive method—by observing the progress of the human mind in the light of science; that is, by ceasing, for the moment, to be psychologists.

The view just given in relation to logical Science becomes yet more striking when we consider the logical Art.

The Positive Method can be judged of only in action. It cannot be looked at by itself, apart from the work on which it is employed. At all events, such a contemplation would be only a dead study, which could produce nothing in the mind which loses time upon it. We may talk for ever about the method, and state it in terms very wisely, without knowing half so much about it as the man who has once put it in practice upon a single particular of actual research, even without any philosophical intention. Thus it is that psychologists, by dint of reading the precepts of Bacon and the discourses of Descartes, have mistaken their own dreams for science.

Without saying whether it will ever be possible to establish *à priori* a true method of investigation, independent of a philosophical study of the sciences, it is clear that the thing has never been done yet, and that we are not capable of doing it now. We cannot as yet explain the great logical procedures, apart from their applications. If we ever do, it will remain as necessary then as now to form good intellectual habits by studying the regular application of the scientific methods which we shall have attained.

This, then, is the first great result of the Positive Philosophy —the manifestation by experiment of the laws which rule the Intellect in the investigation of truth; and, as a consequence the knowledge of the general rules suitable for that object.

§ II. The second effect of the Positive Philosophy, an effect not less important and far more urgently wanted, will be to regenerate Education. The best minds are agreed that our European education, still essentially theological, metaphysical, and literary, must be superseded by a Positive training, conformable to our time and needs. Even the governments of our day have shared, where they have not originated, the attempts to establish positive instruction; and this is a striking indication of the prevalent sense of what is wanted. While encouraging such endeavours to the utmost, we must not however conceal from ourselves that everything yet done is inadequate to the object. The present exclusive specialty of our pursuits, and the consequent isolation of the sciences, spoil our teaching. If any student desires to form an idea of natural philosophy as a whole, he is compelled to go through each department as it is now taught, as if he were to be only an astronomer, or only a chemist; so that, be his intellect what it may, his training must remain very imperfect. And yet his object requires that he should obtain general positive conceptions of all the classes of natural phenomena. It is such an aggregate of conceptions, whether on a great or on a small scale, which must henceforth be the permanent basis of all human combinations. It will constitute the mind of future generations. In order to this regeneration of our intellectual system, it is necessary that the sciences, considered as branches from one trunk, should yield us, as a whole, their chief methods and their most important results. The specialities of science can be pursued by those whose vocation lies in that direction. They are indispensable; and they are not likely to be neglected; but they can never of themselves renovate our system of Education; and, to be of their full use, they must rest upon the basis of that general instruction which is a direct result of the Positive Philosophy.

§ III. The same special study of scientific generalities must also aid the progress of the respective positive sciences: and this constitutes our third head of advantages.

The divisions which we establish between the sciences are, though not arbitrary, essentially artificial. The subject of our researches is one: we divide it for our convenience, in order to deal the more easily with its difficulties. But it sometimes happens—and especially with the most important doctrines of each science—that we need what we cannot obtain under the present isolation of the sciences,—a combination of several special points of view; and for want of this, very important problems wait for their solution much longer than they otherwise need do. To go back into the past for an example: Descartes' grand conception with regard to analytical geometry is a discovery which has changed the whole aspect of mathematical science, and yielded the germ of all future progress; and it issued from the union of two sciences which had always before been separately regarded and pursued. The case of pending questions is yet more impressive; as, for instance, in Chemistry, the doctrine of Definite Proportions. Without entering upon the discussion of the fundamental principle of this theory, we may say with assurance that, in order to determine it—in order to determine whether it is a law of nature that atoms should necessarily combine in fixed numbers,—it will be indispensable that the chemical point of view should be united with the physiological. The failure of the theory with regard to organic bodies indicates that the cause of this immense exception must be investigated; and such an inquiry belongs as much to physiology as to chemistry. Again, it is as yet undecided whether azote is a simple or a compound body. It was concluded by almost all chemists that azote is a simple body; the illustrious Berzelius hesitated, on purely chemical considerations; but he was also influenced by the physiological observation that animals which receive no azote in their food have as much of it in their tissues as carnivorous animals. From this we see how physiology must unite with chemistry to inform us whether azote is simple or compound, and to institute a new series of researches upon the relation between the composition of living bodies and their mode of alimentation.

Such is the advantage which, in the third place, we shall owe to Positive philosophy—the elucidation of the respective sciences by their combination. In the fourth place

§ IV. The Positive Philosophy offers the only solid basis for that Social Reorganization which must succeed the critical condition in which the most civilized nations are now living.

It cannot be necessary to prove to anybody who reads this work that Ideas govern the world, or throw it into chaos; in other words, that all social mechanism rests upon Opinions. The great political and moral crisis that societies are now undergoing is shown by a rigid analysis to arise out of intellectual anarchy. While stability in fundamental maxims is the first condition of genuine social order, we are suffering under an utter disagreement which may be called universal. Till a certain number of general ideas can be acknowledged as a rallying-point of social doctrine, the nations will remain in a revolutionary state; whatever palliatives may be devised; and their institutions can be only provisional. But whenever the necessary agreement on first principles can be obtained, appropriate institutions will issue from them, without shock or resistance; for the causes of disorder will have been arrested by the mere fact of the agreement. It is in this direction that those must look who desire a natural and regular, a normal state of society.

Now, the existing disorder is abundantly accounted for by the existence, all at once, of three incompatible philosophies, —the theological, the metaphysical, and the positive. Any one of these might alone secure some sort of social order; but while the three co-exist, it is impossible for us to understand one another upon any essential point whatever. If this is true, we have only to ascertain which of the philosophies must, in the nature of things, prevail; and, this ascertained, every man, whatever may have been his former views, cannot but concur in its triumph. The problem once recognized cannot remain long unsolved; for all considerations whatever point to the

Positive Philosophy as the one destined to prevail. It alone has been advancing during a course of centuries, throughout which the others have been declining. The fact is incontestable. Some may deplore it, but none can destroy it, nor therefore neglect it but under penalty of being betrayed by illusory speculations. This general revolution of the human mind is nearly accomplished. We have only to complete the Positive Philosophy by bringing Social phenomena within its comprehension, and afterwards consolidating the whole into one body of homogeneous doctrine. The marked preference which almost all minds, from the highest to the commonest, accord to positive knowledge over vague and mystical conceptions, is a pledge of what the reception of this philosophy will be when it has acquired the only quality that it now wants—a character of due generality. When it has become complete, its supremacy will take place spontaneously, and will re-establish order throughout society. There is, at present, no conflict but between the theological and the metaphysical philosophies. They are contending for the task of reorganizing society; but it is a work too mighty for either of them. The positive philosophy has hitherto intervened only to examine both, and both are abundantly discredited by the process. It is time now to be doing something more effective, without wasting our forces in needless controversy. It is time to complete the vast intellectual operation begun by Bacon, Descartes, and Galileo, by constructing the system of general ideas which must henceforth prevail among the human race. This is the way to put an end to the revolutionary crisis which is tormenting the civilized nations of the world.

Leaving these four points of advantage, we must attend to one precautionary reflection.

Because it is proposed to consolidate the whole of our acquired knowledge into one body of homogeneous doctrine, it must not be supposed that we are going to study this vast variety as proceeding from a single principle, and as subjected to a single law. There is something so chimerical in attempts at universal explanation by a single law, that it may be as well to secure this Work at once from any imputation

of the kind, though its development will show how unde-
served such an imputation would be. Our intellectual re-
sources are too narrow, and the universe is too complex, to
leave any hope that it will ever be within our power to carry
scientific perfection to its last degree of simplicity. Moreover,
it appears as if the value of such an attainment, supposing it
possible, were greatly overrated. The only way, for instance,
in which we could achieve the business, would be by connecting all natural phenomena with the most general law we
know,—which is that of Gravitation, by which astronomical
phenomena are already connected with a portion of terrestrial
physics. Laplace has indicated that chemical phenomena may
be regarded as simple atomic effects of the Newtonian attraction, modified by the form and mutual position of the
atoms. But supposing this view provable (which it cannot be
while we are without data about the constitution of bodies),
the difficulty of its application would doubtless be found so
great that we must still maintain the existing division between
astronomy and chemistry, with the difference that we now
regard as natural that division which we should then call
artificial. Laplace himself presented his idea only as a philosophic device, incapable of exercising any useful influence
over the progress of chemical science. Moreover, supposing
this insuperable difficulty overcome, we should be no nearer
to scientific unity, since we then should still have to connect
the whole of physiological phenomena with the same law,
which certainly would not be the least difficult part of the
enterprise. Yet, all things considered, the hypothesis we have
glanced at would be the most favourable to the desired unity.

The consideration of all phenomena as referable to a single
origin is by no means necessary to the systematic formation
of science, any more than to the realization of the great and
happy consequences that we anticipate from the positive
philosophy. The only necessary unity is that of Method,
which is already in great part established. As for the doctrine,
it need not be *one;* it is enough that it should be *homogeneous.*
It is, then, under the double aspect of unity of method and
homogeneousness of doctrine that we shall consider the dif-

ferent classes of positive theories in this work. While pursuing the philosophical aim of all science, the lessening of the number of general laws requisite for the explanation of natural phenomena, we shall regard as presumptuous every attempt, in all future time, to reduce them rigorously to one.

Having thus endeavoured to determine the spirit and influence of the Positive Philosophy, and to mark the goal of our labours, we have now to proceed to the exposition of the system; that is, to the determination of the universal, or encyclopædic order, which must regulate the different classes of natural phenomena, and consequently the corresponding positive sciences.

Charles Darwin

RECAPITULATION AND
CONCLUSION

Charles Darwin
[1809–1882]

In man's long search for an explanation of his descent, no theory has encountered so much theological opposition or so much scientific affirmation as Charles Darwin's observations on natural selection. When his history-making work was published in 1859 violent controversy raged over the book, with Thomas Huxley as its redoubtable defender, because it attempted to throw some light on that mystery of mysteries, the origin of species. Over two decades were required by Darwin to accumulate his material and to prepare it for publication. In the meantime, another naturalist, A. R. Wallace, reached the same general conclusions about evolution. In an act characteristic of the graciousness of great scientists, Charles Darwin presented his own and Wallace's views jointly to the learned Linnean Society. Now, almost a century after its first appearance, *The Origin of Species* remains, in spite of a few minor scientific revisions, one of the magnificent achievements in humanity's struggle for enlightenment. The section, "Recapitulation and Conclusion," is Darwin's summary at the end of the entire work.

RECAPITULATION AND CONCLUSION

CHARLES DARWIN

As this whole volume [*The Origin of Species*] is one long argument, it may be convenient to the reader to have the leading facts and inferences briefly recapitulated.

That many and serious objections may be advanced against the theory of descent with modification through variation and natural selection, I do not deny. I have endeavoured to give them their full force. Nothing at first can appear more difficult to believe than that the more complex organs and instincts have been perfected, not by means superior to, though analogous with, human reason, but by the accumulation of innumerable slight variations, each good for the individual possessor. Nevertheless, this difficulty, though appearing to our imagination insuperably great, cannot be considered real if we admit the following propositions, namely, that all parts of the organisation and instincts offer, at least, individual differences—that there is a struggle for existence leading to the preservation of profitable deviations of structure or instinct—and, lastly, that gradations in the state of perfection of each organ may have existed, each good of its kind. The truth of these propositions cannot, I think, be disputed.

It is, no doubt, extremely difficult even to conjecture by what gradations many structures have been perfected, more especially amongst broken and failing groups of organic beings, which have suffered much extinction, but we see so many strange gradations in nature, that we ought to be extremely cautious in saying that any organ or instinct, or any whole structure, could not have arrived at its present state by many graduated steps. There are, it must be admitted, cases of special difficulty opposed to the theory of natural selection; and one of the most curious of these is the existence in the same community of two or three defined castes of workers or sterile female ants; but I have attempted to show how these difficulties can be mastered.

With respect to the almost universal sterility of species when first crossed, which forms so remarkable a contrast with the almost universal fertility of varieties when crossed, I must refer the reader to the recapitulation of the facts given at the end of the ninth chapter, which seem to me conclusively to show that this sterility is no more a special endowment than is the incapacity of two distinct kinds of trees to be grafted together; but that it is incidental on differences confined to the reproductive systems of the intercrossed species. We see the truth of this conclusion in the vast difference in the results of crossing the same two species reciprocally,—that is, when one species is first used as the father and then as the mother. Analogy from the consideration of dimorphic and trimorphic plants clearly leads to the same conclusion, for when the forms are illegitimately united, they yield few or no seed, and their offspring are more or less sterile; and these forms belong to the same undoubted species, and differ from each other in no respect except in their reproductive organs and functions.

Although the fertility of varieties when intercrossed and of their mongrel offspring has been asserted by so many authors to be universal, this cannot be considered as quite correct after the facts given on the high authority of Gärtner and Kölreuter. Most of the varieties which have been experimented on have been produced under domestication; and as domestication (I do not mean mere confinement) almost certainly tends to eliminate that sterility which, judging from analogy, would have affected the parent-species if inter-crossed, we ought not to expect that domestication would likewise induce sterility in their modified descendants when crossed. This elimination of sterility apparently follows from the same cause which allows our domestic animals to breed freely under diversified circumstances; and this again apparently follows from their having been gradually accustomed to frequent changes in their conditions of life.

A double and parallel series of facts seems to throw much light on the sterility of species, when first crossed, and of their hybrid offspring. On the one side, there is good reason to believe that slight changes in the conditions of life give vigour and fertility to all organic beings. We know also that a cross between the distinct individuals of the same variety, and between distinct varieties, increases the number of their off-spring, and certainly gives to them increased size and vigour. This is chiefly owing to the forms which are crossed having been exposed to somewhat different conditions of life; for I have ascertained by a laborious series of experiments that if all the individuals of the same variety be subjected during several generations to the same conditions, the good derived from crossing is often much diminished or wholly disappears. This is one side of the case. On the other side, we know that species which have long been exposed to nearly uniform conditions, when they are subjected under confinement to new and greatly changed conditions, either perish, or if they survive, are rendered sterile, though retaining perfect health. This does not occur, or only in a very slight degree, with our domesticated productions, which have long been exposed to fluctuating conditions. Hence when we find that hybrids produced by a cross between two distinct species are few in number, owing to their perishing soon after conception or at a very early age, or if surviving that they are rendered more or less sterile, it seems highly probable that this result is due to their having been in fact subjected to a great change in their conditions of life, from being compounded of two distinct organisations. He who will explain in a definite manner why, for instance, an elephant or a fox will not breed under confinement in its native country, whilst the domestic pig or dog will breed freely under the most diversified conditions, will at the same time be able to give a definite answer to the question why two distinct species, when crossed, as well as their hybrid offspring, are generally rendered more or less sterile, whilst two domesticated varieties when crossed and their mongrel offspring are perfectly fertile.

Turning to geographical distribution, the difficulties encountered on the theory of descent with modification are serious enough. All the individuals of the same species, and all the species of the same genus, or even higher group, are descended from common parents; and therefore, in however distant and isolated parts of the world they may now be found, they must in the course of successive generations have travelled from some one point to all the others. We are often wholly unable even to conjecture how this could have been effected. Yet, as we have reason to believe that some species have retained the same specific form for very long periods of time, immensely long as measured by years, too much stress ought not to be laid on the occasional wide diffusion of the same species; for during very long periods there will always have been a good chance for wide migration by many means. A broken or interrupted range may often be accounted for by the extinction of the species in the intermediate regions. It cannot be denied that we are as yet very ignorant as to the full extent of the various climatal and geographical changes which have affected the earth during modern periods; and such changes will often have facilitated migration. As an example, I have attempted to show how potent has been the influence of the Glacial period on the distribution of the same and of allied species throughout the world. We are as yet profoundly ignorant of the many occasional means of transport. With respect to distinct species of the same genus inhabiting distant and isolated regions, as the process of modification has necessarily been slow, all the means of migration will have been possible during a very long period; and consequently the difficulty of the wide diffusion of the species of the same genus is in some degree lessened.

As according to the theory of natural selection an interminable number of intermediate forms must have existed, linking together all the species in each group by gradations as fine as are our existing varieties, it may be asked: Why do we not see these linking forms all around us? Why are not all organic beings blended together in an inextricable chaos? With respect to existing forms, we should remember that we have no right to expect (excepting in rare cases) to discover *directly* connecting links between them, but only between each and some extinct and supplanted form. Even on a wide area, which has during a long period remained continuous, and of which the climatic and other conditions of life change insensibly in proceeding from a district occupied by one species into another district occupied by a closely allied species, we have no just right to expect often to find intermediate varieties in the intermediate zones. For we have reason to believe that only a few species of a genus ever undergo change; the other species becoming utterly extinct and leaving no modified progeny. Of the species which do change, only a few within the same country change at the same time; and all modifications are slowly effected. I have also shown that the intermediate varieties which probably at first existed in the intermediate zones, would be liable to be supplanted by the allied forms on either hand; for the latter, from existing in greater numbers, would generally be modified and improved at a quicker rate than the intermediate varieties, which existed in lesser numbers; so that the intermediate varieties would, in the long run, be supplanted and exterminated.

On this doctrine of the extermination of an infinitude of connecting links, between the living and extinct inhabitants of the world, and at each successive period between the extinct and still older species, why is not every geological formation charged with such links? Why does not every collection of fossil remains afford plain evidence of the gradation and mutation of the forms of life? Although geological research has undoubtedly revealed the former existence of many links, bringing numerous forms of life much closer together, it does not yield the infinitely many fine gradations between past and present species required on the theory; and this is the most obvious of the many objections which may be urged against it. Why, again, do whole groups of allied species appear, though this appearance is often false, to have come in suddenly on the successive geological stages? Although we now know that organic beings appeared on this globe, at a period incalculably remote, long before the lowest bed of the Cambrian system was deposited, why do we not find beneath this system great piles of strata stored with the remains of the progenitors of the Cambrian fossils? For on the theory, such strata must somewhere have been deposited at these ancient and utterly unknown epochs of the world's history.

I can answer these questions and objections only on the supposition that the geological record is far more imperfect than most geologists believe. The number of specimens in all our museums is absolutely as nothing compared with the countless generations of countless species which have certainly existed. The parent-form of any two or more species would not be in all its characters directly intermediate between its modified offspring, any more than the rock-pigeon is directly intermediate in crop and tail between its descendants, the pouter and fantail pigeons. We should not be able to recognise a species as the parent of another and modified species, if we were to examine the two ever so closely, unless we possessed most of the intermediate links; and owing to the imperfection of the geological record, we have no just right to expect to find so many links. If two or three, or even more linking forms were discovered, they would simply be ranked by many naturalists as so many new species, more especially if found in different geological sub-stages, let their differences be ever so slight. Numerous existing doubtful forms could be named which are probably varieties; but who will pretend that in future ages so many fossil links will be discovered, that naturalists will be able to decide whether or not these doubtful forms ought to be called varieties? Only a small portion of the world has been geologically explored. Only organic beings of certain classes can be preserved in a fossil condition, at least in any great number. Many species when once formed never undergo any further change but become extinct without leaving modified descendants; and the periods, during which species have undergone modification, though long as measured by years, have probably been short in comparison with the periods during which they retain the same form. It is the dominant and widely ranging species which vary most frequently and vary most, and varieties are often at first local —both causes rendering the discovery of intermediate links in any one formation less likely. Local varieties will not spread into other and distant regions until they are considerably modified and improved; and when they have spread, and are discovered in a geological formation, they appear as if suddenly created there, and will be simply classed as new species. Most formations have been intermittent in their accumulation; and their duration has probably been shorter than the average duration of specific forms. Successive formations are in most cases separated from each other by blank intervals of time of great length; for fossiliferous formations thick enough to resist future degradations can as a general rule be accumulated only where much sediment is deposited on the subsiding bed of the sea. During the alternate periods of elevation and of stationary level the record will generally be blank. During these latter periods there will probably be more variability in the forms of life; during periods of subsidence, more extinction.

With respect to the absence of strata rich in fossils beneath the Cambrian formation, I can recur only to the hypothesis given in the tenth chapter; namely, that though our continents and oceans have endured for an enormous period in nearly their present relative positions, we have no reason to assume that this has always been the case; consequently formations much older than any now known may lie buried beneath the great oceans. With respect to the lapse of time not having been sufficient since our planet was consolidated for the assumed amount of organic change, and this objection, as urged by Sir William Thompson, is probably one of the gravest as yet advanced, I can only say, firstly, that we do not know at what rate species change as measured by years, and secondly, that many philosophers are not as yet willing to admit that we know enough of the constitution of the universe and of the interior of our globe to speculate with safety on its past duration.

That the geological record is imperfect all will admit; but that it is imperfect to the degree required by our theory, few will be inclined to admit. If we look to long enough intervals of time, geology plainly declares that species have all changed; and they have changed in the manner required by the theory, for they have changed slowly and in a graduated manner. We clearly see this in the fossil remains from consecutive formations invariably being much more closely related to each other, than are the fossils from widely separated formations.

Such is the sum of the several chief objections and difficulties which may be justly urged against the theory; and I have now briefly recapitulated the answers and explanations which, as far as I can see, may be given. I have felt these difficulties far too heavily during many years to doubt their weight. But it deserves especial notice that the more important objections relate to questions on which we are confessedly ignorant; nor do we know how ignorant we are. We do not know all the possible transitional gradations between the simplest and the most perfect organs; it cannot be pretended that we know all the varied means of Distribution during the long lapse of years, or that we know how imperfect is the Geological Record. Serious as these several objections are, in my judgment they are by no means sufficient to overthrow the theory of descent with subsequent modification.

Now let us turn to the other side of the argument. Under domestication we see much variability, caused, or at least excited, by changed conditions of life; but often in so obscure a manner, that we are tempted to consider the variations as spontaneous. Variability is governed by many complex laws, —by correlated growth, compensation, the increased use and disuse of parts, and the definite action of the surrounding conditions. There is much difficulty in ascertaining how largely our domestic productions have been modified; but we may safely infer that the amount has been large, and that modifications can be inherited for long periods. As long as the conditions of life remain the same, we have reason to believe that a modification, which has already been inherited for many generations, may continue to be inherited for an almost infinite number of generations. On the other hand, we have evidence that variability when it has once come into play, does not cease under domestication for a very long period; nor do we know that it ever ceases, for new varieties are still occasionally produced by our oldest domesticated productions.

Variability is not actually caused by man; he only unintentionally exposes organic beings to new conditions of life, and then nature acts on the organisation and causes it to vary. But man can and does select the variations given to him by nature, and thus accumulates them in any desired manner. He thus adapts animals and plants for his own benefit or pleasure. He may do this methodically, or he may do it unconsciously by preserving the individuals most useful or pleasing to him without any intention of altering the breed. It is certain that he can largely influence the character of a breed by selecting, in each successive generation, individual differences so slight as to be inappreciable except by an educated eye. This unconscious process of selection has been the great agency in the formation of the most distinct and useful domestic breeds. That many breeds produced by man have to a large extent the character of natural species, is shown by the inextricable doubts whether many of them are varieties or aboriginally distinct species.

There is no reason why the principles which have acted so efficiently under domestication should not have acted under nature. In the survival of favoured individuals and races, during the constantly-recurrent Struggle for Existence, we see a powerful and ever-acting form of Selection. The struggle for existence inevitably follows from the high geometrical ratio of increase which is common to all organic beings. This high rate of increase is proved by calculation,—by the rapid increase of many animals and plants during a succession of peculiar seasons, and when naturalised in new countries. More individuals are born than can possibly survive. A grain in the balance may determine which individuals shall live and which shall die,—which variety or species shall increase in number, and which shall decrease, or finally become extinct. As the individuals of the same species come in all respects into the closest competition with each other, the struggle will generally be most severe between them; it will be almost equally severe between the varieties of the same species, and next in severity between the species of the same genus. On the other hand the struggle will often be severe between beings remote in the scale of nature. The slightest advantage in certain individuals, at any age or during any season, over those with which they come into competition, or better adaptation in however slight a degree to the surrounding physical conditions, will, in the long run, turn the balance.

With animals having separated sexes, there will be in most cases a struggle between the males for the possession of the females. The most vigorous males, or those which have most successfully struggled with their conditions of life, will generally leave most progeny. But success will often depend on the males having special weapons, or means of defence, or charms; and a slight advantage will lead to victory.

As geology plainly proclaims that each land has undergone great physical changes, we might have expected to find that organic beings have varied under nature, in the same way as they have varied under domestication. And if there has been any variability under nature, it would be an unaccountable fact if natural selection had not come into play. It has often been asserted, but the assertion is incapable of proof, that the amount of variation under nature is a strictly limited quantity. Man, though acting on external characters alone and often capriciously, can produce within a short period a great result by adding up mere individual differences in his domestic productions; and every one admits that species present individual differences. But, besides such differences, all naturalists admit that natural varieties exist, which are considered sufficiently distinct to be worthy of record in systematic works. No one has drawn any clear distinction between individual differences and slight varieties; or between more plainly marked varieties and sub-species, and species. On separate continents, and on different parts of the same continent when divided by barriers of any kind, and on outlying islands, what a multitude of forms exist, which some experienced naturalists rank as varieties, others as geographical races or sub-species, and others as distinct, though closely allied species!

If then, animals and plants do vary, let it be ever so slightly or slowly, why should not variations or individual differences, which are in any way beneficial, be preserved and accumulated through natural selection, or the survival of the fittest? If man can by patience select variations useful to him, why, under changing and complex conditions of life, should not variations useful to nature's living products often arise, and be preserved or selected? What limit can be put to this power, acting during long ages and rigidly scrutinising the whole constitution, structure, and habits of each creature,—favouring the good and rejecting the bad? I can see no limit to this power, in slowly and beautifully adapting each form to the most complex relations of life. The theory of natural selection, even if we look no farther than this, seems to be in the highest degree probable. I have already recapitulated, as fairly as I could, the opposed difficulties and objections: now let us turn to the special facts and arguments in favour of the theory.

On the view that species are only strongly marked and permanent varieties, and that each species first existed as a variety, we can see why it is that no line of demarcation can be drawn between species, commonly supposed to have been produced by special acts of creation, and varieties which are acknowledged to have been produced by secondary laws. On this same view we can understand how it is that in a region where many species of a genus have been produced, and where they now flourish, these same species should present many varieties; for where the manufactory of species has been active, we might expect, as a general rule, to find it still in action; and this is the case if varieties be incipient species. Moreover, the species of the larger genera, which afford the greater number of varieties or incipient species, retain to a certain degree the character of varieties; for they differ from each other by a less amount of difference than do the species of smaller genera. The closely allied species also of the larger genera apparently have restricted ranges, and in their affinities they are clustered in little groups round other species —in both respects resembling varieties. These are strange relations on the view that each species was independently created, but are intelligible if each existed first as a variety.

As each species tends by its geometrical rate of reproduction to increase inordinately in number; and as the modified descendants of each species will be enabled to increase by as much as they become more diversified in habits and structure, so as to be able to seize on many and widely different places in the economy of nature, there will be a constant tendency in natural selection to preserve the most divergent offspring of any one species. Hence, during a long-continued course of modification, the slight differences characteristic of varieties of the same species, tend to be augmented into the greater differences characteristic of the species of the same genus. New and improved varieties will inevitably supplant and exterminate the older, less improved, and intermediate varieties; and thus species are rendered to a large extent defined and distinct objects. Dominant species belonging to the larger groups within each class tend to give birth to new and dominant forms; so that each large group tends to become still larger, and at the same time more divergent in character. But as all groups cannot thus go on increasing in size, for the world would not hold them, the more dominant groups beat the less dominant. This tendency in the large groups to go on increasing in size and diverging in character, together with the inevitable contingency of much extinction, explains the arrangement of all the forms of life in groups subordinate to groups, all within a few great classes, which has prevailed throughout all time. This grand fact of the grouping of all organic beings under what is called the Natural System, is utterly inexplicable on the theory of creation.

As natural selection acts solely by accumulating slight, successive, favourable variations, it can produce no great or sudden modifications; it can act only by short and slow steps. Hence, the canon of "Natura non facit saltum," which every fresh addition to our knowledge tends to confirm, is on this theory intelligible. We can see why throughout nature the same general end is gained by an almost infinite diversity of means, for every peculiarity when once acquired is long inherited, and structures already modified in many different ways have to be adapted for the same general purpose. We can, in short, see why nature is prodigal in variety, though niggard in innovation. But why this should be a law of nature if each species has been independently created no man can explain.

Many other facts are, as it seems to me, explicable on this theory. How strange it is that a bird, under the form of a woodpecker, should prey on insects on the ground; that upland geese which rarely or never swim, should possess webbed feet; that a thrush-like bird should dive and feed on subaquatic insects; and that a petrel should have the habits and structure fitting it for the life of an awk! and so in endless other cases. But on the view of each species constantly trying to increase in number, with natural selection always ready to adapt the slowly varying descendants of each to any unoccupied or ill-occupied place in nature, these facts cease to be strange, or might even have been anticipated.

We can to a certain extent understand how it is that there is so much beauty throughout nature; for this may be largely attributed to the agency of selection. That beauty, according to our sense of it, is not universal, must be admitted by every one who will look at some venomous snakes, at some fishes, and at certain hideous bats with a distorted resemblance to the human face. Sexual selection has given the most brilliant colours, elegant patterns, and other ornaments to the males, and sometimes to both sexes of many birds, butterflies, and other animals. With birds it has often rendered the voice of the male musical to the female, as well as to our ears. Flowers and fruit have been rendered conspicuous by brilliant colours in contrast with the green foliage, in order that the flowers may be readily seen, visited and fertilised by insects, and the seeds disseminated by birds. How it comes that certain colours, sounds, and forms should give pleasure to man and the lower animals,—that is, how the sense of beauty in its simplest form was first acquired,—we do not know any more than how certain odours and flavours were first rendered agreeable.

As natural selection acts by competition, it adapts and improves the inhabitants of each country only in relation to their co-inhabitants; so that we need feel no surprise at the species of any one country, although on the ordinary view supposed to have been created and specially adapted for that country, being beaten and supplanted by the naturalised productions from another land. Nor ought we to marvel if all the contrivances in nature be not, as far as we can judge, absolutely perfect, as in the case even of the human eye; or if some of them be abhorrent to our ideas of fitness. We need not marvel at the sting of the bee, when used against an enemy, causing the bee's own death; at drones being produced in such great numbers for one single act, and being then slaughtered by their sterile sisters; at the astonishing waste of pollen by our fir-trees; at the instinctive hatred of the queen-bee for her own fertile daughters; at the ichneumonidæ feeding within the living bodies of caterpillars; or at other such cases. The wonder indeed is, on the theory of natural selection, that more cases of the want of absolute perfection have not been detected.

The complex and little known laws governing the production of varieties are the same, as far as we can judge, with the laws which have governed the production of distinct species. In both cases physical conditions seem to have produced some direct and definite effect, but how much we cannot say. Thus, when varieties enter any new station, they occasionally assume some of the characters proper to the species of that station. With both varieties and species, use and disuse seem to have produced a considerable effect; for it is impossible to resist this conclusion when we look, for instance, at the logger-headed duck, which has wings incapable of flight, in nearly the same condition as in the domestic duck; or when we look at the burrowing tucu-tucu, which is occasionally blind, and then at certain moles, which are habitually blind and have their eyes covered with skin; or when we look at the blind animals inhabiting the dark caves of America and Europe. With varieties and species, correlated variation seems to have played an important part, so that when one part has been modified other parts have been necessarily modified. With both varieties and species, reversions to long-lost characters occasionally occur. How inexplicable on the theory of creation is the occasional appearance of stripes on the shoulders and legs of the several species of the horse-genus and of their hybrids! How simply is this fact explained if we believe that these species are all descended from a striped progenitor, in the same manner as the several domestic breeds of the pigeon are descended from the blue and barred rock-pigeon!

On the ordinary view of each species having been inde-pendently created, why should specific characters, or those by which the species of the same genus differ from each other, be more variable than generic characters in which they all agree? Why, for instance, should the colour of a flower be more likely to vary in any one species of a genus, if the other species possess differently coloured flowers, than if all pos-sessed the same coloured flowers? If species are only well-marked varieties, of which the characters have become in a high degree permanent, we can understand this fact; for they have already varied since they branched off from a common progenitor in certain characters, by which they have come to be specifically distinct from each other; therefore these same characters would be more likely again to vary than the generic characters which have been inherited without change for an immense period. It is inexplicable on the theory of creation why a part developed in a very unusual manner in one species alone of a genus, and therefore, as we may naturally infer, of great importance to that species, should be eminently liable to variation; but, on our view, this part has undergone, since the several species branched off from a common progenitor, an unusual amount of variability and modification, and therefore we might expect the part generally to be still variable. But a part may be developed in the most unusual manner, like the wing of a bat, and yet not be more variable than any other structure, if the part be common to many subordinate forms, that is, if it has been inherited for a very long period; for in this case, it will have been rendered constant by long-continued natural selection.

Glancing at instincts, marvellous as some are, they offer no greater difficulty than do corporeal structures on the theory of the natural selection of successive slight, but profitable modifications. We can thus understand why nature moves by graduated steps in endowing different animals of the same class with their several instincts. I have attempted to show how much light the principle of gradation throws on the admirable architectural powers of the hive-bee. Habit no doubt often comes into play in modifying instincts; but it certainly is not indispensable, as we see in the case of neuter insects, which leave no progeny to inherit the effects of long-continued habit. On the view of all the species of the same genus having descended from a common parent, and having inherited much in common, we can understand how it is that allied species, when placed under widely different conditions of life, yet follow nearly the same instincts; why the thrushes of tropical and temperate South America, for instance, line their nests with mud like our British species. On the view of instincts having been slowly acquired through natural selection, we need not marvel at some instincts being not perfect and liable to mistakes, and at many instincts causing other animals to suffer.

If species be only well-marked and permanent varieties, we can at once see why their crossed offspring should follow the same complex laws in their degrees and kinds of resemblance to their parents,—in being absorbed into each other by successive crosses, and in other such points,—as do the crossed offspring of acknowledged varieties. This similarity would be a strange fact, if species had been independently created and varieties had been produced through secondary laws.

If we admit that the geological record is imperfect to an extreme degree, then the facts, which the record does give, strongly support the theory of descent with modification. New species have come on the stage slowly and at successive intervals; and the amount of change, after equal intervals of time, is widely different in different groups. The extinction of species and of whole groups of species which has played so conspicuous a part in the history of the organic world, almost inevitably follows from the principle of natural selection; for old forms are supplanted by new and improved forms. Neither single species nor groups of species reappear when the chain of ordinary generation is once broken. The gradual diffusion of dominant forms, with the slow modification of their descendants, causes the forms of life, after long intervals of time, to appear as if they had changed simultaneously throughout the world. The fact of the fossil remains of each formation being in some degree intermediate in character between the fossils in the formations above and below, is simply explained by their intermediate position in the chain of descent. The grand fact that all extinct beings can be classed with all recent beings, naturally follows from the living and the extinct being the offspring of common parents. As species have generally diverged in character during their long course of descent and modification, we can understand why it is that the more ancient forms, or early progenitors of each group, so often occupy a position in some degree intermediate between existing groups. Recent forms are generally looked upon as being, on the whole, higher in the scale of organisation than ancient forms; and they must be higher, in so far as the later and more improved forms have conquered the older and less improved forms in the struggle for life; they have also generally had their organs more specialised for different functions. This fact is perfectly compatible with numerous beings still retaining simple and but little improved structures, fitted for simple conditions of life; it is likewise compatible with some forms having retrograded in organisation, by having become at each stage of descent better fitted for new and degraded habits of life. Lastly, the wonderful law of the long endurance of allied forms on the same continent,—of marsupials in Australia, of edentata in America, and other such cases,—is intelligible, for within the same country the existing and the extinct will be closely allied by descent.

Looking to geographical distribution, if we admit that there has been during the long course of ages much migration from one part of the world to another, owing to former climatal and geographical changes and to the many occasional and unknown means of dispersal, then we can understand, on the theory of descent with modification, most of the great leading facts in Distribution. We can see why there should be so striking a parallelism in the distribution of organic beings throughout space, and in their geological succession throughout time; for in both cases the beings have been connected by the bond of ordinary generation, and the means of modification have been the same. We see the full meaning of the wonderful fact, which has struck every traveller, namely, that on the same continent, under the most diverse conditions, under heat and cold, on mountain and lowland, on deserts and marshes, most of the inhabitants within each great class are plainly related; for they are the descendants of the same progenitors and early colonists. On this same principle of former migration, combined in most cases with modification, we can understand, by the aid of the Glacial period, the identity of some few plants, and the close alliance of many others, on the most distant mountains, and in the northern and southern temperate zones; and likewise the close alliance of some of the inhabitants of the sea in the northern and southern temperate latitudes, though separated by the whole intertropical ocean. Although two countries may present physical conditions as closely similar as the same species ever require, we need feel no surprise at their inhabitants being widely different, if they have been for a long period completely sundered from each other; for as the relation of organism to organism is the most important of all relations, and as the two countries will have received colonists at various periods and in different proportions, from some other country or from each other, the course of modification in the two areas will inevitably have been different.

On this view of migration, with subsequent modification, we see why oceanic islands are inhabited by only few species, but of these, why many are peculiar or endemic forms. We clearly see why species belonging to those groups of animals which cannot cross wide spaces of the ocean, as frogs and terrestrial mammals, do not inhabit oceanic islands; and why, on the other hand, new and peculiar species of bats, animals which can traverse the ocean, are found on islands far distant from any continent. Such cases as the presence of peculiar species of bats on oceanic islands and the absence of all other terrestrial mammals, are facts utterly inexplicable on the theory of independent acts of creation.

The existence of closely allied or representative species in any two areas, implies, on the theory of descent with modification, that the same parent-forms formerly inhabited both areas; and we almost invariably find that wherever many closely allied species inhabit two areas, some identical species are still common to both. Wherever many closely allied yet distinct species occur, doubtful forms and varieties belonging to the same groups likewise occur. It is a rule of high generality that the inhabitants of each area are related to the inhabitants of the nearest source whence immigrants might have been derived. We see this in the striking relation of nearly all plants and animals of the Galapagos archipelago, of Juan Fernandez, and of the other American islands, to the plants and animals of the neighbouring American mainland; and of those of the Cape de Verde archipelago, and of the other African islands to the African mainland. It must be admitted that these facts receive no explanation on the theory of creation.

The fact, as we have seen, that all past and present organic beings can be arranged within a few great classes, in groups subordinate to groups, and with the extinct groups often falling in between the recent groups, is intelligible on the theory of natural selection with its contingencies of extinction and divergence of character. On these same principles we see how it is, that the mutual affinities of the forms within each class are so complex and circuitous. We see why certain characters are far more serviceable than others for classification; —why adaptive characters, though of paramount importance to the beings, are of hardly any importance in classification; why characters derived from rudimentary parts, though of no service to the beings, are often of high classificatory value; and why embryological characters are often the most valuable of all. The real affinities of all organic beings, in contradistinction to their adaptive resemblances, are due to inheritance or community of descent. The Natural System is a genealogical arrangement, with the acquired grades of difference, marked by the terms, varieties, species, genera, families, &c.; and we have to discover the lines of descent by the most permanent characters whatever they may be and of however slight vital importance.

The similar framework of bones in the hand of a man, wing of a bat, fin of the porpoise, and leg of the horse,—the same number of vertebræ forming the neck of the giraffe and of the elephant,—and innumerable other such facts, at once explain themselves on the theory of descent with slow and slight successive modifications. The similarity of pattern in the wing and in the leg of a bat, though used for such different purpose, —in the jaws and legs of a crab,—in the petals, stamens, and pistils of a flower, is likewise, to a large extent, intelligible on the view of the gradual modification of parts or organs, which were aboriginally alike in an early progenitor in each of these classes. On the principle of successive variations not always supervening at an early age, and being inherited at a corresponding not early period of life, we clearly see why the embryos of mammals, birds, reptiles, and fishes should be so closely similar, and so unlike the adult forms. We may cease marvelling at the embryo of an air-breathing mammal or bird having branchial slits and arteries running in loops, like those of a fish which has to breathe the air dissolved in water by the aid of well-developed branchiæ.

Disuse, aided sometimes by natural selection, will often have reduced organs when rendered useless under changed habits or conditions of life; and we can understand on this view the meaning of rudimentary organs. But disuse and selection will generally act on each creature, when it has come to maturity and has to play its full part in the struggle for existence, and will thus have little power on an organ during early life; hence the organ will not be reduced or rendered rudimentary at this early age. The calf, for instance, has inherited teeth, which never cut through the gums of the upper jaw, from an early progenitor having well-developed teeth; and we may believe, that the teeth in the mature animal were formerly reduced by disuse, owing to the tongue and palate, or lips, having become excellently fitted through natural selection to browse without their aid; whereas in the calf, the teeth have been left unaffected, and on the principle of inheritance at corresponding ages have been inherited from a remote period to the present day. On the view of each organism with all its separate parts having been specially created, how utterly inexplicable is it that organs bearing the plain stamp of inutility, such as the teeth in the embryonic calf or the shrivelled wings under the soldered wing-covers of many beetles, should so frequently occur. Nature may be said to have taken pains to reveal her scheme of modification, by means of rudimentary organs, of embryological and homologous structures, but we are too blind to understand her meaning.

I have now recapitulated the facts and considerations which have thoroughly convinced me that species have been modified, during a long course of descent. This has been effected chiefly through the natural selection of numerous successive, slight, favourable variations; aided in an important manner by the inherited effects of the use and disuse of parts; and in an unimportant manner, that is in relation to adaptive structures, whether past or present, by the direct action of external conditions, and by variations which seem to us in our ignorance to arise spontaneously. It appears that I formerly underrated the frequency and value of these latter forms of variation, as leading to permanent modifications of structure independently of natural selection. But as my conclusions have lately been much misrepresented, and it has been stated that I attribute the modification of species exclusively to natural selection, I may be permitted to remark that in the first edition of this work, and subsequently, I placed in a most conspicuous position—namely, at the close of the Introduction—the following words: "I am convinced that natural selection has been the main but not the exclusive means of modification." This has been of no avail. Great is the power of steady misrepresentation; but the history of science shows that fortunately this power does not long endure.

It can hardly be supposed that a false theory would explain, in so satisfactory a manner as does the theory of natural selection, the several large classes of facts above specified. It has recently been objected that this is an unsafe method of arguing; but it is a method used in judging of the common events of life, and has often been used by the greatest natural philosophers. The undulatory theory of light has thus been arrived at; and the belief in the revolution of the earth on its own axis was until lately supported by hardly any direct evidence. It is no valid objection that science as yet throws no light on the far higher problem of the essence or origin of life. Who can explain what is the essence of the attraction of gravity? No one now objects to following out the results consequent on this unknown element of attraction; notwithstanding that Leibnitz formerly accused Newton of introducing "occult qualities and miracles into philosophy."

I see no good reason why the views given in this volume should shock the religious feelings of any one. It is satisfactory, as showing how transient such impressions are, to remember that the greatest discovery ever made by man, namely, the law of the attraction of gravity, was also attacked by Leibnitz, "as subversive of natural, and inferentially of revealed, religion." A celebrated author and divine has written to me that "he has gradually learnt to see that it is just as noble a conception of the Deity to believe that He created a few original forms capable of self-development into other and needful forms, as to believe that He required a fresh act of creation to supply the voids caused by the action of His laws."

Why, it may be asked, until recently did nearly all the most eminent living naturalists and geologists disbelieve in the mutability of species? It cannot be asserted that organic beings in a state of nature are subject to no variation; it cannot be proved that the amount of variation in the course of long ages is a limited quality; no clear distinction has been, or can be, drawn between species and well-marked varieties. It cannot be maintained that species when intercrossed are invariably sterile, and varieties invariably fertile; or that sterility is a special endowment and sign of creation. The belief that species were immutable productions was almost unavoidable as long as the history of the world was thought to be of short duration; and now that we have acquired some idea of the lapse of time, we are too apt to assume, without proof, that the geological record is so perfect that it would have afforded us plain evidence of the mutation of species, if they had undergone mutation.

But the chief cause of our natural unwillingness to admit that one species has given birth to clear and distinct species, is that we are always slow in admitting great changes of which we do not see the steps. The difficulty is the same as that felt by so many geologists, when Lyell first insisted that long lines of inland cliffs had been formed, and great valleys excavated, by the agencies which we see still at work. The mind cannot possibly grasp the full meaning of the term of even a million years; it cannot add up and perceive the full effects of many slight variations, accumulated during an almost infinite number of generations.

Although I am fully convinced of the truth of the views given in this volume under the form of an abstract, I by no means expect to convince experienced naturalists whose minds are stocked with a multitude of facts all viewed, during a long course of years, from a point of view directly opposite to mine. It is so easy to hide our ignorance under such expressions as the "plan of creation," "unity of design," &c., and to think that we give an explanation when we only re-state a fact. Any one whose disposition leads him to attach more weight to unexplained difficulties than to the explanation of a certain number of facts will certainly reject the theory. A few naturalists, endowed with much flexibility of mind, and who have already begun to doubt the immutability of species, may be influenced by this volume; but I look with confidence to the future,—to young and rising naturalists, who will be able to view both sides of the question with impartiality. Whoever is led to believe that species are mutable will do good service by conscientiously expressing his conviction; for thus only can the load of prejudice by which this subject is over-whelmed be removed.

Several eminent naturalists have of late published their be-lief that a multitude of reputed species in each genus are not real species; but that other species are real, that is, have been independently created. This seems to me a strange conclusion to arrive at. They admit that a multitude of forms, which till lately they themselves thought were special creations, and which are still thus looked at by the majority of naturalists, and which consequently have all the external characteristic features of true species,—they admit that these have been produced by variation, but they refuse to extend the same view to other and slightly different forms. Nevertheless they do not pretend that they can define, or even conjecture, which are the created forms of life, and which are those pro-duced by secondary laws. They admit variation as a *vera causa* in one case, they arbitrarily reject it in another, without assigning any distinction in the two cases. The day will come when this will be given as a curious illustration of the blind-ness of preconceived opinion. These authors seem no more startled at a miraculous act of creation than at an ordinary birth. But do they really believe that at innumerable periods in the earth's history certain elemental atoms have been com-manded suddenly to flash into living tissues? Do they believe that at each supposed act of creation one individual or many were produced? Were all the infinitely numerous kinds of animals and plants created as eggs or seed, or as full grown? and in the case of mammals, were they created bearing the false marks of nourishment from the mother's womb? Undoubtedly some of these same questions cannot be answered by those who believe in the appearance or creation of only a few forms of life, or of some one form alone. It has been maintained by several authors that it is as easy to believe in the creation of a million beings as of one; but Maupertuis' philosophical axiom "of least action" leads the mind more willingly to admit the smaller number; and certainly we ought not to believe that innumerable beings within each great class have been created with plain, but deceptive, marks of descent from a single parent.

As a record of a former state of things, I have retained in the foregoing paragraphs, and elsewhere, several sentences which imply that naturalists believe in the separate creation of each species; and I have been much censured for having thus expressed myself. But undoubtedly this was the general belief when the first edition of the present work appeared. I formerly spoke to very many naturalists on the subject of evolution, and never once met with any sympathetic agreement. It is probable that some did then believe in evolution, but they were either silent, or expressed themselves so ambiguously that it was not easy to understand their meaning. Now things are wholly changed, and almost every naturalist admits the great principle of evolution. There are, however, some who still think that species have suddenly given birth, through quite unexplained means, to new and totally different forms: but, as I have attempted to show, weighty evidence can be opposed to the admission of great and abrupt modifications. Under a scientific point of view, and as leading to further investigation, but little advantage is gained by believing that new forms are suddenly developed in an inexplicable manner from old and widely different forms, over the old belief in the creation of species from the dust of the earth.

It may be asked how far I extend the doctrine of the modification of species. The question is difficult to answer, because the more distinct the forms are which we consider, by so much the arguments in favour of community of descent become fewer in number and less in force. But some arguments of the greatest weight extend very far. All the members of whole classes are connected together by a chain of affinities, and all can be classed on the same principle, in groups subordinate to groups. Fossil remains sometimes tend to fill up very wide intervals between existing orders.

Organs in a rudimentary condition plainly show that an early progenitor had the organ in a fully developed condition; and this in some cases implies an enormous amount of modification in the descendants. Throughout whole classes various structures are formed on the same pattern, and at a very early age the embryos closely resemble each other. Therefore I cannot doubt that the theory of descent with modification embraces all the members of the same great class or kingdom. I believe that animals are descended from at most only four or five progenitors, and plants from an equal or lesser number.

Analogy would lead me one step farther, namely, to the belief that all animals and plants are descended from some one prototype. But analogy may be a deceitful guide. Nevertheless all living things have much in common, in their chemical composition, their cellular structure, their laws of growth, and their liability to injurious influences. We see this even in so trifling a fact as that the same poison often similarly affects plants and animals; or that the poison secreted by the gall-fly produces monstrous growths on the wild rose or oak-tree. With all organic beings excepting perhaps some of the very lowest, sexual production seems to be essentially similar. With all, as far as is at present known the germinal vesicle is the same; so that all organisms start from a common origin. If we look even to the two main divisions—namely, to the animal and vegetable kingdoms—certain low forms are so far intermediate in character that naturalists have disputed to which kingdom they should be referred. As Professor Asa Gray has remarked, "the spores and other reproductive bodies of many of the lower algæ may claim to have first a characteristically animal, and then an unequivocally vegetable existence." Therefore, on the principle of natural selection with divergence of character, it does not seem incredible that, from such low and intermediate form, both animals and plants may have been developed; and, if we admit this, we must likewise admit that all the organic beings which have ever lived on this earth may be descended from some one primordial form. But this inference is chiefly grounded on analogy and it is immaterial whether or not it be accepted. No doubt it is possible, as Mr. G. H. Lewes has urged, that at the first commencement of life many different forms were evolved; but if so we may conclude that only a very few have left modified descendants. For, as I have recently remarked in regard to the members of each great kingdom, such as the Vertebrata Articulata &c., we have distinct evidence in their embryological homologous and rudimentary structures that within each kingdom all the members are descended from a single progenitor.

When the views advanced by me in this volume, and by Mr. Wallace, or when analogous views on the origin of species are generally admitted, we can dimly foresee that there will be a considerable revolution in natural history. Systematists will be able to pursue their labours as at present; but they will not be incessantly haunted by the shadowy doubt whether this or that form be a true species. This, I feel sure and I speak after experience, will be no slight relief. The endless disputes whether or not some fifty species of British brambles are good species will cease. Systematists will have only to decide (not that this will be easy) whether any form be sufficiently constant and distinct from other forms, to be capable of definition; and if definable, whether the differences be sufficiently important to deserve a specific name. This latter point will become a far more essential consideration than it is at present; for differences, however slight, between any two forms if not blended by intermediate gradations, are looked at by most naturalists as sufficient to raise both forms to the rank of species.

Hereafter we shall be compelled to acknowledge that the only distinction between species and well-marked varieties is, that the latter are known, or believed, to be connected at the present day by intermediate gradations, whereas species were formerly thus connected. Hence, without rejecting the consideration of the present existence of intermediate gradations between any two forms we shall be led to weigh more carefully and to value higher the actual amount of difference between them. It is quite possible that forms now generally acknowledged to be merely varieties may hereafter be thought worthy of specific names; and in this case scientific and common language will come into accordance. In short, we shall have to treat species in the same manner as those naturalists treat genera, who admit that genera are merely artificial combinations made for convenience. This may not be a cheering prospect; but we shall at least be free from the vain search for the undiscovered and undiscoverable essence of the term species.

The other and more general departments of natural history will rise greatly in interest. The terms used by naturalists, of affinity, relationship, community of type, paternity, morphology, adaptive characters, rudimentary and aborted organs, &c., will cease to be metaphorical, and will have a plain signification. When we no longer look at an organic being as a savage looks at a ship, as something wholly beyond his comprehension; when we regard every production of nature as one which has had a long history; when we contemplate every complex structure and instinct as the summing up of many contrivances, each useful to the possessor, in the same way as any great mechanical invention is the summing up of the labour, the experience, the reason, and even the blunders of numerous workmen; when we thus view each organic being, how far more interesting—I speak from experience—does the study of natural history become!

A grand and almost untrodden field of inquiry will be opened, on the causes and laws of variation, on correlation, on the effects of use and disuse, on the direct action of external conditions, and so forth. The study of domestic productions will rise immensely in value. A new variety raised by man will be a more important and interesting subject for study than one more species added to the infinitude of already recorded species. Our classifications will come to be, as far as they can be so made, genealogies; and will then truly give what may be called the plan of creation. The rules for classifying will no doubt become simpler when we have a definite object in view. We possess no pedigrees or armorial bearings; and we have to discover and trace the many diverging lines of descent in our natural genealogies, by characters of any kind which have long been inherited. Rudimentary organs will speak infallibly with respect to the nature of long-lost structures. Species and groups of species which are called aberrant, and which may fancifully be called living fossils, will aid us in forming a picture of the ancient forms of life. Embryology will often reveal to us the structure, in some degree obscured, of the prototype of each great class.

When we feel assured that all the individuals of the same species, and all the closely allied species of most genera, have within a not very remote period descended from one parent, and have migrated from some one birth-place; and when we better know the many means of migration, then, by the light which geology now throws, and will continue to throw, on former changes of climate and of the level of the land, we shall surely be enabled to trace in an admirable manner the former migrations of the inhabitants of the whole world. Even at present, by comparing the differences between the inhabitants of the sea on the opposite sides of a continent, and the nature of the various inhabitants on that continent, in relation to their apparent means of immigration, some light can be thrown on ancient geography.

The noble science of Geology loses glory from the extreme imperfection of the record. The crust of the earth with its imbedded remains must not be looked at as a well-filled museum, but as a poor collection made at hazard and at rare intervals. The accumulation of each great fossiliferous formation will be recognised as having depended on an unusual concurrence of favourable circumstances, and the blank intervals between the successive stages as having been of vast duration. But we shall be able to gauge with some security the duration of these intervals by a comparison of the preceding and succeeding organic forms. We must be cautious in attempting to correlate as strictly contemporaneous two formations, which do not include many identical species, by the general succession of the forms of life. As species are produced and exterminated by slowly acting and still existing causes, and not by miraculous acts of creation; and as the most important of all causes of organic change is one which is almost independent of altered and perhaps suddenly altered physical conditions, namely, the mutual relation of organism to organism,—the improvement of one organism entailing the improvement or the extermination of others; it follows, that the amount of organic change in the fossils of consecutive formations probably serves as a fair measure of the relative though not actual lapse of time. A number of species, however, keeping in a body might remain for a long period unchanged, whilst within the same period several of these species by migrating into new countries and coming into competition with foreign associates, might become modified; so that we must not overrate the accuracy of organic change as a measure of time.

In the future I see open fields for far more important researches. Psychology will be securely based on the foundation already well laid by Mr. Herbert Spencer, that of the necessary acquirement of each mental power and capacity by gradation. Much light will be thrown on the origin of man and his history.

Authors of the highest eminence seem to be fully satisfied with the view that each species has been independently created. To my mind it accords better with what we know of the laws impressed on matter by the Creator, that the production and extinction of the past and present inhabitants of the world should have been due to secondary causes, like those determing the birth and death of the individual. When I view all beings not as special creations, but as the lineal descendants of some few beings which lived long before the first bed of the Cambrian system was deposited, they seem to me to become ennobled. Judging from the past, we may safely infer that not one living species will transmit its unaltered likeness to a distant futurity. And of the species now living very few will transmit progeny of any kind to a far distant futurity; for the manner in which all organic beings are grouped, shows that the greater number of species in each genus, and all the species in many genera, have left no descendants, but have become utterly extinct. We can so far take a prophetic glance into futurity as to foretell that it will be the common and widely-spread species, belonging to the larger and dominant groups within each class, which will ultimately prevail and procreate new and dominant species. As all the living forms of life are the lineal descendants of those which lived long before the Cambrian epoch, we may feel certain that the ordinary succession by generation has never once been broken, and that no cataclysm has desolated the whole world. Hence we may look with some confidence to a secure future of great length. And as natural selection works solely by and for the good of each being, all corporeal and mental endowments will tend to progress towards perfection.

It is interesting to contemplate a tangled bank, clothed with many plants of many kinds, with birds singing on the bushes, with various insects flitting about, and with worms crawling through the damp earth, and to reflect that these elaborately constructed forms, so different from each other, and dependent upon each other in so complex a manner, have all been produced by laws acting around us. These laws, taken in the largest sense, being Growth with Reproduction; Inheritance which is almost implied by reproduction; Variability from the indirect and direct action of the conditions of life, and from use and disuse: a Ratio of Increase so high as to lead to a Struggle for Life, and as a consequence to Natural Selection, entailing Divergence of Character and the Extinction of less-improved forms. Thus, from the war of nature, from famine and death, the most exalted object which we are capable of conceiving, namely, the production of the higher animals, directly follows. There is grandeur in this view of life, with its several powers, having been originally breathed by the Creator into a few forms or into one; and that, whilst this planet has gone cycling on according to the fixed law of gravity, from so simple a beginning endless forms most beautiful and most wonderful have been, and are being evolved.

Henri Bergson

THE EVOLUTION OF LIFE

Henri Bergson
[1859–1941]

There is perhaps a special significance in the fact that the 1927 Nobel Prize for Literature was awarded to Henri Bergson; at least it immediately suggests recognition for a creative writer rather than for a thinker who might have founded a philosophical school. Judged by the range and variety of Bergson's interests, he was far from being the architect of a system of ideas. In the interval between 1907, when *Creative Evolution* was published, and 1935, which marked the appearance of *Two Sources of Morality and Religion* in English, the professor of philosophy at the Collège de France became a world figure identified popularly by such literary phrases as "*élan vital,*" "the flow of reality," and "the full stream of experience." Laughter interested him as much as conscience. In all his works, however, emphasis is given to his conception of the continuity of change in the process of growth, and growth itself an unending creation, with freedom as its ultimate goal. Basic to his study of existence in *Creative Evolution* is his concern with duration and movement. "Duration," he writes, "is the continuous progress of the past which gnaws into the future and which swells as it advances." "The Evolution of Life," which follows, states the thesis of Bergson's *Creative Evolution*.

THE EVOLUTION OF LIFE

HENRI BERGSON

The existence of which we are most assured and which we know best is unquestionably our own, for of every other object we have notions which may be considered external and superficial, whereas, of ourselves, our perception is internal and profound. What, then, do we find? In this privileged case, what is the precise meaning of the word "exist"? Let us recall here briefly the conclusions of an earlier work.

I find, first of all, that I pass from state to state. I am warm or cold, I am merry or sad, I work or I do nothing, I look at what is around me or I think of something else. Sensations, feelings, volitions, ideas—such are the changes into which my existence is divided and which color it in turns. I change, then, without ceasing. But this is not saying enough. Change is far more radical than we are at first inclined to suppose.

For I speak of each of my states as if it formed a block and were a separate whole. I say indeed that I change, but the change seems to me to reside in the passage from one state to the next: of each state, taken separately, I am apt to think that it remains the same during all the time that it prevails. Nevertheless, a slight effort of attention would reveal to me that there is no feeling, no idea, no volition which is not undergoing change every moment: if a mental state ceased to vary, its duration would cease to flow. Let us take the most stable of internal states, the visual perception of a motionless external object. The object may remain the same, I may look

275

at it from the same side, at the same angle, in the same light;
nevertheless the vision I now have of it differs from that
which I have just had, even if only because the one is an instant older than the other. My memory is there, which con-
veys something of the past into the present. My mental state,
as it advances on the road of time, is continually swelling with
the duration which it accumulates: it goes on increasing—
rolling upon itself, as a snowball on the snow. Still more is
this the case with states more deeply internal, such as sensations, feelings, desires, etc., which do not correspond, like
a simple visual perception, to an unvarying external object.
But it is expedient to disregard this uninterrupted change,
and to notice it only when it becomes sufficient to impress a
new attitude on the body, a new direction on the attention.
Then, and then only, we find that our state has changed. The
truth is that we change without ceasing, and that the state
itself is nothing but change.

This amounts to saying that there is no essential difference
between passing from one state to another and persisting in
the same state. If the state which "remains the same" is more
varied than we think, on the other hand the passing from one
state to another resembles, more than we imagine, a single
state being prolonged; the transition is continuous. But, just
because we close our eyes to the unceasing variation of every
psychical state, we are obliged, when the change has become
so considerable as to force itself on our attention, to speak
as if a new state were placed alongside the previous one. Of
this new state we assume that it remains unvarying in its turn,
and so on endlessly. The apparent discontinuity of the psychical life is then due to our attention being fixed on it by a
series of separate acts: actually there is only a gentle slope;
but in following the broken line of our acts of attention, we
think we perceive separate steps. True, our psychic life is full
of the unforeseen. A thousand incidents arise, which seem to
be cut off from those which precede them, and to be discon-
nected from those which follow. Discontinuous though they
appear, however, in point of fact they stand out against the
continuity of a background on which they are designed, and

to which indeed they owe the intervals that separate them; they are the beats of the drum which break forth here and there in the symphony. Our attention fixes on them because they interest it more, but each of them is borne by the fluid mass of our whole psychical existence. Each is only the best illuminated point of a moving zone which comprises all that we feel or think or will—all, in short, that we are at any given moment. It is this entire zone which in reality makes up our state. Now, states thus defined cannot be regarded as distinct elements. They continue each other in an endless flow.

But, as our attention has distinguished and separated them artificially, it is obliged next to reunite them by an artificial bond. It imagines, therefore, a formless *ego*, indifferent and unchangeable, on which it threads the psychic states which it has set up as independent entities. Instead of a flux of fleeting shades merging into each other, it perceives distinct and, so to speak, *solid* colors, set side by side like the beads of a necklace; it must perforce then suppose a thread, also itself solid, to hold the beads together. But if this colorless substratum is perpetually colored by that which covers it, it is for us, in its indeterminateness, as if it did not exist, since we only perceive what is colored, or, in other words, psychic states. As a matter of fact, this substratum has no reality; it is merely a symbol intended to recall unceasingly to our consciousness the artificial character of the process by which the attention places clean-cut states side by side, where actually there is a continuity which unfolds. If our existence were composed of separate states with an impassive ego to unite them, for us there would be no duration. For an ego which does not change does not *endure*, and a psychic state which remains the same so long as it is not replaced by the following state does not *endure* either. Vain, therefore, is the attempt to range such states beside each other on the ego supposed to sustain them: never can these solids strung upon a solid make up that duration which flows. What we actually obtain in this way is an artificial imitation of the internal life, a static equivalent which will lend itself better to the requirements of logic

and language, just because we have eliminated from it the
element of real time. But, as regards the psychical life unfolding beneath the symbols which conceal it, we readily perceive that time is just the stuff it is made of.

There is, moreover, no stuff more resistant nor more substantial. For our duration is not merely one instant replacing
another; if it were, there would never be anything but the
present—no prolonging of the past into the actual, no evolution, no concrete duration. Duration is the continuous progress of the past which gnaws into the future and which swells
as it advances. And as the past grows without ceasing, so also
there is no limit to its preservation. Memory, as we have tried
to prove,[1] is not a faculty of putting away recollections in a
drawer, or of inscribing them in a register. There is no register, no drawer; there is not even, properly speaking, a faculty, for a faculty works intermittently, when it will or when
it can, whilst the piling up of the past upon the past goes on
without relaxation. In reality, the past is preserved by itself,
automatically. In its entirety, probably, it follows us at every
instant; all that we have felt, thought and willed from our
earliest infancy is there, leaning over the present which is
about to join it, pressing against the portals of consciousness
that would fain leave it outside. The cerebral mechanism is
arranged just so as to drive back into the unconscious almost
the whole of this past, and to admit beyond the threshold only
that which can cast light on the present situation or further
the action now being prepared—in short, only that which can
give *useful* work. At the most, a few superfluous recollections
may succeed in smuggling themselves through the half-open
door. These memories, messengers from the unconscious, remind us of what we are dragging behind us unawares. But,
even though we may have no distinct idea of it, we feel
vaguely that our past remains present to us. What are we, in
fact, what is our *character*, if not the condensation of the history that we have lived from our birth—nay, even before our
birth, since we bring with us prenatal dispositions? Doubtless

[1] *Matière et mémoire*, Paris, 1896, chaps. ii. and iii.

we think with only a small part of our past, but it is with our entire past, including the original bent of our soul, that we desire, will and act. Our past, then, as a whole, is made manifest to us in its impulse; it is felt in the form of tendency, although a small part of it only is known in the form of idea.

From this survival of the past it follows that consciousness cannot go through the same state twice. The circumstances may still be the same, but they will act no longer on the same person, since they find him at a new moment of his history. Our personality, which is being built up each instant with its accumulated experience, changes without ceasing. By changing, it prevents any state, although superficially identical with another, from ever repeating it in its very depth. That is why our duration is irreversible. We could not live over again a single moment, for we should have to begin by effacing the memory of all that had followed. Even could we erase this memory from our intellect, we could not from our will.

Thus our personality shoots, grows and ripens without ceasing. Each of its moments is something new added to what was before. We may go further: it is not only something new, but something unforeseeable. Doubtless, my present state is explained by what was in me and by what was acting on me a moment ago. In analyzing it I should find no other elements. But even a superhuman intelligence would not have been able to foresee the simple indivisible form which gives to these purely abstract elements their concrete organization. For to foresee consists of projecting into the future what has been perceived in the past, or of imagining for a later time a new grouping, in a new order, of elements already perceived. But that which has never been perceived, and which is at the same time simple, is necessarily unforeseeable. Now such is the case with each of our states, regarded as a moment in a history that is gradually unfolding: it is simple, and it cannot have been already perceived, since it concentrates in its indivisibility all that has been perceived and what the present is adding to it besides. It is an original moment of a no less original history.

The finished portrait is explained by the features of the

model, by the nature of the artist, by the colors spread out on the palette; but, even with the knowledge of what explains it, no one, not even the artist, could have foreseen exactly what the portrait would be, for to predict it would have been to produce it before it was produced—an absurd hypothesis which is its own refutation. Even so with regard to the moments of our life, of which we are the artisans. Each of them is a kind of creation. And just as the talent of the painter is formed or deformed—in any case, is modified—under the very influence of the works he produces, so each of our states, at the moment of its issue, modifies our personality, being indeed the new form that we are just assuming. It is then right to say that what we do depends on what we are; but it is necessary to add also that we are, to a certain extent, what we do, and that we are creating ourselves continually. This creation of self by self is the more complete, the more one reasons on what one does. For reason does not proceed in such matters as in geometry, where impersonal premises are given once for all, and an impersonal conclusion must perforce be drawn. Here, on the contrary, the same reasons may dictate to different persons, or to the same person at different moments, acts profoundly different, although equally reasonable. The truth is that they are not quite the same reasons, since they are not those of the same person, nor of the same moment. That is why we cannot deal with them in the abstract, from outside, as in geometry, nor solve for another the problems by which he is faced in life. Each must solve them from within, on his own account. But we need not go more deeply into this. We are seeking only the precise meaning that our consciousness gives to this word "exist," and we find that, for a conscious being, to exist is to change, to change is to mature, to mature is to go on creating oneself endlessly. Should the same be said of existence in general?

A material object, of whatever kind, presents opposite characters to those which we have just been describing. Either it remains as it is, or else, if it changes under the influence of an external force, our idea of this change is that of a displacement of parts which themselves do not change. If these parts took to changing, we should split them up in their turn. We should thus descend to the molecules of which the fragments are made, to the atoms that make up the molecules, to the corpuscles that generate the atoms, to the "imponderable" within which the corpuscle is perhaps a mere vortex. In short, we should push the division or analysis as far as necessary. But we should stop only before the unchangeable.

Now, we say that a composite object changes by the displacement of its parts. But when a part has left its position, there is nothing to prevent its return to it. A group of elements which has gone through a state can therefore always find its way back to that state, if not by itself, at least by means of an external cause able to restore everything to its place. This amounts to saying that any state of the group may be repeated as often as desired, and consequently that the group does not grow old. It has no history.

Thus nothing is created therein, neither form nor matter. What the group will be is already present in what it is, provided "what it is" includes all the points of the universe with which it is related. A superhuman intellect could calculate, for any moment of time, the position of any point of the system in space. And as there is nothing more in the form of the whole than the arrangement of its parts, the future forms of the system are theoretically visible in its present configuration.

All our belief in objects, all our operations on the systems that science isolates, rest in fact on the idea that time does not bite into them. We have touched on this question in an earlier work, and shall return to it in the course of the present study. For the moment, we will confine ourselves to pointing out that the abstract time t attributed by science to a material object or to an isolated system consists only in a certain number of simultaneities or more generally of correspondences, and that this number remains the same, whatever be the nature of the intervals between the correspondences. With these intervals we are never concerned when dealing with inert matter; or, if they are considered, it is in order to count therein fresh correspondences, between which again we shall not care what happens. Common sense, which is occupied with detached objects, and also science, which considers isolated systems, are concerned only with the ends of the intervals and not with the intervals themselves. Therefore the flow of time might assume an infinite rapidity, the entire past, present, and future of material objects or of isolated systems might be spread out all at once in space, without there being anything to change either in the formulae of the scientist or even in the language of common sense. The number t would always stand for the same thing; it would still count the same number of correspondences between the states of the objects or systems and the points of the line, ready drawn, which would be then the "course of time."

Yet succession is an undeniable fact, even in the material world. Though our reasoning on isolated systems may imply that their history, past, present and future, might be instantaneously unfurled like a fan, this history, in point of fact, unfolds itself gradually, as if it occupied a duration like our own. If I want to mix a glass of sugar and water, I must, willy-nilly, wait until the sugar melts. This little fact is big with meaning. For here the time I have to wait is not that mathematical time which would apply equally well to the entire history of the material world, even if that history were spread out instantaneously in space. It coincides with my impatience, that is to say, with a certain portion of my own duration, which I cannot protract or contract as I like. It is no longer something *thought*, it is something *lived*. It is no longer a relation, it is an absolute. What else can this mean than that the glass of water, the sugar, and the process of the sugar's melting in the water are abstractions, and that the Whole within which they have been cut out by my senses and understanding progresses, it may be in the manner of a consciousness?

Certainly, the operation by which science isolates and closes a system is not altogether artificial. If it had no objective foundation, we could not explain why it is clearly indicated in some cases and impossible in others. We shall see that matter has a tendency to constitute *isolable* systems, that can be treated geometrically. In fact, we shall define matter by just this tendency. But it is only a tendency. Matter does not go to the end, and the isolation is never complete. If science does go to the end and isolate completely, it is for convenience of study; it is understood that the so-called isolated system remains subject to certain external influences. Science merely leaves these alone, either because it finds them slight enough to be negligible, or because it intends to take them into account later on. It is none the less true that these influences are so many threads which bind up the system to another more extensive, and to this a third which includes both, and so on to the system most objectively isolated and most independent of all, the solar system complete. But, even here, the isolation is not absolute. Our sun radiates heat and light beyond the farthest planet. And, on the other hand, it moves in a certain fixed direction, drawing with it the planets and their satellites. The thread attaching it to the rest of the universe is doubtless very tenuous. Nevertheless it is along this thread that is transmitted down to the smallest particle of the world in which we live the duration immanent to the whole of the universe.

The universe *endures*. The more we study the nature of time, the more we shall comprehend that duration means invention, the creation of forms, the continual elaboration of the absolutely new. The systems marked off by science *endure* only because they are bound up inseparably with the rest of the universe. It is true that in the universe itself two opposite movements are to be distinguished, as we shall see later on, "descent" and "ascent." The first only unwinds a roll ready prepared. In principle, it might be accomplished almost instantaneously, like releasing a spring. But the ascending movement, which corresponds to an inner work of ripening or creating, *endures* essentially, and imposes its rhythm on the first, which is inseparable from it.

There is no reason, therefore, why a duration, and so a form of existence like our own, should not be attributed to the systems that science isolates, provided such systems are reintegrated into the Whole. But they must be so reintegrated. The same is even more obviously true of the objects cut out by our perception. The distinct outlines which we see in an object, and which give it its individuality, are only the design of a certain kind of *influence* that we might exert on a certain point of space: it is the plan of our eventual actions that is sent back to our eyes, as though by a mirror, when we see the surfaces and edges of things. Suppress this action, and with it consequently those main directions which by perception are traced out for it in the entanglement of the real, and the individuality of the body is reabsorbed in the universal interaction which, without doubt, is reality itself.

Now, we have considered material objects generally. Are there not some objects privileged? The bodies we perceive are, so to speak, cut out of the stuff of nature by our *perception,* and the scissors follow, in some way, the marking of lines along which *action* might be taken. But the body which is to perform this action, the body which marks out upon matter the design of its eventual actions even before they are actual, the body that has only to point its sensory organs on the flow of the real in order to make that flow crystallize into definite forms and thus to create all the other bodies—in short, the *living* body—is this a body as others are?

Doubtless it, also, consists in a portion of extension bound up with the rest of extension, an intimate part of the Whole, subject to the same physical and chemical laws that govern any and every portion of matter. But, while the subdivision of matter into separate bodies is relative to our perception, while the building up of closed-off systems of material points is relative to our science, the living body has been separated and closed off by nature herself. It is composed of unlike parts that complete each other. It performs diverse functions that involve each other. It is an *individual,* and of no other object, not even of the crystal, can this be said, for a crystal has neither difference of parts nor diversity of functions. No doubt, it is hard to decide, even in the organized world, what is individual and what is not. The difficulty is great, even in the animal kingdom; with plants it is almost insurmountable.

This difficulty is, moreover, due to profound causes, on which we shall dwell later. We shall see that individuality admits of any number of degrees, and that it is not fully realized anywhere, even in man. But that is no reason for thinking it is not a characteristic property of life. The biologist who proceeds as a geometrician is too ready to take advantage here of our inability to give a precise and general definition of individuality. A perfect definition applies only to a *completed* reality; now, vital properties are never entirely realized, though always on the way to become so; they are not so much *states* as *tendencies*. And a tendency achieves all that it aims at only if it is not thwarted by another tendency. How, then, could this occur in the domain of life, where, as we shall show, the interaction of antagonistic tendencies is always implied? In particular, it may be said of individuality that, while the tendency to individuate is everywhere present in the organized world, it is everywhere opposed by the tendency toward reproduction. For the individuality to be perfect, it would be necessary that no detached part of the organism could live separately. But then reproduction would be impossible. For what is reproduction, but the building up of a new organism with a detached fragment of the old? Individuality therefore harbors its enemy at home. Its very need of perpetuating itself in time condemns it never to be complete in space. The biologist must take due account of both tendencies in every instance, and it is therefore useless to ask him for a definition of individuality that shall fit all cases and work automatically.

But too often one reasons about the things of life in the same way as about the conditions of crude matter. Nowhere is the confusion so evident as in discussions about individuality. We are shown the stumps of a Lumbriculus, each regenerating its head and living thenceforward as an independent individual; a hydra whose pieces become so many fresh hydras; a sea-urchin's egg whose fragments develop complete embryos: where then, we are asked, was the individuality of the egg, the hydra, the worm?—But, because there are several individuals now, it does not follow that there was not a single

individual just before. No doubt, when I have seen several
drawers fall from a chest, I have no longer the right to say
that the article was all of one piece. But the fact is that there
can be nothing more in the present of the chest of drawers
than there was in its past, and if it is made up of several different pieces now, it was so from the date of its manufacture.
Generally speaking, unorganized bodies, which are what we
have need of in order that we may act, and on which we have
modeled our fashion of thinking, are regulated by this simple
law: *the present contains nothing more than the past, and
what is found in the effect was already in the cause*. But suppose that the distinctive feature of the organized body is that
it grows and changes without ceasing, as indeed the most superficial observation testifies, there would be nothing astonishing in the fact that it was *one* in the first instance, and
afterwards *many*. The reproduction of unicellular organisms
consists in just this—the living being divides into two halves,
of which each is a complete individual. True, in the more
complex animals, nature localizes in the almost independent
sexual cells the power of producing the whole anew. But
something of its power may remain diffused in the rest of
the organism, as the facts of regeneration prove, and it is conceivable that in certain privileged cases the faculty may persist integrally in a latent condition and manifest itself on the
first opportunity. In truth, that I may have the right to speak
of individuality, it is not necessary that the organism should
be without the power to divide into fragments that are able
to live. It is sufficient that it should have presented a certain
systematization of parts before the division, and that the same
systematization tend to be reproduced in each separate portion afterwards. Now, that is precisely what we observe in
the organic world. We may conclude, then, that individuality
is never perfect, and that it is often difficult, sometimes impossible, to tell what is an individual, and what is not, but that
life nevertheless manifests a search for individuality, as if it
strove to constitute systems naturally isolated, naturally
closed.

By this is a living being distinguished from all that our perception or our science isolates or closes artificially. It would therefore be wrong to compare it to an *object*. Should we wish to find a term of comparison in the inorganic world, it is not to a determinate material object, but much rather to the totality of the material universe that we ought to compare the living organism. It is true that the comparison would not be worth much, for a living being is observable, whilst the whole of the universe is constructed or reconstructed by thought. But at least our attention would thus have been called to the essential character of organization. Like the universe as a whole, like each conscious being taken separately, the organism which lives is a thing that *endures*. Its past, in its entirety, is prolonged into its present, and abides there, actual and acting. How otherwise could we understand that it passes through distinct and well-marked phases, that it changes its age—in short, that it has a history? If I consider my body in particular, I find that, like my consciousness, it matures little by little from infancy to old age; like myself, it grows old. Indeed, maturity and old age are, properly speaking, attributes only of my body; it is only metaphorically that I apply the same names to the corresponding changes of my conscious self. Now, if I pass from the top to the bottom of the scale of living beings, from one of the most to one of the least differentiated, from the multicellular organism of man to the unicellular organism of the Infusorian, I find, even in this simple cell, the same process of growing old. The Infusorian is exhausted at the end of a certain number of divisions, and though it may be possible, by modifying the environment, to put off the moment when a rejuvenation by conjugation becomes necessary, this cannot be indefinitely postponed.[2] It is true that between these two extreme cases, in which the organism is completely individualized, there might be found a multitude of others in which the individual-

[2] Calkins, *Studies on the Life History of Protozoa* (*Archiv f. Entwick-lungsmechanik*, vol. xv., 1903, pp. 139–186).

ity is less well marked, and in which, although there is doubtless an aging somewhere, one cannot say exactly what it is
that grows old. Once more, there is no universal biological
law which applies precisely and automatically to every living
thing. There are only *directions* in which life throws out species in general. Each particular species, in the very act by
which it is constituted, affirms its independence, follows its
caprice, deviates more or less from the straight line, sometimes even remounts the slope and seems to turn its back on
its original direction. It is easy enough to argue that a tree
never grows old, since the tips of its branches are always
equally young, always equally capable of engendering new
trees by budding. But in such an organism—which is, after all,
a society rather than an individual—*something* ages, if only
the leaves and the interior of the trunk. And each cell, considered separately, evolves in a specific way. *Wherever anything lives, there is, open somewhere, a register in which
time is being inscribed.*

This, it will be said, is only a metaphor.—It is of the very
essence of mechanism, in fact, to consider as metaphorical
every expression which attributes to time an effective action
and a reality of its own. In vain does immediate experience
show us that the very basis of our conscious existence is memory, that is to say, the prolongation of the past into the present, or, in a word, *duration*, acting and irreversible. In vain
does reason prove to us that the more we get away from the
objects cut out and the systems isolated by common sense and
by science and the deeper we dig beneath them, the more we
have to do with a reality which changes as a whole in its inmost states, as if an accumulative memory of the past made it
impossible to go back again. The mechanistic instinct of the
mind is stronger than reason, stronger than immediate experience. The metaphysician that we each carry unconsciously within us, and the presence of which is explained,
as we shall see later on, by the very place that man occupies
amongst the living beings, has its fixed requirements, its
ready-made explanations, its irreducible propositions: all
unite in denying concrete duration. Change *must* be reducible

to an arrangement or rearrangement of parts; the irreversibility of time *must* be an appearance relative to our ignorance; the impossibility of turning back *must* be only the inability of man to put things in place again. So growing old can be nothing more than the gradual gain or loss of certain substances, perhaps both together. Time is assumed to have just as much reality for a living being as for an hour-glass, in which the top part empties while the lower fills, and all goes where it was before when you turn the glass upside down.

True, biologists are not agreed on what is gained and what is lost between the day of birth and the day of death. There are those who hold to the continual growth in the volume of protoplasm from the birth of the cell right on to its death.[3] More probable and more profound is the theory according to which the diminution bears on the quantity of nutritive substance contained in that "inner environment" in which the organism is being renewed, and the increase on the quantity of unexcreted residual substances which, accumulating in the body, finally "crust it over."[4] Must we however—with an eminent bacteriologist—declare any explanation of growing old insufficient that does not take account of phagocytosis?[5] We do not feel qualified to settle the question. But the fact that the two theories agree in affirming the constant accumulation or loss of a certain kind of matter, even though they have little in common as to what is gained and lost, shows pretty well that the frame of the explanation has been furnished *a priori*. We shall see this more and more as we proceed with our study: it is not easy, in thinking of time, to escape the image of the hour-glass.

The cause of growing old must lie deeper. We hold that

---

[3] Sedgwick Minot, *On Certain Phenomena of Growing Old* (*Proc. Amer. Assoc. for the Advancement of Science*, 39th Meeting, Salem, 1891, pp. 271–288).

[4] Le Dantec, *L'Individualité et l'erreur individualiste*, Paris, 1905, pp. 84 ff.

[5] Metchnikoff, *La Dégénérescence sénile* (*Année biologique*, iii., 1897, pp. 249 ff.). Cf. by the same author, *La Nature humaine*, Paris, 1903, pp. 312 ff.

there is unbroken continuity between the evolution of the
embryo and that of the complete organism. The impetus
which causes a living being to grow larger, to develop and
to age, is the same that has caused it to pass through the phases
of the embryonic life. The development of the embryo is a
perpetual change of form. Anyone who attempts to note all
its successive aspects becomes lost in an infinity, as is inevitable in dealing with a continuum. Life does but prolong this
prenatal evolution. The proof of this is that it is often impossible for us to say whether we are dealing with an organism growing old or with an embryo continuing to evolve;
such is the case, for example, with the larvae of insects and
crustacea. On the other hand, in an organism such as our own,
crises like puberty or the menopause, in which the individual
is completely transformed, are quite comparable to changes
in the course of larval or embryonic life—yet they are part
and parcel of the process of our aging. Although they occur
at a definite age and within a time that may be quite short,
no one would maintain that they appear then *ex abrupto*,
from without, simply because a certain age is reached, just
as a legal right is granted to us on our one-and-twentieth
birthday. It is evident that a change like that of puberty is in
course of preparation at every instant from birth, and even
before birth, and that the aging up to that crisis consists, in
part at least, of this gradual preparation. In short, what is
properly vital in growing old is the insensible, infinitely graduated, continuance of the change of form. Now, this change
is undoubtedly accompanied by phenomena of organic destruction: to these, and to these alone, will a mechanistic explanation of aging be confined. It will note the facts of scle-
rosis, the gradual accumulation of residual substances, the
growing hypertrophy of the protoplasm of the cell. But under
these visible effects an inner cause lies hidden. The evolution
of the living being, like that of the embryo, implies a continual recording of duration, a persistence of the past in the
present, and so an appearance, at least, of organic memory.

The present state of an unorganized body depends exclusively on what happened at the previous instant; and like-

wise the position of the material points of a system defined and isolated by science is determined by the position of these same points at the moment immediately before. In other words, the laws that govern unorganized matter are expressible, in principle, by differential equations in which time (in the sense in which the mathematician takes this word) would play the role of independent variable. Is it so with the laws of life? Does the state of a living body find its complete explanation in the state immediately before? Yes, if it is agreed *a priori* to liken the living body to other bodies, and to identify it, for the sake of the argument, with the artificial systems on which the chemist, physicist and astronomer operate. But in astronomy, physics and chemistry the proposition has a perfectly definite meaning: it signifies that certain aspects of the present, important for science, are calculable as functions of the immediate past. Nothing of the sort in the domain of life. Here calculation touches, at most, certain phenomena of organic *destruction*. Organic *creation*, on the contrary, the evolutionary phenomena which properly constitute life, we cannot in any way subject to a mathematical treatment. It will be said that this impotence is due only to our ignorance. But it may equally well express the fact that the present moment of a living body does not find its explanation in the moment immediately before, that *all* the past of the organism must be added to that moment, its heredity—in fact, the whole of a very long history. In the second of these two hypotheses, not in the first, is really expressed the present state of the biological sciences, as well as their direction. As for the idea that the living body might be treated by some superhuman calculator in the same mathematical way as our solar system, this has gradually arisen from a metaphysic which has taken a more precise form since the physical discoveries of Galileo, but which, as we shall show, was always the natural metaphysic of the human mind. Its apparent clearness, our impatient desire to find it true, the enthusiasm with which so many excellent minds accept it without proof—all the seductions, in short, that it exercises on our thought, should put us on our guard against it. The attraction it has for us proves well enough that it gives satisfaction to an innate inclination. But, as will be seen further on, the intellectual tendencies innate today, which life must have created in the course of its evolution, are not at all meant to supply us with an explanation of life: they have something else to do.

Any attempt to distinguish between an artificial and a natural system, between the dead and the living, runs counter to this tendency at once. Thus it happens that we find it equally difficult to imagine that the organized has duration and that the unorganized has not. When we say that the state of an artificial system depends exclusively on its state at the moment before, does it not seem as if we were bringing time in, as if the system had something to do with real duration? And, on the other hand, though the whole of the past goes into the making of the living being's present moment, does not organic memory press it into the moment immediately before the present, so that the moment immediately before becomes the sole cause of the present one?—To speak thus is to ignore the cardinal difference between *concrete* time, along which a real system develops, and that *abstract* time which enters into our speculations on artificial systems. What does it mean, to say that the state of an artificial system depends on what it was at the moment immediately before? There is no instant immediately before another instant; there could not be, any more than there could be one mathematical point touching another. The instant "immediately before" is, in reality, that which is connected with the present instant by the interval dt. All that you mean to say, therefore, is that the present state of the system is defined by equations into which differential coefficients enter, such as ds/dt, dv/dt, that is to say, at bottom, *present* velocities and *present* accelerations. You are therefore really speaking only of the present—a present, it is true, considered along with its *tendency*. The systems science works with are, in fact, in an instantaneous present that is always being renewed; and such systems are never in that real, concrete duration in which the past remains bound up with the present. When the mathematician calculates the future state of a system at the end of a time t, there is nothing to prevent him from supposing that the universe vanishes from this moment till that, and suddenly reappears. It is the t-th moment only that counts—and that will be a mere instant. What will flow on in the interval—that is to say, real time—does not count, and cannot enter into the calculation. If the mathematician says that he puts himself inside this interval, he means that he is placing himself at a certain point, at a particular moment, therefore at the extremity again of a certain time t'; with the interval up to T' he is not concerned. If he divides the interval into infinitely small parts by considering the differential dt, he thereby expresses merely the fact that he will consider accelerations and velocities—that is to say, numbers which denote tendencies and enable him to calculate the state of the system at a given moment. But he is always speaking of a given moment—a static moment, that is—and not of flowing time. In short, *the world the mathematician deals with is a world that dies and is reborn at every instant—the world which Descartes was thinking of when he spoke of continued creation*. But, in time thus conceived, how could evolution, which is the very essence of life, ever take place? Evolution implies a real persistence of the past in the present, a duration which is, as it were, a hyphen, a connecting link. In other words, to know a living being or *natural system* is to get at the very interval of duration, while the knowledge of an *artificial* or *mathematical system* applies only to the extremity.

Continuity of change, preservation of the past in the present, real duration—the living being seems, then, to share these attributes with consciousness. Can we go further and say that life, like conscious activity, is invention, is unceasing creation?

Sigmund Freud

THE METHOD

OF DREAM-INTERPRETATION

THE DREAM

AS WISH-FULFILMENT

Sigmund Freud
[1856–1939]

Until Sigmund Freud began his studies of neuroses, the immeasurable world of the unconscious was a virtual *terra incognita*. Now, because of his explorations and discoveries in psychoanalysis, a new and vigorous impetus has been given to related sciences, to art, to literature, and to the whole cultural complex of twentieth-century life. According to Dr. A. A. Brill, Freud's apostle and translator in America, "The dream is the royal road to the unconscious." It represents the hidden fulfillment of unconscious wishes, which, when repressed, produce a chain of psychic consequences, frequently disastrous. The new Freudian psychology, based upon the tracing of unconscious psychic patterns, opened vistas far beyond the scope of the clinical therapist. Its method has been adapted, with ever-widening implications, to interpret the problems of man and his institutions. "The Method of Dream-Interpretation" and "The Dream as Wish-Fulfilment" are from Freud's *The Interpretation of Dreams*, in the A. A. Brill translation.

THE METHOD
OF DREAM-INTERPRETATION

SIGMUND FREUD

The Analysis of a Specimen Dream

THE epigraph on the title-page of this volume indicates the tradition to which I prefer to ally myself in my conception of the dream. I am proposing to show that dreams are capable of interpretation; and any contributions to the solution of the problem which have already been discussed will emerge only as possible by-products in the accomplishment of my special task. On the hypothesis that dreams are susceptible of interpretation, I at once find myself in disagreement with the prevailing doctrine of dreams—in fact, with all the theories of dreams, excepting only that of Scherner, for "to interpret a dream" is to specify its "meaning," to replace it by something which takes its position in the concatenation of our psychic activities as a link of definite importance and value. But, as we have seen, the scientific theories of the dream leave no room for a problem of dream-interpretation; since, in the first place, according to these theories, dreaming is not a psychic activity at all, but a somatic process which makes itself known to the psychic apparatus by means of symbols. Lay opinion has always been opposed to these theories. It asserts its privilege of proceeding illogically, and although it admits that dreams are incomprehensible and absurd, it cannot summon up the courage to deny that dreams have any significance. Led by a dim intuition, it seems rather to assume that dreams have a meaning, albeit a hidden one; that they are intended as a substitute for some other thought-process, and that we have only to disclose this substitute correctly in order to discover the hidden meaning of the dream.

The unscientific world, therefore, has always endeavored to "interpret" dreams, and by applying one or the other of two essentially different methods. The first of these methods envisages the dream-content as a whole, and seeks to replace it by another content, which is intelligible and in certain respects analogous. This is symbolic dream-interpretation; and of course it goes to pieces at the very outset in the case of those dreams which are not only unintelligible but confused. The construction which the biblical Joseph placed upon the dream of Pharaoh furnishes an example of this method. The seven fat kine, after which came seven lean ones that devoured the former, were a symbolic substitute for seven years of famine in the land of Egypt, which according to the prediction were to consume all the surplus that seven fruitful years had produced. Most of the artificial dreams contrived by the poets [1] are intended for some such symbolic interpretation, for they reproduce the thought conceived by the poet in a guise not unlike the disguise which we are wont to find in our dreams.

The idea that the dream concerns itself chiefly with the

---

[1] In a novel *Gradiva*, by the poet, W. Jensen, I chanced to discover several fictitious dreams, which were perfectly correct in their construction, and could be interpreted as though they had not been invented, but had been dreamt by actual persons. The poet declared, upon my inquiry, that he was unacquainted with my theory of dreams. I have made use of this agreement between my investigations and the creations of the poet as a proof of the correctness of my method of dream-analysis (*Der Wahn und die Träume* in W. Jensen's *Gradiva*, vol. i of the *Schriften zur angewandten Seelenkunde*, 1906, edited by myself, *Ges. Schriften*, vol. ix).

future, whose form it surmises in advance—a relic of the prophetic significance with which dreams were once invested —now becomes the motive for translating into the future the meaning of the dream which has been found by means of symbolic interpretation.

A demonstration of the manner in which one arrives at such a symbolic interpretation cannot, of course, be given. Success remains a matter of ingenious conjecture, of direct intuition, and for this reason dream-interpretation has naturally been elevated into an art which seems to depend upon extraordinary gifts.[2] The second of the two popular methods of dream-interpretation entirely abandons such claims. It might be described as the "cipher method," since it treats the dream as a kind of secret code in which every sign is translated into another sign of known meaning, according to an established key. For example, I have dreamt of a letter, and also of a funeral or the like; I consult a "dream-book," and I find that "letter" is to be translated by "vexation" and "funeral" by "engagement." It now remains to establish a connection, which I am again to assume as pertaining to the future, by means of the rigmarole which I have deciphered. An interesting variant of this cipher procedure, a variant in which its character of purely mechanical transference is to a certain extent corrected, is presented in the work on dream-interpretation by Artemidoros of Daldis.[3] Here not only the

---

[2] Aristotle expressed himself in this connection by saying that the best interpreter of dreams is he who can best grasp similarities. For dream-pictures, like pictures in water, are disfigured by the motion (of the water), so that he hits the target best who is able to recognize the true picture in the distorted one (Büchsenschütz, p. 65).

[3] Artemidoros of Daldis, born probably in the beginning of the second century of our calendar, has furnished us with the most complete and careful elaboration of dream-interpretation as it existed in the Graeco-Roman world. As Gompertz has emphasized, he ascribed great importance to the consideration that dreams ought to be interpreted on the basis of observation and experience, and he drew a definite line between his own art and other methods, which he considered fraudulent. The principle of his art of interpretation is, according to Gompertz, identical with that of magic:

dream-content, but also the personality and social position of the dreamer are taken into consideration, so that the same dream-content has a significance for the rich man, the married man, or the orator, which is different from that which applies to the poor man, the bachelor, or, let us say, the merchant. The essential point, then, in this procedure is that the work of interpretation is not applied to the entirety of the dream, but to each portion of the dream-content severally, as though the dream were a conglomerate in which each fragment calls for special treatment. Incoherent and confused dreams are certainly those that have been responsible for the invention of the cipher method.[4]

---

i.e. the principle of association. The thing dreamed meant what it recalled to the memory—to the memory, of course, of the dream-interpreter! This fact—that the dream may remind the interpreter of various things, and every interpreter of different things—leads, of course, to uncontrollable arbitrariness and uncertainty. The technique which I am about to describe differs from that of the ancients in one essential point, namely, in that it imposes upon the dreamer himself the work of interpretation. Instead of taking into account whatever may occur to the dream-interpreter, it considers only what occurs to the dreamer in connection with the dream-element concerned. According to the recent records of the missionary, Tfinkdjit (*Anthropos*, 1913), it would seem that the modern dream-interpreters of the Orient likewise attribute much importance to the co-operation of the dreamer. Of the dream-interpreters among the Mesopotamian Arabs this writer relates as follows: "*Pour interpréter exactement un songe les oniromanciens les plus habiles s'informent de ceux qui les consultent de toutes les circonstances qu'ils regardent nécessaires pour la bonne explication. . . . En un mot, nos oniromanciens ne laissent aucune circonstance leur échapper et ne donnent l'interprétation désirée avant d'avoir parfaitement saisi et reçu toutes les interrogations désirables.*" Among these questions one always finds demands for precise information in respect to near relatives (parents, wife, children) as well as the following formula: *habistine in hoc nocte copulam conjugalem ante vel post somnium?*—"*L'idée dominante dans l'interprétation des songes consiste à expliquer le rêve par son opposé.*"

[4] Dr. Alfred Robitsek calls my attention to the fact that Oriental dream-books, of which ours are pitiful plagiarisms, commonly undertake the interpretation of dream-elements in accordance with the assonance and similarity of words. Since these relationships must be lost by translation into our language, the incomprehensibil-

The worthlessness of both these popular methods of interpretation does not admit of discussion. As regards the scientific treatment of the subject, the symbolic method is limited in its application, and is not susceptible of a general exposition. In the cipher method everything depends upon whether the "key," the dream-book, is reliable, and for that all guarantees are lacking. So that one might be tempted to grant the contention of the philosophers and psychiatrists, and to dismiss the problem of dream-interpretation as altogether fanciful.[5]

I have, however, come to think differently. I have been forced to perceive that here, once more, we have one of those not infrequent cases where an ancient and stubbornly retained popular belief seems to have come nearer to the truth of the matter than the opinion of modern science. I must insist that the dream actually does possess a meaning, and that a scientific method of dream-interpretation is pos-

---

ity of the equivalents in our popular "dream-books" is hereby explained. Information as to the extraordinary significance of puns and the play upon words in the old Oriental cultures may be found in the writings of Hugo Winckler. The finest example of a dream-interpretation which has come down to us from antiquity is based on a play upon words. Artemidoros relates the following (p. 225): "But it seems to me that Aristandros gave a most happy interpretation to Alexander of Macedon. When the latter held Tyros encompassed and in a state of siege, and was angry and depressed over the great waste of time, he dreamed that he saw a Satyr dancing on his shield. It happened that Aristandros was in the neighbourhood of Tyros, and in the escort of the king, who was waging war on the Syrians. By dividing the word Satyros into σὰ and τύρος, he induced the king to become more aggressive in the siege. And thus Alexander became master of the city." (Σὰ Τύρος = thine is Tyros.) The dream, indeed, is so intimately connected with verbal expression that Ferenczi justly remarks that every tongue has its own dream-language. A dream is, as a rule, not to be translated into other languages.

[5] After the completion of my manuscript, a paper by Stumpf came to my notice which agrees with my work in attempting to prove that the dream is full of meaning and capable of interpretation. But the interpretation is undertaken by means of an allegorizing symbolism, and there is no guarantee that the procedure is generally applicable.

sible. I arrived at my knowledge of this method in the following manner:

For years I have been occupied with the resolution of certain psychopathological structures—hysterical phobias, obsessional ideas, and the like—with therapeutic intentions. I have been so occupied, in fact, ever since I heard the significant statement of Joseph Breuer, to the effect that in these structures, regarded as morbid symptoms, solution and treatment go hand in hand.[6] Where it has been possible to trace a pathological idea back to those elements in the psychic life of the patient to which it owed its origin, this idea has crumbled away, and the patient has been relieved of it. In view of the failure of our other therapeutic efforts, and in the face of the mysterious character of these pathological conditions, it seemed to me tempting, in spite of all the difficulties, to follow the method initiated by Breuer until a complete elucidation of the subject had been achieved. I shall have occasion elsewhere to give a detailed account of the form which the technique of this procedure has finally assumed, and of the results of my efforts. In the course of these psychoanalytic studies, I happened upon the question of dream-interpretation. My patients, after I had pledged them to inform me of all the ideas and thoughts which occurred to them in connection with a given theme, related their dreams, and thus taught me that a dream may be interpolated in the psychic concatenation, which may be followed backwards from a pathological idea into the patient's memory. The next step was to treat the dream itself as a symptom, and to apply to it the method of interpretation which had been worked out for such symptoms.

For this a certain psychic preparation on the part of the patient is necessary. A twofold effort is made, to stimulate his attentiveness in respect of his psychic perceptions, and to eliminate the critical spirit in which he is ordinarily in the habit of viewing such thoughts as come to the surface. For the purpose of self-observation with concentrated attention

[6] *Selected Papers on Hysteria and other Psychoneuroses.* Monograph series, Journ. Nerv. Mental Dis. Pub. Co.

it is advantageous that the patient should take up a restful position and close his eyes; he must be explicitly instructed to renounce all criticism of the thought-formations which he may perceive. He must also be told that the success of the psychoanalysis depends upon his noting and communicating everything that passes through his mind, and that he must not allow himself to suppress one idea because it seems to him unimportant or irrelevant to the subject, or another because it seems nonsensical. He must preserve an absolute impartiality in respect to his ideas; for if he is unsuccessful in finding the desired solution of the dream, the obsessional idea, or the like, it will be because he permits himself to be critical of them.

I have noticed in the course of my psychoanalytical work that the psychological state of a man in an attitude of reflection is entirely different from that of a man who is observing his psychic processes. In reflection there is a greater play of psychic activity than in the most attentive self-observation; this is shown even by the tense attitude and the wrinkled brow of the man in a state of reflection, as opposed to the mimic tranquillity of the man observing himself. In both cases there must be concentrated attention, but the reflective man makes use of his critical faculties, with the result that he rejects some of the thoughts which rise into consciousness after he has become aware of them, and abruptly interrupts others, so that he does not follow the lines of thought which they would otherwise open up for him; while in respect of yet other thoughts he is able to behave in such a manner that they do not become conscious at all—that is to say, they are suppressed before they are perceived. In self-observation, on the other hand, he has but one task—that of suppressing criticism; if he succeeds in doing this, an unlimited number of thoughts enter his consciousness which would otherwise have eluded his grasp. With the aid of the material thus obtained—material which is new to the self-observer—it is possible to achieve the interpretation of pathological ideas, and also that of dream-formations. As will be seen, the point is to induce a psychic state which is in some degree analogous, as regards the distribution of psychic energy (mobile attention), to the state of the mind before falling asleep—and also, of course, to the hypnotic state. On falling asleep the "undesired ideas" emerge, owing to the slackening of a certain arbitrary (and, of course, also critical) action, which is allowed to influence the trend of our ideas; we are accustomed to speak of fatigue as the reason of this slackening; the emerging undesired ideas are changed into visual and auditory images. In the condition which it utilized for the analysis of dreams and pathological ideas, this activity is purposely and deliberately renounced, and the psychic energy thus saved (or some part of it) is employed in attentively tracking the undesired thoughts which now come to the surface—thoughts which retain their identity as ideas (in which the condition differs from the state of falling asleep). *"Undesired ideas" are thus changed into "desired" ones.*

There are many people who do not seem to find it easy to adopt the required attitude toward the apparently "freely rising" ideas, and to renounce the criticism which is otherwise applied to them. The "undesired ideas" habitually evoke the most violent resistance, which seeks to prevent them from coming to the surface. But if we may credit our great poet-philosopher Friedrich Schiller, the essential condition of poetical creation includes a very similar attitude. In a certain passage in his correspondence with Körner (for the tracing of which we are indebted to Otto Rank), Schiller replies in the following words to a friend who complains of his lack of creative power: "The reason for your complaint lies, it seems to me, in the constraint which your intellect imposes upon your imagination. Here I will make an observation, and illustrate it by an allegory. Apparently it is not good—and indeed it hinders the creative work of the mind—if the intellect examines too closely the ideas already pouring in, as it were, at the gates. Regarded in isolation, an idea may be quite insignificant, and venturesome in the extreme, but it may acquire importance from an idea which follows it; perhaps, in a certain collocation with other ideas, which may seem equally absurd, it may be capable of furnishing a very serv-

iceable link. The intellect cannot judge all these ideas unless
it can retain them until it has considered them in connection
with these other ideas. In the case of a creative mind, it seems
to me, the intellect has withdrawn its watchers from the
gates, and the ideas rush in pell-mell, and only then does it
review and inspect the multitude. You worthy critics, or
whatever you may call yourselves, are ashamed or afraid of
the momentary and passing madness which is found in all
real creators, the longer or shorter duration of which distinguishes the thinking artist from the dreamer. Hence your
complaints of unfruitfulness, for you reject too soon and
discriminate too severely" (letter of December 1, 1788).

And yet, such a withdrawal of the watchers from the gates
of the intellect, as Schiller puts it, such a translation into the
condition of uncritical self-observation, is by no means difficult.

Most of my patients accomplish it after my first instructions. I myself can do so very completely, if I assist the
process by writing down the ideas that flash through my
mind. The quantum of psychic energy by which the critical
activity is thus reduced, and by which the intensity of self-
observation may be increased, varies considerably according
to the subject-matter upon which the attention is to be fixed.

The first step in the application of this procedure teaches
us that one cannot make the dream as a whole the object of
one's attention, but only the individual components of its
content. If I ask a patient who is as yet unpractised: "What
occurs to you in connection with this dream?" he is unable,
as a rule, to fix upon anything in his psychic field of vision.
I must first dissect the dream for him; then, in connection
with each fragment, he gives me a number of ideas which
may be described as the "thoughts behind" this part of the
dream. In this first and important condition, then, the method
of dream-interpretation which I employ diverges from the
popular, historical and legendary method of interpretation by
symbolism and approaches more nearly to the second or
"cipher method." Like this, it is an interpretation in detail,
not *en masse;* like this, it conceives the dream, from the out-

set, as something built up, as a conglomerate of psychic formations.

In the course of my psychoanalysis of neurotics I have already subjected perhaps more than a thousand dreams to interpretation, but I do not wish to use this material now as an introduction to the theory and technique of dream-interpretation. For quite apart from the fact that I should lay myself open to the objection that these are the dreams of neuropaths, so that the conclusions drawn from them would not apply to the dreams of healthy persons, there is another reason that impels me to reject them. The theme to which these dreams point is, of course, always the history of the malady that is responsible for the neurosis. Hence every dream would require a very long introduction, and an investigation of the nature and etiological conditions of the psychoneuroses, matters which are in themselves novel and exceedingly strange, and which would therefore distract attention from the dream-problem proper. My purpose is rather to prepare the way, by the solution of the dream-problem, for the solution of the more difficult problems of the psychology of the neuroses. But if I eliminate the dreams of neurotics, which constitute my principal material, I cannot be too fastidious in my treatment of the rest. Only those dreams are left which have been incidentally related to me by healthy persons of my acquaintance, or which I find given as examples in the literature of dream-life. Unfortunately, in all these dreams I am deprived of the analysis without which I cannot find the meaning of the dream. My mode of procedure is, of course, less easy than that of the popular cipher method, which translates the given dream-content by reference to an established key; I, on the contrary, hold that the same dream-content may conceal a different meaning in the case of different persons, or in different connections. I must, therefore, resort to my own dreams as a source of abundant and convenient material, furnished by a person who is more or less normal, and containing references to many incidents of everyday life. I shall certainly be confronted with doubts as to the trustworthiness of these "self-analyses," and it will be said that arbitrariness is by no means excluded in such analyses. In my own judgment, conditions are more likely to be favourable in self-observation than in the observation of others; in any case, it is permissible to investigate how much can be accomplished in the matter of dream-interpretation by means of self-analysis. There are other difficulties which must be overcome in my own inner self. One has a comprehensible aversion to exposing so many intimate details of one's own psychic life, and one does not feel secure against the misinterpretations of strangers. But one must be able to transcend such considerations. "*Tout psychologiste*," writes Delbœuf, "*est obligé de faire l'aveu même de ses faiblesses s'il croît par là jeter du jour sur quelque problème obscur.*" And I may assume for the reader that his initial interest in the indiscretions which I must commit will very soon give way to an exclusive engrossment in the psychological problems elucidated by them.[7]

I shall therefore select one of my own dreams for the purpose of elucidating my method of interpretation. Every such dream necessitates a preliminary statement; so that I must now beg the reader to make my interests his own for a time, and to become absorbed, with me, in the most trifling details of my life; for an interest in the hidden significance of dreams imperatively demands just such a transference.

Preliminary Statement

In the summer of 1895 I had treated psycho-analytically a young lady who was an intimate friend of mine and of my family. It will be understood that such complicated relations

---

[7] However, I will not omit to mention, in qualification of the above statement, that I have practically never reported a complete interpretation of a dream of my own. And I was probably right not to trust too far to the reader's discretion.

may excite manifold feelings in the physician, and especially the psychotherapist. The personal interest of the physician is greater, but his authority less. If he fails, his friendship with the patient's relatives is in danger of being undermined. In this case, however, the treatment ended in partial success; the patient was cured of her hysterical anxiety, but not of all her somatic symptoms. At that time I was not yet quite sure of the criteria which denote the final cure of an hysterical case, and I expected her to accept a solution which did not seem acceptable to her. In the midst of this disagreement we discontinued the treatment for the summer holidays. One day a younger colleague, one of my most intimate friends, who had visited the patient—Irma—and her family in their country residence, called upon me. I asked him how Irma was, and received the reply: "She is better, but not quite well." I realize that these words of my friend Otto's, or the tone of voice in which they were spoken, annoyed me. I thought I heard a reproach in the words, perhaps to the effect that I had promised the patient too much, and—rightly or wrongly —I attributed Otto's apparent "taking sides" against me to the influence of the patient's relatives, who, I assumed, had never approved of my treatment. This disagreeable impression, however, did not become clear to me, nor did I speak of it. That same evening I wrote the clinical history of Irma's case, in order to give it, as though to justify myself, to Dr. M., a mutual friend, who was at that time the leading personality in our circle. During the night (or rather in the early morning) I had the following dream, which I recorded immediately after waking:— [8]

DREAM OF JULY 23–24, 1895

A great hall—a number of guests, whom we are receiving— among them Irma, whom I immediately take aside, as though to answer her letter, and to reproach her for not yet accepting the "solution." I say to her: "If you still have pains, it is

[8] This is the first dream which I subjected to an exhaustive interpretation.

really only your own fault."—She answers: "If you only knew what pains I have now in the throat, stomach, and abdomen—I am choked by them." I am startled, and look at her. She looks pale and puffy. I think that after all I must be overlooking some organic affection. I take her to the window and look into her throat. She offers some resistance to this, like a woman who has a set of false teeth. I think, surely, she doesn't need them.—The mouth then opens wide, and I find a large white spot on the right, and elsewhere I see extensive grayish-white scabs adhering to curiously curled formations, which are evidently shaped like the turbinal bones of the nose.—I quickly call Dr. M., who repeats the examination and confirms it. . . . Dr. M. looks quite unlike his usual self; he is very pale, he limps, and his chin is clean-shaven. . . . Now my friend Otto, too, is standing beside her, and my friend Leopold percusses her covered chest, and says: "She has a dullness below, on the left," and also calls attention to an infiltrated portion of skin on the left shoulder (which I can feel, in spite of the dress). . . . M. says: "There's no doubt that it's an infection, but it doesn't matter; dysentery will follow and the poison will be eliminated." . . . We know, too, precisely how the infection originated. My friend Otto, not long ago, gave her, when she was feeling unwell, an injection of a preparation of propyl . . . propyls . . . propionic acid . . . trimethylamin (the formula of which I see before me, printed in heavy type). . . . One doesn't give such injections so rashly. . . . Probably, too, the syringe was not clean.

This dream has an advantage over many others. It is at once obvious to what events of the preceding day it is related, and of what subject it treats. The preliminary statement explains these matters. The news of Irma's health which I had received from Otto, and the clinical history, which I was writing late into the night, had occupied my psychic activities even during sleep. Nevertheless, no one who had read the preliminary report, and had knowledge of the content of the dream, could guess what the dream signified. Nor do I myself know. I am puzzled by the morbid symptoms of which Irma com-

plains in the dream, for they are not the symptoms for which
I treated her. I smile at the nonsensical idea of an injection
of propionic acid, and at Dr. M.'s attempt at consolation.
Towards the end of the dream seems more obscure and
quicker in tempo than at the beginning. In order to learn the
significance of all these details I resolve to undertake an exhaustive analysis.

Analysis

The hall—a number of guests, whom we are receiving. We
were living that summer at *Bellevue,* an isolated house on one
of the hills adjoining the Kahlenberg. This house was originally built as a place of entertainment, and therefore has un-
usually lofty, hall-like rooms. The dream was dreamed in
Bellevue, a few days before my wife's birthday. During the
day my wife had mentioned that she expected several friends,
and among them Irma, to come to us as guests for her birthday. My dream, then, anticipates this situation: It is my wife's
birthday, and we are receiving a number of people, among
them Irma, as guests in the large hall of *Bellevue.*

*I reproach Irma for not having accepted the "solution," I
say, "If you still have pains, it is really your own fault."* I
might even have said this while awake; I may have actually
said it. At that time I was of the opinion (recognized later to
be incorrect) that my task was limited to informing patients
of the hidden meaning of their symptoms. Whether they then
accepted or did not accept the solution upon which success
depended—for that I was not responsible. I am grateful to
this error, which, fortunately, has now been overcome, since
it made life easier for me at a time when, with all my unavoidable ignorance, I was expected to effect successful cures.
But I note that in the speech which I make to Irma in the
dream I am above all anxious that I shall not be blamed for

the pains which she still suffers. If it is Irma's own fault, it cannot be mine. Should the purpose of the dream be looked for in this quarter?

Irma's complaints—pains in the neck, abdomen, and stomach; she is choked by them. Pains in the stomach belonged to the symptom-complex of my patient, but they were not very prominent; she complained rather of qualms and a feeling of nausea. Pains in the neck and abdomen and constriction of the throat played hardly any part in her case. I wonder why I have decided upon this choice of symptoms in the dream; for the moment I cannot discover the reason.

She looks pale and puffy. My patient had always a rosy complexion. I suspect that here another person is being substituted for her.

I am startled at the idea that I may have overlooked some organic affection. This, as the reader will readily believe, is a constant fear with the specialist who sees neurotics almost exclusively, and who is accustomed to ascribe to hysteria so many manifestations which other physicians treat as organic. On the other hand, I am haunted by a faint doubt—I do not know whence it comes—whether my alarm is altogether honest. If Irma's pains are indeed of organic origin, it is not my duty to cure them. My treatment, of course, removes only hysterical pains. It seems to me, in fact, that I wish to find an error in the diagnosis; for then I could not be reproached with failure to effect a cure.

I take her to the window in order to look into her throat. She resists a little, like a woman who has false teeth. I think to myself, she does not need them. I had never had occasion to inspect Irma's oral cavity. The incident in the dream reminds me of an examination, made some time before, of a governess who at first produced an impression of youthful beauty, but who, upon opening her mouth, took certain measures to conceal her denture. Other memories of medical examinations, and of petty secrets revealed by them, to the embarrassment of both physician and patient, associate themselves with this case.—"She surely does not need them," is perhaps in the first place a compliment to Irma; but I suspect yet another meaning. In a careful analysis one is able to feel whether or not the *arrière-pensées* which are to be expected have all been exhausted. The way in which Irma stands at the window suddenly reminds me of another experience. Irma has an intimate woman friend of whom I think very highly. One evening, on paying her a visit, I found her at the window in the position reproduced in the dream, and her physician, the same Dr. M., declared that she had a diphtheritic membrane. The person of Dr. M. and the membrane return, indeed, in the course of the dream. Now it occurs to me that during the past few months I have had every reason to suppose that this lady too is hysterical. Yes, Irma herself betrayed the fact to me. But what do I know of her condition? Only the one thing, that like Irma in the dream she suffers from hysterical choking. Thus, in the dream I have replaced my patient by her friend. Now I remember that I have often played with the supposition that this lady, too, might ask me to relieve her of her symptoms. But even at the time I thought it improbable, since she is extremely reserved. She *resists*, as the dream shows. Another explanation might be that *she does not need it;* in fact, until now she has shown herself strong enough to master her condition without outside help. Now only a few features remain, which I can assign neither to Irma nor to her friend; pale, puffy, false teeth. The false teeth led me to the governess; I now feel inclined to be satisfied with bad teeth. Here another person, to whom these features may allude, occurs to me. She is not my patient, and I do not wish her to be my patient, for I have noticed that she is not at her ease with me, and I do not consider her a docile patient. She is generally pale, and once, when she had not felt particularly well, she was puffy.[9] I have thus compared my patient Irma

---

[9] The complaint of pains in the abdomen, as yet unexplained, may also be referred to this third person. It is my own wife, of course, who is in question; the abdominal pains remind me of one of the occasions on which her shyness became evident to me. I must admit that I do not treat Irma and my wife very gallantly in this dream, but let it be said, in my defence, that I am measuring both of them against the ideal of the courageous and docile female patient.

with two others, who would likewise resist treatment. What is the meaning of the fact that I have exchanged her for her friend in the dream? Perhaps that I wish to exchange her; either her friend arouses in me stronger sympathies, or I have a higher regard for her intelligence. For I consider Irma foolish because she does not accept my solution. The other woman would be more sensible, and would thus be more likely to yield. *The mouth then opens readily;* she would tell more than Irma.[10]

What I see in the throat: a white spot and scabby turbinal bones. The white spot recalls diphtheria, and thus Irma's friend, but it also recalls the grave illness of my eldest daughter two years earlier, and all the anxiety of that unhappy time. The scab on the turbinal bones reminds me of my anxiety concerning my own health. At that time I frequently used cocaine in order to suppress distressing swellings in the nose, and I had heard a few days previously that a lady patient who did likewise had contracted an extensive necrosis of the nasal mucous membrane. In 1885 it was I who had recommended the use of cocaine, and I had been gravely reproached in consequence. A dear friend, who had died before the date of this dream, had hastened his end by the misuse of this remedy.

I quickly call Dr. M., who repeats the examination. This would simply correspond to the position which M. occupied among us. But the word "quickly" is striking enough to demand a special examination. It reminds me of a sad medical experience. By continually prescribing a drug (sulphonal), which at that time was still considered harmless, I was once responsible for a condition of acute poisoning in the case of a woman patient, and hastily turned for assistance to my older and more experienced colleague. The fact that I really had this case in mind is confirmed by a subsidiary circum-

---

[10] I suspect that the interpretation of this portion has not been carried far enough to follow every hidden meaning. If I were to continue the comparison of the three women, I should go far afield. Every dream has at least one point at which it is unfathomable; a central point, as it were, connecting it with the unknown.

stance. The patient, who succumbed to the toxic effects of the drug, bore the same name as my eldest daughter. I had never thought of this until now; but now it seems to me almost like a retribution of fate—as though the substitution of persons had to be continued in another sense: this Matilda for that Matilda; an eye for an eye, a tooth for a tooth. It is as though I were seeking every opportunity to reproach myself for a lack of medical conscientiousness.

Dr. M. is pale; his chin is shaven, and he limps. Of this so much is correct, that his unhealthy appearance often arouses the concern of his friends. The other two characteristics must belong to another person. An elder brother living abroad occurs to me, for he, too, shaves his chin, and if I remember him rightly, the M. of the dream bears on the whole a certain resemblance to him. And some days previously the news arrived that he was limping on account of an arthritic affection of the hip. There must be some reason why I fuse the two persons into one in my dream. I remember that, in fact, I was on bad terms with both of them for similar reasons. Both had rejected a certain proposal which I had recently made them.

My friend Otto is now standing next to the patient, and my friend Leopold examines her and calls attention to a dulness low down on the left side. My friend Leopold also is a physician, and a relative of Otto's. Since the two practise the same speciality, fate has made them competitors, so that they are constantly being compared with one another. Both of them assisted me for years, while I was still directing a public clinic for neurotic children. There, scenes like that reproduced in my dream had often taken place. While I would be discussing the diagnosis of a case with Otto, Leopold would examine the child anew and make an unexpected contribution towards our decision. There was a difference of character between the two men like that between Inspector Brasig and his friend Karl. Otto was remarkably prompt and alert; Leopold was slow and thoughtful, but thorough. If I contrast Otto and the cautious Leopold in the dream I do so, apparently, in order to extol Leopold. The comparison is like that made above between the disobedient patient Irma and her friend, who was believed to be more sensible. I now become aware of one of the tracks along which the association of ideas in the dream proceeds: from the sick child to the children's clinic. Concerning the dulness low on the left side, I have the impression that it corresponds with a certain case of which all the details were similar, a case in which Leopold impressed me by his thoroughness. I thought vaguely, too, of something like a metastatic affection, but it might also be a reference to the patient whom I should have liked to have in Irma's place. For this lady, as far as I can gather, exhibited symptoms which imitated tuberculosis.

An infiltrated portion of skin on the left shoulder. I know at once that this is my own rheumatism of the shoulder, which I always feel if I lie awake long at night. The very phrasing of the dream sounds ambiguous: "Something which I can feel, as he does, in spite of the dress." "Feel on my own body" is intended. Further, it occurs to me how unusual the phrase "infiltrated portion of skin" sounds. We are accustomed to the phrase: "an infiltration of the upper posterior left"; this would refer to the lungs, and thus, once more, to tuberculosis.

In spite of the dress. This, to be sure, is only an interpolation. At the clinic the children were, of course, examined undressed; here we have some contrast to the manner in which adult female patients have to be examined. The story used to be told of an eminent physician that he always examined his patients through their clothes. The rest is obscure to me; I have, frankly, no inclination to follow the matter further.

Dr. M. says: "It's an infection, but it doesn't matter; dysentery will follow, and the poison will be eliminated." This, at first, seems to me ridiculous; nevertheless, like everything else, it must be carefully analysed; more closely observed it seems after all to have a sort of meaning. What I had found in the patient was a local diphtheritis. I remember the discussion about diphtheritis and diphtheria at the time of my daughter's illness. Diphtheria is the general infection which proceeds from local diphtheritis. Leopold demonstrates the existence of such a general infection by the dulness, which also suggests a metastatic focus. I believe, however, that just this kind of metastasis does not occur in the case of diphtheria. It reminds me rather of pyaemia.

It doesn't matter is a consolation. I believe it fits in as follows: The last part of the dream has yielded a content to the effect that the patient's sufferings are the result of a serious organic affection. I begin to suspect that by this I am only trying to shift the blame from myself. Psychic treatment cannot be held responsible for the continued presence of a diphtheritic affection. Now, indeed, I am distressed by the thought of having invented such a serious illness for Irma, for the sole purpose of exculpating myself. It seems so cruel. Accordingly, I need the assurance that the outcome will be benign, and it seems to me that I made a good choice when I put the words that consoled me into the mouth of Dr. M. But here I am placing myself in a position of superiority to the dream; a fact which needs explanation.

But why is this consolation so nonsensical?

Dysentery. Some sort of far-fetched theoretical notion that the toxins of disease might be eliminated through the intestines. Am I thereby trying to make fun of Dr. M.'s remarkable store of far-fetched explanations, his habit of conceiving curious pathological relations? Dysentery suggests something else. A few months ago I had in my care a young man who was suffering from remarkable intestinal troubles; a case which had been treated by other colleagues as one of "anaemia with malnutrition." I realized that it was a case of hysteria; I was unwilling to use my psychotherapy on him, and sent him off on a sea-voyage. Now a few days previously I had received a despairing letter from him; he wrote from Egypt, saying that he had had a fresh attack, which the doctor had declared to be dysentery. I suspect that the diagnosis is merely an error on the part of an ignorant colleague, who is allowing himself to be fooled by the hysteria; yet I cannot help reproaching myself for putting the invalid in a position where he might contract some organic affection of the bowels in addition to his hysteria. Furthermore, dysentery sounds not unlike diphtheria, a word which does not occur in the dream.

Yes, it must be the case that with the consoling prognosis, "Dysentery will develop, etc.," I am making fun of Dr. M., for I recollect that years ago he once jestingly told a very similar story of a colleague. He had been called in to consult with him in the case of a woman who was very seriously ill, and he felt obliged to confront his colleague, who seemed very hopeful, with the fact that he found albumen in the patient's urine. His colleague, however, did not allow this to worry him, but answered calmly: "*That does not matter*, my dear sir; the albumen will soon be excreted!" Thus I can no longer doubt that this part of the dream expresses derision for those of my colleagues who are ignorant of hysteria. And, as though in confirmation, the thought enters my mind: "Does Dr. M. know that the appearances in Irma's friend, his patient, which gave him reason to fear tuberculosis, are likewise due to hysteria? Has he recognized this hysteria, or has he allowed himself to be fooled?"

But what can be my motive in treating this friend so badly? That is simple enough: Dr. M. agrees with my solution as little as does Irma herself. Thus, in this dream I have already revenged myself on two persons: on Irma in the words, "If you still have pains, it is your own fault," and on Dr. M. in the wording of the nonsensical consolation which has been put into his mouth.

We know precisely how the infection originated. This precise knowledge in the dream is remarkable. Only a moment before this we did not yet know of the infection, since it was first demonstrated by Leopold.

My friend Otto gave her an injection not long ago, when she was feeling unwell. Otto had actually related during his short visit to Irma's family that he had been called in to a neighbouring hotel in order to give an injection to someone who had been suddenly taken ill. Injections remind me once more of the unfortunate friend who poisoned himself with cocaine. I had recommended the remedy for internal use only during the withdrawal of morphia; but he immediately gave himself injections of cocaine.

With a preparation of propyl . . . propyls . . . propionic acid. How on earth did this occur to me? On the evening of the day after I had written the clinical history and dreamed about the case, my wife opened a bottle of liqueur labelled "Ananas," [11] which was a present from our friend Otto. He had, as a matter of fact, a habit of making presents on every possible occasion; I hope he will some day be cured of this by a wife.[12] This liqueur smelt so strongly of fusel oil that I refused to drink it. My wife suggested: "We will give the bottle to the servants," and I, more prudent, objected, with the philanthropic remark: "They shan't be poisoned either." The smell of fusel oil (amyl . . .) has now apparently awakened my memory of the whole series: propyl, methyl, etc., which furnished the preparation of propyl mentioned in the dream. Here, indeed, I have effected a substitution: I dreamt of propyl after smelling amyl; but substitutions of this kind are perhaps permissible, especially in organic chemistry.

Trimethylamin. In the dream I see the chemical formula of this substance—which at all events is evidence of a great effort on the part of my memory—and the formula is even printed in heavy type, as though to distinguish it from the context as something of particular importance. And where does trimethylamin, thus forced on my attention, lead me? To a conversation with another friend, who for years has been familiar with all my germinating ideas, and I with his. At that time he had just informed me of certain ideas concerning a sexual chemistry, and had mentioned, among others, that he thought he had found in trimethylamin one of the products of sexual metabolism. This substance thus leads me

---

[11] "Ananas," moreover, has a remarkable assonance with the family name of my patient Irma.

[12] In this the dream did not turn out to be prophetic. But in another sense it proved correct, for the "unsolved" stomach pains, for which I did not want to be blamed, were the forerunners of a serious illness, due to gall-stones.

to sexuality, the factor to which I attribute the greatest significance in respect of the origin of these nervous affections which I am trying to cure. My patient Irma is a young widow; if I am required to excuse my failure to cure her, I shall perhaps do best to refer to this condition, which her admirers would be glad to terminate. But in what a singular fashion such a dream is fitted together! The friend who in my dream becomes my patient in Irma's place is likewise a young widow.

I surmise why it is that the formula of trimethylamin is so insistent in the dream. So many important things are centred about this one word: trimethylamin is an allusion, not merely to the all-important factor of sexuality, but also to a friend whose sympathy I remember with satisfaction whenever I feel isolated in my opinions. And this friend, who plays such a large part in my life: will he not appear yet again in the concatenation of ideas peculiar to this dream? Of course; he has a special knowledge of the results of affections of the nose and the sinuses, and has revealed to science several highly remarkable relations between the turbinal bones and the female sexual organs. (The three curly formations in Irma's throat.) I got him to examine Irma, in order to determine whether her gastric pains were of nasal origin. But he himself suffers from suppurative rhinitis, which gives me concern, and to this perhaps there is an allusion in pyaemia, which hovers before me in the metastasis of the dream.

One doesn't give such injections so rashly. Here the reproach of rashness is hurled directly at my friend Otto. I believe I had some such thought in the afternoon, when he seemed to indicate, by word and look, that he had taken sides against me. It was, perhaps: "How easily he is influenced; how irresponsibly he pronounces judgment." Further, the above sentence points once more to my deceased friend, who so irresponsibly resorted to cocaine injections. As I have said, I had not intended that injections of the drug should be taken. I note that in reproaching Otto I once more touch upon the story of the unfortunate Matilda, which was the pretext for the same reproach against me. Here, obviously, I am collecting examples of my conscientiousness, and also of the reverse.

Probably too the syringe was not clean. Another reproach directed at Otto, but originating elsewhere. On the previous day I happened to meet the son of an old lady of eighty-two, to whom I am obliged to give two injections of morphia daily. At present she is in the country, and I have heard that she is suffering from phlebitis. I immediately thought that this might be a case of infiltration caused by a dirty syringe. It is my pride that in two years I have not given her a single infiltration; I am always careful, of course, to see that the syringe is perfectly clean. For I am conscientious. From the phlebitis I return to my wife, who once suffered from thrombosis during a period of pregnancy, and now three related situations come to the surface in my memory, involving my wife, Irma, and the dead Matilda, whose identity has apparently justified my putting these three persons in one another's places.

I have now completed the interpretation of the dream.[13] In the course of this interpretation I have taken great pains to avoid all those notions which must have been suggested by a comparison of the dream-content with the dream-thoughts hidden behind this content. Meanwhile the "meaning" of the dream has dawned upon me. I have noted an intention which is realized through the dream, and which must have been my motive in dreaming. The dream fulfils several wishes, which were awakened within me by the events of the previous evening (Otto's news, and the writing of the clinical history). For the result of the dream is, that it is not I who am to blame for the pain which Irma is still suffering, but that Otto is to blame for it. Now Otto has annoyed me by his remark about Irma's imperfect cure; the dream avenges me upon him, in that it turns the reproach upon himself. The dream acquits me of responsibility for Irma's condition, as it refers this condition to other causes (which do, indeed, furnish quite a num-

---

[13] Even if I have not, as might be expected, accounted for everything that occurred to me in connection with the work of interpretation.

ber of explanations). The dream represents a certain state of affairs, such as I might wish to exist; *the content of the dream is thus the fulfilment of a wish; its motive is a wish.*

This much is apparent at first sight. But many other details of the dream become intelligible when regarded from the standpoint of wish-fulfilment. I take my revenge on Otto, not merely for too readily taking sides against me, in that I accuse him of careless medical treatment (the injection), but I revenge myself also for the bad liqueur which smells of fusel oil, and I find an expression in the dream which unites both these reproaches: the injection of a preparation of propyl. Still I am not satisfied, but continue to avenge myself by comparing him with his more reliable colleague. Thereby I seem to say: "I like him better than you." But Otto is not the only person who must be made to feel the weight of my anger. I take my revenge on the disobedient patient, by exchanging her for a more sensible and more docile one. Nor do I pass over Dr. M.'s contradiction; for I express, in an obvious allusion, my opinion of him: namely, that his attitude in this case is that of an ignoramus ("Dysentery will develop, etc."). Indeed, it seems as though I were appealing from him to someone better informed (my friend, who told me about trimethylamin), just as I have turned from Irma to her friend, and from Otto to Leopold. It is as though I were to say: Rid me of these three persons, replace them by three others of my own choice, and I shall be rid of the reproaches which I am not willing to admit that I deserve! In my dream the unreasonableness of these reproaches is demonstrated for me in the most elaborate manner. Irma's pains are not attributable to me, since she herself is to blame for them, in that she refuses to accept my solution. They do not concern me, for being as they are of an organic nature, they cannot possibly be cured by psychic treatment.—Irma's sufferings are satisfactorily explained by her widowhood (trimethylamin!); a state which I cannot alter.—Irma's illness has been caused by an incautious injection administered by Otto, an injection of an unsuitable drug, such as I should never have administered. —Irma's complaint is the result of an injection made with an unclean syringe, like the phlebitis of my old lady patient, whereas my injections have never caused any ill effects. I am aware that these explanations of Irma's illness, which unite in acquitting me, do not agree with one another; that they even exclude one another. The whole plea—for this dream is nothing else—recalls vividly the defence offered by a man who was accused by his neighbour of having returned a kettle in a damaged condition. In the first place, he said, he had returned the kettle undamaged; in the second place it already had holes in it when he borrowed it; and in the third place, he had never borrowed it at all. A complicated defence, but so much the better; if only one of these three lines of defence is recognized as valid, the man must be acquitted.

Still other themes play a part in the dream, and their relation to my non-responsibility for Irma's illness is not so apparent: my daughter's illness, and that of a patient with the same name; the harmfulness of cocaine; the affection of my patient, who was traveling in Egypt; concern about the health of my wife; my brother, and Dr. M.; my own physical troubles, and anxiety concerning my absent friend, who is suffering from suppurative rhinitis. But if I keep all these things in view, they combine into a single train of thought, which might be labelled: concern for the health of myself and others; professional conscientiousness. I recall a vaguely disagreeable feeling when Otto gave me the news of Irma's condition. Lastly, I am inclined, after the event, to find an expression of this fleeting sensation in the train of thoughts which forms part of the dream. It is as though Otto had said to me: "You do not take your medical duties seriously enough; you are not conscientious; you do not perform what you promise." Thereupon this train of thought placed itself at my service, in order that I might give proof of my extreme conscientiousness, of my intimate concern about the health of my relatives, friends and patients. Curiously enough, there are also some painful memories in this material, which confirm the blame attached to Otto rather than my own exculpation. The material is apparently impartial, but the connection between this broader material, on which the dream is based, and the more limited theme from which emerges the wish to be innocent of Irma's illness, is, nevertheless, unmistakable.

I do not wish to assert that I have entirely revealed the meaning of the dream, or that my interpretation is flawless.

I could still spend much time upon it; I could draw further explanations from it, and discuss further problems which it seems to propound. I can even perceive the points from which further mental associations might be traced; but such considerations as are always involved in every dream of one's own prevent me from interpreting it farther. Those who are overready to condemn such reserve should make the experiment of trying to be more straightforward. For the present I am content with the one fresh discovery which has just been made: If the method of dream-interpretation here indicated is followed, it will be found that dreams do really possess a meaning, and are by no means the expression of a disintegrated cerebral activity, as the writers on the subject would have us believe. *When the work of interpretation has been completed the dream can be recognized as a wish-fulfilment.*

THE DREAM
AS WISH-FULFILMENT

WHEN, after passing through a narrow defile, one suddenly reaches a height beyond which the ways part and a rich prospect lies outspread in different directions, it is well to stop for a moment and consider whither one shall turn next. We are in somewhat the same position after we have mastered this first interpretation of a dream. We find ourselves standing in the light of a sudden discovery. The dream is not comparable to the irregular sounds of a musical instrument, which, instead of being played by the hand of a musician, is struck by some external force; the dream is not meaningless, not absurd, does not presuppose that one part of our store of ideas is dormant while another part begins to awake. It is a perfectly valid psychic phenomenon, actually a wish-fulfilment; it may be enrolled in the continuity of the intelligible psychic activities of the waking state; it is built up by a highly complicated intellectual activity. But at the very moment when we are about to rejoice in this discovery a host of problems besets us. If the dream, as this theory defines it, represents a fulfilled wish, what is the cause of the striking and unfamiliar manner in which this fulfilment is expressed? What transformation has occurred in our dream-thoughts before the manifest dream, as we remember it on waking, shapes itself out of them? How has this transformation taken place? Whence comes the material that is worked up into the dream? What causes many of the peculiarities which are to be observed in our dream-thoughts; for example, how is it that they are able to contradict one another? (see the analogy of the kettle). Is the dream capable of teaching us something new concerning our internal psychic processes, and can its content correct opinions which we have held during the day? I suggest that for the present all these problems be laid aside, and that a single path be pursued. We have found that the dream represents a wish as fulfilled. Our next purpose should be to ascertain whether this is a general characteristic of dreams, or whether it is only the accidental content of the particular dream ("the dream about Irma's injection") with which we have begun our analysis; for even if we conclude that every dream has a meaning and psychic value, we must nevertheless allow for the possibility that this meaning may not be the same in every dream. The first dream which we have considered was the fulfilment of a wish; another may turn out to be the realization of an apprehension; a third may have a reflection as its content; a fourth may simply reproduce a reminiscence. Are there, then, dreams other than wish-dreams; or are there none but wish-dreams?

It is easy to show that the wish-fulfilment in dreams is often undisguised and easy to recognize, so that one may wonder why the language of dreams has not long since been understood. There is, for example, a dream which I can evoke as often as I please, experimentally, as it were. If, in the evening, I eat anchovies, olives, or other strongly salted foods, I am thirsty at night, and therefore I wake. The waking, however, is preceded by a dream, which has always the same content, namely, that I am drinking. I am drinking long draughts of water; it tastes as delicious as only a cool drink can taste when one's throat is parched; and then I wake, and find that I have an actual desire to drink. The cause of this dream is thirst, which I perceive when I wake. From this sensation arises the wish to drink, and the dream shows me this wish as fulfilled. It thereby serves a function, the nature of which I soon surmise. I sleep well, and am not accustomed to being waked by a bodily need. If I succeed in appeasing my thirst by means of the dream that I am drinking, I need not wake up in order to satisfy that thirst. It is thus a *dream of convenience*. The dream takes the place of action, as elsewhere in life. Unfortunately, the need of water to quench the thirst cannot be satisfied by a dream, as can my thirst for revenge upon Otto

and Dr. M., but the intention is the same. Not long ago I had
the same dream in a somewhat modified form. On this occasion I felt thirsty before going to bed, and emptied the glass
of water which stood on the little chest beside my bed. Some
hours later, during the night, my thirst returned, with the
consequent discomfort. In order to obtain water, I should
have had to get up and fetch the glass which stood on my
wife's bed-table. I thus quite appropriately dreamt that my
wife was giving me a drink from a vase; this vase was an
Etruscan cinerary urn, which I had brought home from Italy,
and had since given away. But the water in it tasted so salty
(apparently on account of the ashes) that I was forced to
wake. It may be observed how conveniently the dream is
capable of arranging matters. Since the fulfilment of a wish
is its only purpose, it may be perfectly egoistic. Love of comfort is really not compatible with consideration for others.
The introduction of the cinerary urn is probably once again
the fulfilment of a wish; I regret that I no longer possess this
vase; it, like the glass of water at my wife's side, is inaccessible to me. The cinerary urn is appropriate also in connection with the sensation of an increasingly salty taste, which I
know will compel me to wake.[1]

---

[1] The facts relating to dreams of thirst were known also to Wey-
gandt, who speaks of them as follows: "It is just this sensation of
thirst which is registered most accurately of all; it always causes
a representation of quenching the thirst. The manner in which the
dream represents the act of quenching the thirst is manifold, and
is specified in accordance with some recent recollection. A universal phenomenon noticeable here is the fact that the representation of quenching the thirst is immediately followed by disappointment in the inefficacy of the imagined refreshment." But he
overlooks the universal character of the reaction of the dream to
the stimulus. If other persons who are troubled by thirst at night
awake without dreaming beforehand, this does not constitute an
objection to my experiment, but characterizes them as persons who
sleep less soundly. Cf. here *Isaiah xxix.* 8: "It shall even be as when
an hungry man dreameth, and, behold, he eateth; but he awaketh,
and his soul is empty: or as when a thirsty man dreameth, and,
behold he drinketh; but he awaketh, and, behold, he is faint. . . ."

Such convenience-dreams came very frequently to me in my youth. Accustomed as I had always been to working until late at night, early waking was always a matter of difficulty. I used then to dream that I was out of bed and standing at the wash-stand. After a while I could no longer shut out the knowledge that I was not yet up; but in the meantime I had continued to sleep. The same sort of lethargy-dream was dreamed by a young colleague of mine, who appears to share my propensity for sleep. With him it assumed a particularly amusing form. The landlady with whom he was lodging in the neighbourhood of the hospital had strict orders to wake him every morning at a given hour, but she found it by no means easy to carry out his orders. One morning sleep was especially sweet to him. The woman called into his room: "Herr Pepi, get up; you've got to go to the hospital." Where-upon the sleeper dreamt of a room in the hospital, of a bed in which he was lying, and of a chart pinned over his head, which read as follows: "Pepi M., medical student, 22 years of age." He told himself in the dream: "If I am already at the hospital, I don't have to go there," turned over, and slept on. He had thus frankly admitted to himself his motive for dreaming.

Here is yet another dream of which the stimulus was active during sleep: One of my women patients, who had been obliged to undergo an unsuccessful operation on the jaw, was instructed by her physicians to wear by day and night a cooling apparatus on the affected cheek; but she was in the habit of throwing it off as soon as she had fallen asleep. One day I was asked to reprove her for doing so; she had again thrown the apparatus on the floor. The patient defended her-self as follows: "This time I really couldn't help it; it was the result of a dream which I had during the night. In the dream I was in a box at the opera, and was taking a lively interest in the performance. But Herr Karl Meyer was lying in the sanatorium and complaining pitifully on account of pains in his jaw. I said to myself, 'Since I haven't the pains, I don't need the apparatus either'; that's why I threw it away." The dream of this poor sufferer reminds me of an expression which comes to our lips when we are in a disagreeable situation: "Well, I can imagine more amusing things!" The dream presents these "more amusing things!" Herr Karl Meyer, to whom the dreamer attributed her pains, was the most casual acquaintance of whom she could think.

It is quite as simple a matter to discover the wish-fulfilment in several other dreams which I have collected from healthy persons. A friend who was acquainted with my theory of dreams, and had explained it to his wife, said to me one day: "My wife asked me to tell you that she dreamt yesterday that she was having her menses. You will know what that means." Of course I know: if the young wife dreams that she is having her menses, the menses have stopped. I can well imagine that she would have liked to enjoy her freedom a little longer, before the discomforts of maternity began. It was a clever way of giving notice of her first pregnancy. Another friend writes that his wife had dreamt not long ago that she noticed milk-stains on the front of her blouse. This also is an indication of pregnancy, but not of the first one; the young mother hoped she would have more nourishment for the second child than she had for the first.

A young woman who for weeks had been cut off from all society because she was nursing a child who was suffering from an infectious disease dreamt, after the child had recovered, of a company of people in which Alphonse Daudet, Paul Bourget, Marcel Prévost and others were present; they were all very pleasant to her and amused her enormously. In her dream these different authors had the features which their portraits give them. M. Prévost, with whose portrait she is not familiar, looked like the man who had disinfected the sickroom the day before, the first outsider to enter it for a long time. Obviously the dream is to be translated thus: "It is about time now for something more entertaining than this eternal nursing."

Perhaps this collection will suffice to prove that frequently, and under the most complex conditions, dreams may be noted which can be understood only as wish-fulfilments, and which present their content without concealment. In most cases these are short and simple dreams, and they stand in pleasant contrast to the confused and overloaded dream-compositions which have almost exclusively attracted the attention of the writers on the subject. But it will repay us if we give some time to the examination of these simple dreams. The simplest dreams of all are, I suppose, to be expected in the case of children whose psychic activities are certainly less complicated than those of adults. Child psychology, in my opinion, is destined to render the same services to the psychology of adults as a study of the structure or development of the lower animals renders to the investigation of the structure of the higher orders of animals. Hitherto but few deliberate efforts have been made to make use of the psychology of the child for such a purpose.

The dreams of little children are often simple fulfilments of wishes, and for this reason are, as compared with the dreams of adults, by no means interesting. They present no problem to be solved, but they are invaluable as affording proof that the dream, in its inmost essence, is the fulfilment of a wish. I have been able to collect several examples of such dreams from the material furnished by my own children.

For two dreams, one that of a daughter of mine, at that time eight and a half years of age, and the other that of a boy of five and a quarter, I am indebted to an excursion to Hallstatt, in the summer of 1896. I must first explain that we were living that summer on a hill near Aussee, from which, when the weather was fine, we enjoyed a splendid view of the Dachstein. With a telescope we could easily distinguish the Simony hut. The children often tried to see it through the telescope—I do not know with what success. Before the excursion I had told the children that Hallstatt lay at the foot of the Dachstein. They looked forward to the outing with the greatest delight. From Hallstatt we entered the valley of Eschern, which enchanted the children with its constantly changing scenery. One of them, however, the boy of five, gradually became discontented. As often as a mountain came into view, he would ask: "Is that the Dachstein?" whereupon I had to reply: "No, only a foot-hill." After this question had been repeated several times he fell quite silent, and did not wish to accompany us up the steps leading to the waterfall. I thought he was tired. But the next morning he came to me, perfectly happy, and said: "Last night I dreamt that we went to the Simony hut." I understood him now; he had expected, when I spoke of the Dachstein, that on our excursion to Hall-statt he would climb the mountain, and would see at close quarters the hut which had been so often mentioned when the telescope was used. When he learned that he was ex-pected to content himself with foot-hills and a waterfall he was disappointed, and became discontented. But the dream compensated him for all this. I tried to learn some details of the dream; they were scanty. "You go up steps for six hours," as he had been told.

On this excursion the girl of eight and a half had likewise cherished wishes which had to be satisfied by a dream. We had taken with us to Hallstatt our neighbour's twelve-year-old boy; quite a polished little gentleman, who, it seemed to me, had already won the little woman's sympathies. Next morning she related the following dream: "Just think, I dreamt that Emil was one of the family, that he said 'papa' and 'mamma' to you, and slept at our house, in the big room, like one of the boys. Then mamma came into the room and threw a handful of big bars of chocolate, wrapped in blue and green paper, under our beds." The girl's brothers, who evidently had not inherited an understanding of dream-inter-pretation, declared, just as the writers we have quoted would have done: "That dream is nonsense." The girl defended at least one part of the dream, and from the standpoint of the theory of the neuroses it is interesting to learn which part it was that she defended: "That Emil was one of the family was nonsense, but that about the bars of chocolate wasn't." It was just this latter part that was obscure to me, until my wife furnished the explanation. On the way home from the railway-station the children had stopped in front of a slot-machine, and had wanted exactly such bars of chocolate, wrapped in paper with a metallic lustre, such as the machine, in their experience, provided. But the mother thought, and rightly so, that the day had brought them enough wish-fulfilments, and therefore left this wish to be satisfied in the dream. This little scene had escaped me. That portion of the dream which had been condemned by my daughter I understood without any difficulty. I myself had heard the well-behaved little guest enjoining the children, as they were walking ahead of us, to wait until "papa" or "mamma" had come up. For the little girl the dream turned this temporary relationship into a permanent adoption. Her affection could not as yet conceive of any other way of enjoying her friend's company permanently than the adoption pictured in her dream, which was suggested by her brothers. Why the bars of chocolate were thrown under the bed could not, of course, be explained without questioning the child.

From a friend I have learned of a dream very much like that of my little boy. It was dreamed by a little girl of eight. Her father, accompanied by several children, had started on a walk to Dornbach, with the intention of visiting the Rohrer hut, but had turned back, as it was growing late, promising the children to take them some other time. On the way back they passed a signpost which pointed to the Hameau. The children now asked him to take them to the Hameau, but once more, and for the same reason, they had to be content with the promise that they should go there some other day. Next morning the little girl went to her father and told him, with a satisfied air: "Papa, I dreamed last night that you were with us at the Rohrer hut, and on the Hameau." Thus, in the dream her impatience had anticipated the fulfilment of the promise made by her father.

Another dream, with which the picturesque beauty of the Aussee inspired my daughter, at that time three and a quarter years of age, is equally straightforward. The little girl had crossed the lake for the first time, and the trip had passed too quickly for her. She did not want to leave the boat at the landing, and cried bitterly. The next morning she told us: "Last night I was sailing on the lake." Let us hope that the duration of this dream-voyage was more satisfactory to her.

My eldest boy, at that time eight years of age, was already dreaming of the realization of his fancies. He had ridden in a chariot with Achilles, with Diomedes as charioteer. On the previous day he had shown a lively interest in a book on the myths of Greece which had been given to his elder sister.*

If it can be admitted that the talking of children in their sleep belongs to the sphere of dreams, I can relate the following as one of the earliest dreams in my collection: My youngest daughter, at that time nineteen months old, vomited one morning, and was therefore kept without food all day. During the night she was heard to call excitedly in her sleep: "Anna F(r)eud, st'awbewy, wild st'awbewy, om'lette, pap!" She used her name in this way in order to express the act of appropriation; the menu presumably included everything that would seem to her a desirable meal; the fact that two varieties of strawberry appeared in it was a demonstration against the sanitary regulations of the household, and was based on the circumstance, which she had by no means overlooked, that the nurse had ascribed her indisposition to an over-plentiful consumption of strawberries; so in her dream she avenged herself for this opinion which met with her disapproval.[2]

When we call childhood happy because it does not yet know sexual desire, we must not forget what a fruitful source of disappointment and renunciation, and therefore of dream-stimulation, the other great vital impulse may be for the

---

[2] The dream afterwards accomplished the same purpose in the case of the child's grandmother, who is older than the child by about seventy years. After she had been forced to go hungry for a day on account of the restlessness of her floating kidney, she dreamed, being apparently translated into the happy years of her girlhood, that she had been "asked out," invited to lunch and dinner, and had at each meal been served with the most delicious titbits.

child.[3] Here is a second example. My nephew, twenty-two months of age, had been instructed to congratulate me on my birthday, and to give me a present of a small basket of cherries, which at that time of the year were scarce, being hardly in season. He seemed to find the task a difficult one, for he repeated again and again: "Cherries in it," and could not be induced to let the little basket go out of his hands. But he knew how to indemnify himself. He had, until then, been in the habit of telling his mother every morning that he had dreamt of the "white soldier," an officer of the guard in a white cloak, whom he had once admired in the street. On the day after the sacrifice on my birthday he woke up joyfully with the announcement, which could have referred only to a dream: *"He[r] man eaten all the cherries!"* [4]

---

[3] A more searching investigation into the psychic life of the child teaches us, of course, that sexual motives, in infantile forms, play a very considerable part, which has been too long overlooked, in the psychic activity of the child. This permits us to doubt to some extent the happiness of the child, as imagined later by adults. Cf. *Three Contributions to the Theory of Sex.*

[4] It should be mentioned that young children often have more complex and obscure dreams, while, on the other hand, adults, in certain circumstances, often have dreams of a simple and infantile character. How rich in unsuspected content the dreams of children no more than four or five years of age may be is shown by the examples in my *Analyse der Phobie eines fünfjährigen Knaben* (*Jahrbuch von Bleuler-Freud*, vol. i, 1909), and Jung's "Experiences Concerning the Psychic Life of the Child," translated by Brill, *American Journal of Psychology*, April, 1910. For analytically interpreted dreams of children, see also von Hug-Hellmuth, Putnam, Raalte, Spielrein, and Tausk; others by Banchieri, Busemann, Doglia, and especially Wigam, who emphasizes the wish-fulfilling tendency of such dreams. On the other hand, it seems that dreams of an infantile type reappear with especial frequency in adults who are transferred into the midst of unfamiliar conditions. Thus Otto Nordenskjöld, in his book, *Antarctic* (1904, vol. i, p. 336), writes as follows of the crew who spent the winter with him: "Very characteristic of the trend of our inmost thoughts were our dreams, which were never more vivid and more numerous. Even those of our comrades with whom dreaming was formerly exceptional had long stories to tell in the morning, when we exchanged our ex-

What animals dream of I do not know. A proverb for which I am indebted to one of my pupils professes to tell us, for it asks the question: "What does the goose dream of?" and answers: "Of maize." [5] The whole theory that the dream is the fulfilment of a wish is contained in these two sentences. [6]

---

periences in the world of phantasy. They all had reference to that outside world which was now so far removed from us, but they often fitted into our immediate circumstances. An especially characteristic dream was that in which one of our comrades believed himself back at school, where the task was assigned to him of skinning miniature seals, which were manufactured especially for purposes of instruction. Eating and drinking constituted the pivot around which most of our dreams revolved. One of us, who was especially fond of going to big dinner-parties, was delighted if he could report in the morning 'that he had had a three-course dinner.' Another dreamed of tobacco, whole mountains of tobacco; yet another dreamed of a ship approaching on the open sea under full sail. Still another dream deserves to be mentioned: The postman brought the post and gave a long explanation of why it was so long delayed; he had delivered it at the wrong address, and only with great trouble was he able to get it back. To be sure, we were often occupied in our sleep with still more impossible things, but the lack of phantasy in almost all the dreams which I myself dreamed, or heard others relate, was quite striking. It would certainly have been of great psychological interest if all these dreams could have been recorded. But one can readily understand how we longed for sleep. That alone could afford us everything that we all most ardently desired." I will continue by a quotation from Du Prel (p. 231): "Mungo Park, nearly dying of thirst on one of his African expeditions, dreamed constantly of the well-watered valleys and meadows of his home. Similarly Trenck, tortured by hunger in the fortress of Magdeburg, saw himself surrounded by copious meals. And George Back, a member of Franklin's first expedition, when he was on the point of death by starvation, dreamed continually and invariably of plenteous meals."

[5] A Hungarian proverb cited by Ferenczi states more explicitly that "the pig dreams of acorns, the goose of maize." A Jewish proverb asks: "Of what does the hen dream?"—"Of millet" (*Sammlung jüd. Sprichw. u. Redensarten.*, edit. by Bernstein, 2nd ed., p. 116).

[6] I am far from wishing to assert that no previous writer has ever thought of tracing a dream to a wish. Those interested in the subject will find that even in antiquity the physician Herophilos, who lived under the First Ptolemy, distinguished between three kinds of

We now perceive that we should have reached our theory of the hidden meaning of dreams by the shortest route had we merely consulted the vernacular. Proverbial wisdom, it is true, often speaks contemptuously enough of dreams—it apparently seeks to justify the scientists when it says that "dreams are bubbles"; but in colloquial language the dream is predominantly the gracious fulfiller of wishes. "I should never have imagined that in my wildest dreams," we exclaim in delight if we find that the reality surpasses our expectations.

---

dreams: dreams sent by the gods; natural dreams—those which come about whenever the soul creates for itself an image of that which is beneficial to it, and will come to pass; and mixed dreams—those which originate spontaneously from the juxtaposition of images, when we see that which we desire. From the examples collected by Scherner, J. Stärcke cites a dream which was described by the author himself as a wish-fulfilment. Scherner says: "The phantasy immediately fulfills the dreamer's wish, simply because this existed vividly in the mind." This dream belongs to the "emotional dreams." Akin to it are dreams due to "masculine and feminine erotic longing," and to "irritable moods." As will readily be seen, Scherner does not ascribe to the wish any further significance for the dream than to any other psychic condition of the waking state; least of all does he insist on the connection between the wish and the essential nature of the dream.

A. N. Whitehead

SCIENCE AND PHILOSOPHY

Alfred North Whitehead
[1861-   ]

The new locutions used by contemporary philosophers to communicate with one another become more and more involved and private. More particularly in the field of the philosophy of science does a code language seem unavoidable. Alfred North Whitehead, the distinguished British author of *Process and Reality*, co-author with Bertrand Russell of *Principia Mathematica* and Emeritus Professor of Philosophy at Harvard University, demands of his reader a changed orientation in language and ideas as he devaluates our previous concepts of science. He deplores the separation of science from the affirmations of our aesthetic and ethical experience; life and matter are interwoven into the pattern of process and should be fused instead of being isolated. He sustains the doctrine that "neither physical nature nor life can be understood unless we fuse them together as essential factors in the composition of 'really real' things whose interconnections and individual characters constitute the universe." One of the eight Lowell Lectures delivered at Harvard in 1925, "Science and Philosophy" is from *Science in the Modern World*.

SCIENCE AND PHILOSOPHY

A. N. WHITEHEAD

In the present lecture, it is my object to consider some reactions of science upon the stream of philosophic thought
during the modern centuries with which we are concerned.
I shall make no attempt to compress a history of modern
philosophy within the limits of one lecture. We shall merely
consider some contacts between science and philosophy, in
so far as they lie within the scheme of thought which it is
the purpose of these lectures to develop. For this reason the
whole of the great German idealistic movement will be
ignored, as being out of effective touch with its contemporary
science so far as reciprocal modification of concepts is concerned. Kant, from whom this movement took its rise, was
saturated with Newtonian physics, and with the ideas of the
great French physicists—such as Clairaut,[1] for instance—who
developed the Newtonian ideas. But the philosophers who
developed the Kantian school of thought, or who transformed
it into Hegelianism, either lacked Kant's background of
scientific knowledge, or lacked his potentiality of becoming

---

[1] Cf. the curious evidence of Kant's scientific reading in the
*Critique of Pure Reason, Transcendental Analytic, Second Analogy
of Experience*, where he refers to the phenomenon of capillary action. This is an unnecessarily complex illustration; a book resting
on a table would have equally well sufficed. But the subject had
just been adequately treated for the first time by Clairaut in an
appendix to his *Figure of the Earth*. Kant evidently had read this
appendix, and his mind was full of it.

a great physicist if philosophy had not absorbed his main energies.

The origin of modern philosophy is analogous to that of science, and is contemporaneous. The general trend of its development was settled in the seventeenth century, partly at the hands of the same men who established the scientific principles. This settlement of purpose followed upon a transitional period dating from the fifteenth century. There was in fact a general movement of European mentality, which carried along with its stream, religion, science and philosophy. It may shortly be characterised as being the direct recurrence to the original sources of Greek inspiration on the part of men whose spiritual shape had been derived from inheritance from the Middle Ages. There was therefore no revival of Greek mentality. Epochs do not rise from the dead. The principles of aesthetics and of reason, which animated the Greek civilisation, were reclothed in a modern mentality. Between the two there lay other religions, other systems of law, other anarchies, and other racial inheritances, dividing the living from the dead.

Philosophy is peculiarly sensitive to such differences. For, whereas you can make a replica of an ancient statue, there is no possible replica of an ancient state of mind. There can be no nearer approximation than that which a masquerade bears to real life. There may be understanding of the past, but there is a difference between the modern and the ancient reactions to the same stimuli.

In the particular case of philosophy, the distinction in tonality lies on the surface. Modern philosophy is tinged with subjectivism, as against the objective attitude of the ancients. The same change is to be seen in religion. In the early history of the Christian Church, the theological interest centred in discussions on the nature of God, the meaning of the Incarnation, and apocalyptic forecasts of the ultimate fate of the world. At the Reformation, the Church was torn asunder by dissension as to the individual experiences of believers in respect to justification. The individual subject of experience had been substituted for the total drama of all

reality. Luther asked, "How am I justified?"; modern philosophers have asked, "How do I have knowledge?" The
emphasis lies upon the subject of experience. This change
of standpoint is the work of Christianity in its pastoral aspect
of shepherding the company of believers. For century after
century it insisted upon the infinite worth of the individual
human soul. Accordingly, to the instinctive egotism of
physical desires, it has superadded an instinctive feeling of
justification for an egotism of intellectual outlook. Every
human being is the natural guardian of his own importance.
Without a doubt, this modern direction of attention em-
phasises truths of the highest value. For example, in the field
of practical life, it has abolished slavery, and has impressed
upon the popular imagination the primary rights of mankind.

Descartes, in his *Discourse on Method*, and in his *Meditations*, discloses with great clearness the general conceptions
which have since influenced modern philosophy. There is a
subject receiving experience: in the *Discourse* this subject is
always mentioned in the first person, that is to say, as being
Descartes himself. Descartes starts with himself as being a
mentality, which in virtue of its consciousness of its own
inherent presentations of sense and of thought, is thereby
conscious of its own existence as a unit entity. The subsequent history of philosophy revolves round the Cartesian
formulation of the primary datum. The ancient world takes
its stand upon the drama of the Universe, the modern world
upon the inward drama of the Soul. Descartes, in his *Meditations*, expressly grounds the existence of this inward drama
upon the possibility of error. There may be no correspondence with objective fact, and thus there must be a soul with
activities whose reality is purely derivative from itself. For
example, here is a quotation [2] from *Meditation II*: "But it
will be said that these presentations are false, and that I am
dreaming. Let it be so. At all events it is certain that I seem
to see light, hear a noise, and feel heat; this cannot be false,
and this is what in me is properly called perceiving (*sentire*),

---

[2] Quoted from Veitch's translation.

which is nothing else than thinking. From this I begin to know what I am with somewhat greater clearness and distinctness than heretofore." Again in *Meditation III*: ". . . ; for, as I before remarked, although the things which I perceive or imagine are perhaps nothing at all apart from me, I am nevertheless assured that those modes of consciousness which I call perceptions and imaginations, in as far only as they are modes of consciousness, exist in me."

The objectivism of the medieval and the ancient worlds passed over into science. Nature is there conceived as for itself, with its own mutual reactions. Under the recent influence of relativity, there has been a tendency towards subjectivist formulations. But, apart from this recent exception, nature, in scientific thought, has had its laws formulated without any reference to dependence on individual observers. There is, however, this difference between the older and the later attitudes towards science. The anti-rationalism of the moderns has checked any attempt to harmonise the ultimate concepts of science with ideas drawn from a more concrete survey of the whole of reality. The material, the space, the time, the various laws concerning the transition of material configurations, are taken as ultimate stubborn facts, not to be tampered with.

The effect of this antagonism to philosophy has been equally unfortunate both for philosophy and for science. In this lecture we are concerned with philosophy. Philosophers are rationalists. They are seeking to go behind stubborn and irreducible facts: they wish to explain in the light of universal principles the mutual reference between the various details entering into the flux of things. Also, they seek such principles as will eliminate mere arbitrariness; so that, whatever portion of fact is assumed or given, the existence of the remainder of things shall satisfy some demand of rationality. They demand meaning. In the words of Henry Sidgwick [3]— "It is the primary aim of philosophy to unify completely, bring into clear coherence, all departments of rational

---

[3] *Cf. Henry Sidgwick: A Memoir*, Appendix I.

thought, and this aim cannot be realised by any philosophy that leaves out of its view the important body of judgments and reasonings which form the subject matter of ethics." Accordingly, the bias towards history on the part of the physical and social sciences with their refusal to rationalise below some ultimate mechanism, has pushed philosophy out of the effective currents of modern life. It has lost its proper rôle as a constant critic of partial formulations. It has retreated into the subjectivist sphere of mind, by reason of its expulsion by science from the objectivist sphere of matter. Thus the evolution of thought in the seventeenth century coöperated with the enhanced sense of individual personality derived from the Middle Ages. We see Descartes taking his stand upon his own ultimate mind, which his philosophy assures him of; and asking about its relations to the ultimate matter—exemplified, in the second *Meditation*, by the human body and a lump of wax—which his science assumes. There is Aaron's rod, and the magicians' serpents; and the only question for philosophy is, which swallows which; or whether, as Descartes thought, they all lived happily together. In this stream of thought are to be found Locke, Berkeley, Hume, Kant. Two great names lie outside this list, Spinoza and Leibniz. But there is a certain isolation of both of them in respect to their philosophical influence so far as science is concerned; as though they had strayed to extremes which lie outside the boundaries of safe philosophy, Spinoza by retaining older ways of thought, and Leibniz by the novelty of his monads.

The history of philosophy runs curiously parallel to that of science. In the case of both, the seventeenth century set the stage for its two successors. But with the twentieth century a new act commences. It is an exaggeration to attribute a general change in a climate of thought to any one piece of writing, or to any one author. No doubt Descartes only expressed definitely and in decisive form what was already in the air of his period. Analogously, in attributing to William James the inauguration of a new stage in philosophy, we should be neglecting other influences of his time. But, admitting this, there still remains a certain fitness in contrasting his essay, *Does Consciousness Exist*, published in 1904, with Descartes' *Discourse on Method*, published in 1637. James clears the stage of the old paraphernalia; or rather he entirely alters its lighting. Take for example these two sentences from his essay: "To deny plumply that 'consciousness' exists seems so absurd on the face of it—for undeniably 'thoughts' do exist—that I fear some readers will follow me no farther. Let me then immediately explain that I mean only to deny that the word stands for an entity, but to insist most emphatically that it does stand for a function."

The scientific materialism and the Cartesian Ego were both challenged at the same moment, one by science and the other by philosophy, as represented by William James with his psychological antecedents; and the double challenge marks the end of a period which lasted for about two hundred and fifty years. Of course, "matter" and "consciousness" both express something so evident in ordinary experience that any philosophy must provide some things which answer to their respective meanings. But the point is that, in respect to both of them, the seventeenth century settlement was infected with a presupposition which is now challenged. James denies that consciousness is an entity, but admits that it is a function. The discrimination between an entity and a function is therefore vital to the understanding of the challenge which James is advancing against the older modes of thought. In the essay in question, the character which James assigns to consciousness is fully discussed. But he does not unambiguously explain what he means by the notion of an entity, which he refuses to apply to consciousness. In the sentence which immediately follows the one which I have already quoted, he says:

"There is, I mean, no aboriginal stuff or quality of being, contrasted with that of which material objects are made, out of which our thoughts of them are made; but there is a function in experience which thoughts perform, and for the performance of which this quality of being is invoked. That function is *knowing*. 'Consciousness' is supposed necessary to explain the fact that things not only are, but get reported, are known."

Thus James is denying that consciousness is a "stuff."

The term "entity," or even that of "stuff," does not fully tell its own tale. The notion of "entity" is so general that it may be taken to mean anything that can be thought about. You cannot think of mere nothing; and the something which is an object of thought may be called an entity. In this sense, a function is an entity. Obviously, this is not what James had in his mind.

In agreement with the organic theory of nature which I have been tentatively putting forward in these lectures, I shall for my own purposes construe James as denying exactly what Descartes asserts in his *Discourse* and his *Meditations*. Descartes discriminates two species of entities, *matter* and *soul*. The essence of matter is spatial extension; the essence of soul is its cogitation, in the full sense which Descartes assigns to the word *cogitare*. For example, in Section Fifty-three of Part I of his *Principles of Philosophy*, he enunciates: "That of every substance there is one principal attribute, as thinking of the mind, extension of the body." In the earlier, Fifty-first Section, Descartes states: "By substance we can conceive nothing else than a thing which exists in such a way as to stand in need of nothing beyond itself in order to its existence." Furthermore, later on, Descartes says: "For example, because any substance which ceases to endure ceases also to exist, duration is not distinct from substance except in thought; . . ." Thus we conclude that, for Descartes, minds and bodies exist in such a way as to stand in need of nothing beyond themselves individually (God only excepted, as being the foundation of all things); that both minds and bodies endure, because without endurance they would cease to exist; that spatial extension is the essential attribute of bodies; and that cogitation is the essential attribute of minds.

It is difficult to praise too highly the genius exhibited by Descartes in the complete sections of his *Principles* which deal with these questions. It is worthy of the century in which he writes, and of the clearness of the French intellect.

Descartes in his distinction between time and duration, and in his way of grounding time upon motion, and in his close relation between matter and extension, anticipates, as far as it was possible at his epoch, modern notions suggested by the doctrine of relativity, or by some aspects of Bergson's doctrine of the generation of things. But the fundamental principles are so set out as to presuppose independently existing substances with simple location in the community of temporal durations, and in the case of bodies, with simple location in the community of spatial extensions. Those principles lead straight to the theory of a materialistic, mechanistic nature, surveyed by cogitating minds. After the close of the seventeenth century, science took charge of the materialistic nature, and philosophy took charge of the cogitating minds. Some schools of philosophy admitted an ultimate dualism; and the various idealistic schools claimed that nature was merely the chief example of the cogitations of minds. But all schools admitted that Cartesian analysis of the ultimate elements of nature. I am excluding Spinoza and Leibniz from these statements as to the main stream of modern philosophy, as derivative from Descartes; though of course they were influenced by him, and in their turn influenced philosophers. I am thinking mainly of the effective contacts between science and philosophy.

This division of territory between science and philosophy was not a simple business; and in fact it illustrated the weakness of the whole cut-and-dried presupposition upon which it rested. We are aware of nature as an interplay of bodies, colours, sounds, scents, tastes, touches and other various bodily feelings, displayed as in space, in patterns of mutual separation by intervening volumes, and of individual shape. Also the whole is a flux, changing with the lapse of time. This systematic totality is disclosed to us as one complex of things. But the seventeenth century dualism cuts straight across it. The objective world of science was confined to mere spatial material with simple location in space and time, and subjected to definite rules as to its locomotion. The subjective world of philosophy annexed the colours, sounds, scents, tastes, touches, bodily feelings, as forming the subjective content of the cogitations of the individual minds. Both worlds shared in the general flux; but time, as measured, is assigned by Descartes to the cogitations of the observer's mind. There is obviously one fatal weakness to this scheme. The cogitations of mind exhibit themselves as holding up entities, such as colours for instance, before the mind as the termini of contemplation. But in this theory these colours are, after all, merely the furniture of the mind. Accordingly, the mind seems to be confined to its own private world of cogitations. The subject-object conformation of experience in its entirety lies within the mind as one of its private passions. This conclusion from the Cartesian data is the starting point from which Berkeley, Hume, and Kant developed their respective systems. And, antecedently to them, it was the point upon which Locke concentrated as being the vital question. Thus the question as to how any knowledge is obtained of the truly objective world of science becomes a problem of the first magnitude. Descartes states that the objective body is perceived by the intellect. He says (*Meditation II*): "I must, therefore, admit that I cannot even comprehend by imagination what the piece of wax is, and that it is the mind alone which perceives it. I speak of one piece in particular; for, as to wax in general, this is still more evident. But what is the piece of wax that can be perceived only by the mind? . . . The perception of it is neither an act of sight, of touch, nor of imagination, and never was either of these, though it might formerly seem so, but is simply an *intuition* (*inspectio*) of the mind, . . ." It must be noted that the Latin word "inspectio" is associated in its classical use with the notion of theory as opposed to practice.

The two great preoccupations of modern philosophy now lie clearly before us. The study of mind divides into psychology, or the study of mental functionings as considered in themselves and in their mutual relations, and into epistemology, or the theory of the knowledge of a common objective world. In other words, there is the study of the cogitations, *qua* passions of the mind, and their study *qua* leading to an inspection (*intuition*) of an objective world. This is a very uneasy division, giving rise to a host of perplexities whose consideration has occupied the intervening centuries.

As long as men thought in terms of physical notions for the objective world and of mentality for the subjective world, the setting out of the problem, as achieved by Descartes, sufficed as a starting point. But the balance has been upset by the rise of physiology. In the seventeenth century men passed from the study of physics to the study of philosophy. Towards the end of the nineteenth century, notably in Germany, men passed from the study of physiology to the study of psychology. The change in tone has been decisive. Of course, in the earlier period the intervention of the human body was fully considered, for example, by Descartes in Part V of the *Discourse on Method*. But the physiological instinct had not been developed. In considering the human body, Descartes thought with the outfit of a physicist; whereas the modern psychologists are clothed with the mentalities of medical physiologists. The career of William James is an example of this change in standpoint. He also possessed the clear, incisive genius which could state in a flash the exact point at issue.

The reason why I have put Descartes and James in close juxtaposition is now evident. Neither philosopher finished an epoch by a final solution of a problem. Their great merit is of the opposite sort. They each of them open an epoch by their clear formulation of terms in which thought could profitably express itself at particular stages of knowledge, one for the seventeenth century, the other for the twentieth century. In this respect, they are both to be contrasted with St. Thomas Aquinas, who expressed the culmination of Aristotelian scholasticism.

In many ways neither Descartes nor James were the most characteristic philosophers of their respective epochs. I should be disposed to ascribe these positions to Locke and to Bergson respectively, at least so far as concerns their relations to the science of their times. Locke developed the lines of thought which kept philosophy on the move; for example he emphasised the appeal to psychology. He initiated the age of epoch-making enquiries into urgent problems of limited scope. Undoubtedly, in so doing, he infected philosophy with something of the anti-rationalism of science. But the very groundwork of a fruitful methodology is to start from those clear postulates which must be held to be ultimate so far as concerns the occasion in question. The criticism of such methodological postulates is thus reserved for another opportunity. Locke discovered that the philosophical situation bequeathed by Descartes involved the problems of epistemology and psychology.

Bergson introduced into philosophy the organic conceptions of physiological science. He has most completely moved away from the static materialism of the seventeenth century. His protest against spatialisation is a protest against taking the Newtonian conception of nature as being anything except a high abstraction. His so-called anti-intellectualism should be construed in this sense. In some respects he recurs to Descartes; but the recurrence is accompanied with an instinctive grasp of modern biology.

There is another reason for associating Locke and Bergson. The germ of an organic theory of nature is to be found in Locke. His most recent expositor, Professor Gibson,[4] states that Locke's way of conceiving the identity of self-consciousness "like that of a living organism, involves a genuine transcending of the mechanical view of nature and of mind, embodied in the composition theory." But it is to be noticed that in the first place Locke wavers in his grasp of this position; and in the second place, what is more important still, he only applies his idea to self-consciousness. The physiological attitude has not yet established itself. The effect of physiology was to put mind back into nature. The neurologist traces first the effect of stimuli along the bodily nerves, then integration at nerve centres, and finally the rise of a projective reference beyond the body with a resulting motor

---

[4] Cf. his book, Locke's Theory of Knowledge and its Historical Relations, Camb. Univ. Press, 1917.

efficacy in renewed nervous excitement. In biochemistry, the
delicate adjustment of the chemical composition of the parts
to the preservation of the whole organism is detected. Thus
the mental cognition is seen as the reflective experience of a
totality, reporting for itself what it is in itself as one unit
occurrence. This unit is the integration of the sum of its
partial happenings, but it is not their numerical aggregate.
It has its own unity as an event. This total unity, considered
as an entity for its own sake, is the prehension into unity of
the patterned aspects of the universe of events. Its knowledge
of itself arises from its own relevance to the things of which
it prehends the aspects. It knows the world as a system of
mutual relevance, and thus sees itself as mirrored in other
things. These other things include more especially the various
parts of its own body.

It is important to discriminate the bodily pattern, which
endures, from the bodily event, which is pervaded by the
enduring pattern, and from the parts of the bodily event.
The parts of the bodily event are themselves pervaded by
their own enduring patterns, which form elements in the
bodily pattern. The parts of the body are really portions of
the environment of the total bodily event, but so related that
their mutual aspects, each in the other, are peculiarly effective in modifying the pattern of either. This arises from the
intimate character of the relation of whole to part. Thus
the body is a portion of the environment for the part, and the
part is a portion of the environment for the body; only they
are peculiarly sensitive, each to modifications of the other.
This sensitiveness is so arranged that the part adjusts itself
to preserve the stability of the pattern of the body. It is a
particular example of the favourable environment shielding
the organism. The relation of part to whole has the special
reciprocity associated with the notion of organism, in which
the part is for the whole; but this relation reigns throughout
nature and does not start with the special case of the higher
organisms.

Further, viewing the question as a matter of chemistry,
there is no need to construe the actions of each molecule in

a living body by its exclusive particular reference to the pattern of the complete living organism. It is true that each molecule is affected by the aspect of this pattern as mirrored in it, so as to be otherwise than what it would have been if placed elsewhere. In the same way, under some circumstances an electron may be a sphere, and under other circumstances an egg-shaped volume. The mode of approach to the problem, so far as science is concerned, is merely to ask if molecules exhibit in living bodies properties which are not to be observed amid inorganic surroundings. In the same way, in a magnetic field soft iron exhibits magnetic properties which are in abeyance elsewhere. The prompt self-preservative actions of living bodies, and our experience of the physical actions of our bodies following the determinations of will, suggest the modification of molecules in the body as the result of the total pattern. It seems possible that there may be physical laws expressing the modification of the ultimate basic organisms when they form part of higher organisms with adequate compactness of pattern. It would, however, be entirely in consonance with the empirically observed action of environments, if the direct effects of aspects as between the whole body and its parts were negligible. We should expect transmission. In this way the modification of total pattern would transmit itself by means of a series of modifications of a descending series of parts, so that finally the modification of the cell changes its aspect in the molecule, thus effecting a corresponding alteration in the molecule—or in some subtler entity. Thus the question for physiology is the question of the physics of molecules in cells of different characters.

We can now see the relation of psychology to physiology and to physics. The private psychological field is merely the event considered from its own standpoint. The unity of this field is the unity of the event. But it is the event as one entity, and not the event as a sum of parts. The relations of the parts, to each other and to the whole, are their aspects, each in the other. A body for an external observer is the aggregate of the aspects for him of the body as a whole, and also of the body as a sum of parts. For the external observer the aspects of shape and of sense-objects are dominant, at least for cognition. But we must also allow for the possibility that we can detect in ourselves direct aspects of the mentalities of higher organisms. The claim that the cognition of alien mentalities must necessarily be by means of indirect inferences from aspects of shape and of sense-objects is wholly unwarranted by this philosophy of organism. The fundamental principle is that whatever merges into actuality, implants its aspects in every individual event.

Further, even for self-cognition, the aspects of the parts of our own bodies partly take the form of aspects of shape, and of sense-objects. But that part of the bodily event, in respect to which the cognitive mentality is associated, is for itself the unit psychological field. Its ingredients are not referent to the event itself; they are aspects of what lies beyond that event. Thus the self-knowledge inherent in the bodily event is the knowledge of itself as a complex unity, whose ingredients involve all reality beyond itself, restricted under the limitation of its pattern of aspects. Thus we know ourselves as a function of unification of a plurality of things which are other than ourselves. Cognition discloses an event as being an activity, organising a real togetherness of alien things. But this psychological field does not depend on its cognition; so that this field is still a unit event as abstracted from its self-cognition.

Accordingly, consciousness will be the function of knowing. But what is known is already a prehension of aspects of the one real universe. These aspects are aspects of other events as mutually modifying, each the others. In the pattern of aspects they stand in their pattern of mutual relatedness.

The aboriginal data in terms of which the pattern weaves itself are the aspects of shapes, of sense-objects, and of other eternal objects whose self-identity is not dependent on the flux of things. Wherever such objects have ingression into the general flux, they interpret events, each to the other. They are here in the perceiver; but, as perceived by him, they convey for him something of the total flux which is beyond himself. The subject-object relation takes its origin in the double rôle of these eternal objects. They are modifications of the subject, but only in their character of conveying aspects of other subjects in the community of the universe. Thus no individual subject can have independent reality, since it is a prehension of limited aspects of subjects other than itself.

The technical phrase "subject-object" is a bad term for the fundamental situation disclosed in experience. It is really reminiscent of the Aristotelian "subject-predicate." It already presupposes the metaphysical doctrine of diverse subjects qualified by their private predicates. This is the doctrine of subjects with private worlds of experience. If this be granted, there is no escape from solipsism. The point is that the phrase "subject-object" indicates a fundamental entity underlying the objects. Thus the "objects," as thus conceived, are merely the ghosts of Aristotelian predicates. The primary situation disclosed in cognitive experience is "ego-object amid objects." By this I mean that the primary fact is an impartial world transcending the "here-now" which marks the ego-object, and transcending the "now" which is the spatial world of simultaneous realisation. It is a world also including the actuality of the past, and the limited potentiality of the future, together with the complete world of abstract potentiality, the realm of eternal objects, which transcends, and finds exemplification in and comparison with, the actual course of realisation. The ego-object, as consciousness here-now, is conscious of its experient essence as constituted by its internal relatedness to the world of realities, and to the world of ideas. But the ego-object, in being thus constituted, is within the world of realities, and exhibits itself as an organism requiring the ingression of ideas for the purpose of this status among realities. This question of consciousness must be reserved for treatment on another occasion.

The point to be made for the purpose of the present discussion is that a philosophy of nature as organic must start at the opposite end to that requisite for a materialistic philosophy. The materialistic starting point is from independently existing substances, matter and mind. The matter suffers modifications of its external relations of locomotion, and the mind suffers modifications of its contemplated objects. There are, in this materialistic theory, two sorts of independent substances, each qualified by their appropriate passions. The organic starting point is from the analysis of process as the realisation of events disposed in an interlocked community. The event is the unit of things real. The emergent enduring pattern is the stabilisation of the emergent achievement so as to become a fact which retains its identity throughout the process. It will be noted that endurance is not primarily the property of enduring beyond itself, but of enduring within itself. I mean that endurance is the property of finding its pattern reproduced in the temporal parts of the total event. It is in this sense that a total event carries an enduring pattern. There is an intrinsic value identical for the whole and for its succession of parts. Cognition is the emergence, into some measure of individualised reality, of the general substratum of activity, poising before itself possibility, actuality, and purpose.

It is equally possible to arrive at this organic conception of the world if we start from the fundamental notions of modern physics, instead of, as above, from psychology and physiology. In fact by reason of my own studies in mathematics and mathematical physics, I did in fact arrive at my convictions in this way. Mathematical physics presumes in the first place an electromagnetic field of activity pervading space and time. The laws which condition this field are nothing else than the conditions observed by the general activity of the flux of the world, as it individualises itself in the events. In physics, there is an abstraction. The science ignores what anything is in itself. Its entities are merely considered in respect to their extrinsic reality, that is to say, in respect to their aspects in other things. But the abstraction reaches even further than that; for it is only the aspects in other things, as modifying the spatio-temporal specifications of the life histories of those other things, which count. The intrinsic reality of the observer comes in: I mean what the observer is for himself is appealed to. For example, the fact that he will see red or blue enters into scientific statements. But the red which the observer sees does not in truth enter into science. What is relevant is merely the bare diversity of the observer's red experiences from all of his other experiences. Accordingly, the intrinsic character of the observer is merely relevant in order to fix the self-identical individuality of the physical entities. These entities are only considered as agencies in fixing the routes in space and in time of the life histories of enduring entities.

The phraseology of physics is derived from the materialistic ideas of the seventeenth century. But we find that, even in its extreme abstraction, what it is really presupposing is the organic theory of aspects as explained above. First, consider any event in empty space where the word "empty" means devoid of electrons, or protons, or of any other form of electric charge. Such an event has three rôles in physics. In the first place, it is the actual scene of an adventure of energy, either as its *habitat* or as the locus of a particular stream of energy: anyhow, in this rôle the energy is there, either as located in space during the time considered, or as streaming through space.

In its second rôle, the event is a necessary link in the pattern of transmission, by which the character of every event receives some modification from the character of every other event.

In its third rôle, the event is the repository of a possibility, as to what would happen to an electric charge, either by way of deformation or of locomotion, if it should have happened to be there.

If we modify our assumption by considering an event which includes in itself a portion of the life-history of an electric charge, then the analysis of its three rôles still remains; except that the possibility embodied in the third rôle is now transformed into an actuality. In this replacement of possibility by actuality, we obtain the distinction between empty and occupied events.

Recurring to the empty events, we note the deficiency in them of individuality of intrinsic content. Considering the first rôle of an empty event, as being a *habitat* of energy, we note that there is no individual discrimination of an individual bit of energy, either as statically located, or as an element in the stream. There is simply a quantitative determination of activity, without individualisation of the activity in itself. This lack of individualisation is still more evident in the second and third rôles. An empty event is something in itself, but it fails to realise a stable individuality of content. So far as its content is concerned, the empty event is one realised element in a general scheme of organised activity.

Some qualification is required when the empty event is the scene of the transmission of a definite train of recurrent waveforms. There is now a definite pattern which remains permanent in the event. We find here the first faint trace of enduring individuality. But it is individuality without the faintest capture of originality: for it is merely a permanence arising solely from the implication of the event in a larger scheme of patterning.

Turning now to the examination of an occupied event, the electron has a determinate individuality. It can be traced throughout its life-history through a variety of events. A collection of electrons, together with the analogous atomic charges of positive electricity, forms a body such as we ordinarily perceive. The simplest body of this kind is a molecule, and a set of molecules forms a lump of ordinary matter, such as a chair, or a stone. Thus a charge of electricity is the mark of individuality of content, as additional to the individuality of an event in itself. This individuality of content is the strong point of the materialistic doctrine.

It can, however, be equally well explained on the theory of organism. When we look into the function of the electric charge, we note that its rôle is to mark the origination of a pattern which is transmitted through space and time. It is the key of some particular pattern. For example, the field of force in any event is to be constructed by attention to the adventures of electrons and protons, and so also are the streams and distributions of energy. Further, the electric waves find their origin in the vibratory adventures of these charges. Thus the transmitted pattern is to be conceived as the flux of aspects throughout space and time derived from the life history of the atomic charge. The individualisation of the charge arises by a conjunction of two characters, in the first place by the continued identity of its mode of functioning as a key for the determination of a diffusion of pattern; and, in the second place, by the unity and continuity of its life history.

We may conclude, therefore, that the organic theory represents directly what physics actually does assume respecting its ultimate entities. We also notice the complete futility of these entities, if they are conceived as fully concrete individuals. So far as physics is concerned, they are wholly occupied in moving each other about, and they have no reality outside this function. In particular for physics, there is no intrinsic reality.

It is obvious that the basing of philosophy upon the presupposition of organism must be traced back to Leibniz.[5] His monads are for him the ultimately real entities. But he retained the Cartesian substances with their qualifying passions, as also equally expressing for him the final characterisation of real things. Accordingly for him there was no concrete reality of internal relations. He had therefore on his hands two distinct points of view. One was that the final real entity is an organising activity, fusing ingredients into a unity, so that this unity is the reality. The other point of view is that the final real entities are substances supporting qualities. The first point of view depends upon the acceptance of internal relations binding together all reality. The latter is inconsistent with the reality of such relations. To combine these two points of view, his monads were therefore windowless; and their passions merely mirrored the universe by the divine arrangement of a preëstablished harmony. This system thus presupposed an aggregate of independent entities. He did not discriminate the event, as the unit of experience, from the enduring organism as its stabilisation into importance, and from

---

[5] Cf. Bertrand Russell, *The Philosophy of Leibniz*, for the suggestion of this line of thought.

the cognitive organism as expressing an increased completeness of individualisation. Nor did he admit the many-termed relations, relating sense-data to various events in diverse ways. These many-termed relations are in fact the perspectives which Leibniz does admit, but only on the condition that they are purely qualities of the organising monads. The difficulty really arises from the unquestioned acceptance of the notion of simple location as fundamental for space and time, and from the acceptance of the notion of independent individual substance as fundamental for a real entity. The only road open to Leibniz was thus the same as that later taken by Berkeley [in a prevalent interpretation of his meaning], namely an appeal to a *deus ex machina* who was capable of rising superior to the difficulties of metaphysics.

In the same way as Descartes introduced the tradition of thought which kept subsequent philosophy in some measure of contact with the scientific movement, so Leibniz introduced the alternative tradition that the entities, which are the ultimate actual things, are in some sense procedures of organisation. This tradition has been the foundation of the great achievements of German philosophy. Kant reflected the two traditions, one upon the other. Kant was a scientist, but the schools derivative from Kant have had but slight effect on the mentality of the scientific world. It should be the task of the philosophical schools of this century to bring together the two streams into an expression of the world-picture derived from science, and thereby end the divorce of science from the affirmations of our aesthetic and ethical experiences.

Sir James Jeans

SOME PROBLEMS

OF PHILOSOPHY

Sir James Jeans
[1877–1946]

Modern scientists are conducting a critical examination of the methods by which scientific knowledge has been acquired. Their researches have made all science undergo change and become more and more contiguous to philosophy. For Sir James Jeans, the British physicist whose work on radiation and stellar dynamics had brought him world eminence, the two fields are closely related, and he was convinced that "philosophy has become less concerned with ourselves and more concerned with the universe outside ourselves." The new physics, dealing with quanta, laws of radioactivity and phenomena on the atomic and sub-atomic scale, has revolutionized our conceptions of classical physics in its analysis of matter and has created not only a new mathematical symbolism, but a revision of our ideas of time and space, determinism and free will. The lucidity with which Jeans expounded his scientific and philosophical principles makes their interrelation, in all their complexity, understandable and inevitable. "Some Problems of Philosophy" is the concluding portion of his book, *Physics and Philosophy*.

SOME PROBLEMS OF
PHILOSOPHY

SIR JAMES JEANS

Because we are human beings and not mere animals, we try to discover as much as we can about the world in which our lives are cast. We have seen that there is only one method of gaining such knowledge—the method of science, which consists in a direct questioning of nature by observation and experiment.

The first thing we learn from such questioning is that the world is rational; its happenings are not determined by caprice but by law. There exists what we have called a "pattern of events," and the primary aim of physical science is the discovery of this pattern. This, as we have seen, will be capable of description only in mathematical terms.

The new quantum theory explained in the preceding chapter has provided a mathematical description of the pattern of events which is believed to be complete and perfect. For it enables us—in principle at least—to predict every possible phenomenon of physics, and not one of its predictions has so far proved to be wrong. In a sense, then, we might say that theoretical physics has achieved the main purpose of its being, and that nothing remains but to work out the details.

But we not only wish to predict phenomena, but also to understand them. Thus it is not surprising that philosophy and science have alike found this mathematical description unsatisfying, and have tried to attach concrete meanings to the mathematical symbols involved—to replace unintelligible universals by intelligible particulars. We may argue that if there is a pattern, there must be some sort of loom for ever weaving it; we want to know what this loom is, how it works, and why it works thus rather than otherwise.

The physicists of the last century thought that one of the primary concerns of science should be to devise models or draw pictures to illustrate the workings of this loom. It was supposed that a model which reproduced all the phenomena of a science, and so made it possible to predict them all, must in some way correspond to the reality underlying the phenomena. But obviously this cannot be so. After one perfect model had been found, a second of equal perfection might appear, and as both models could not correspond to reality, we should have at least one perfect model which did not correspond to reality. Thus we could never be sure that any model corresponded to reality. In brief, we can never have certain knowledge as to the nature of reality.

We know now that there is no danger of even one perfect model appearing—at least of a kind which is intelligible to our minds. For a model or picture will only be intelligible to us if it is made up of ideas which are already in our minds. Of such ideas some, as for instance the ideas of abstract mathematics, have no special relation to our particular world; all those which have must, as we have seen, have entered our minds through the gateways of the senses. These are restricted by our having only five senses of which only two are at all important for our present purpose.

A detailed investigation of the sources of our ideas has shown that there is only one type of model or picture which could be intelligible to our restricted minds, namely one in mechanical terms. Yet a review of recent physics has shown that all attempts at mechanical models or pictures have failed and must fail. For a mechanical model or picture must represent things as happening in space and time, while it has recently become clear that the ultimate processes of nature neither occur in, nor admit of representation in, space and time. Thus an understanding of the ultimate processes of nature is for ever beyond our reach; we shall never be able—even in imagination—to open the case of our watch and see how the wheels go round. The true object of scientific study can never be the realities of nature, but only our own observations on nature.

THE PARTICLE-PICTURE AND THE WAVE-PICTURE

Although there can be no complete picture of the workings of nature which will be intelligible to our minds, yet we can still draw pictures to represent partial aspects of the truth in an intelligible way. The new physics places two such partial pictures before us—one in terms of particles, and one in terms of waves. Neither of these can of course tell the whole truth.

In the same way, an atlas may contain two maps of North America drawn on different projections: neither of them will represent the whole truth, but each will faithfully represent some aspect of it. An equal-area projection, for instance, represents the relative areas of any two regions accurately, but their shapes wrongly, while a Mercator projection represents the shapes rightly, but the areas wrongly. So long as we can only draw our maps on flat pieces of paper, such imperfections are inevitable; they are the price we pay for limiting our maps to the kind that can be bound up in an atlas.

The pictures we draw of nature show similar limitations; these are the price we pay for limiting our pictures of nature to the kinds that can be understood by our minds. As we cannot draw one perfect picture, we make two imperfect pictures and turn to one or the other according as we want one property or another to be accurately delineated. Our observations tell us which is the right picture to use for each particular purpose—for instance, we know we must use the particle-picture for the photo-electric effect, the wave-picture for illumination effects, and so on.

Yet some properties of nature are so far-reaching and general that neither picture can depict them properly of itself.

In such cases we must appeal to both pictures, and these some-times give us different and inconsistent information. Where, then, shall we find the truth?

For instance, is nature governed by causal laws or not? The particle-picture answers: No, the motions of my particles can only be compared to the random jumps of kangaroos, with no causal laws controlling the jumps. But the wave-picture says: Yes, at every instant my waves follow uniquely, and so inevitably, from those of the preceding instant.

Or again, is reality ultimately atomic or is it not? The particle-picture tells us of a material world in which matter, electricity and radiation occur only in indivisible units; the wave-picture merely tells us that it knows of none of these things.

The two pictures seem to tell different stories, but we must remember that they are not equally trustworthy. The particle-picture embodies the findings of the old quantum theory which we discussed in Chapter v. This proved to be both in-accurate and incomplete, so that the new quantum theory was brought into being to remedy its deficiencies—which it has successfully done. The wave-picture is not only a pictorial representation of the new quantum theory, but also, as regards the mathematical facts involved, is its exact equivalent. Thus the predictions of the wave-picture cannot be other than true, whereas those of the particle-picture may or may not be true. When there is a conflict, the evidence of the wave-picture must be accepted, while we may be sure that the con-flict results from some imperfection of the particle-picture. In the instances just given, it is not difficult to trace out a possible origin for the conflict.

The mathematical laws of the quantum theory show that radiant energy is transferred by complete quanta. But in de-picting a beam of light as a hail of bullet-like photons, the particle-picture is clearly going further than the facts war-rant. A man's balance at the bank always changes by an integral number of pence, but this does not justify him in pic-turing its changes as caused by a flight of bronze pennies. If he does, his child may ask him what decides which particular pennies shall be sent to pay the rent. The father may reply: Mere chance—a foolish answer but no more foolish than the question. In the same way, if we make the initial mistake of depicting radiation as identifiable photons, we shall have to call on mere chance to get us out of our difficulties—and here is the origin of the indeterminacy of the particle-picture.

For instance, when a beam of light falls on a half-silvered mirror, the particle-picture shows half the photons being turned back by the silvering of the mirror, while the other half pass on their way undisturbed. We ask at once: What singles out the lucky photons? It is a question which had confronted Newton's corpuscular theory of light, and he had answered it by a vague wave of the hand towards Fortune's wheel—his corpuscles, he had said, were "subject to alternate fits of easy transmission and easy reflection." In the same way, if we depict radiation as identifiable photons, we can find nothing but the finger of Fate to separate the sheep from the goats. But the finger of Fate, like the sheep and the goats, is mere pictorial detail. As soon as we turn to the more trustworthy wave-picture, all this pictorial drapery drops out of the picture, and we find a complete determinism. Yet this determinism, as we have seen, does not control events, but our knowledge of events. The wave-picture does not show the future following inexorably from the present, but the imperfections of our future knowledge following inexorably from the imperfections of our present knowledge.

What is true of radiation is true also of electricity. We know that electricity is always transferred from place to place by complete electron-units, but this does not justify us in replacing a current of electricity by a shower of identifiable particles. Indeed, the quantum theory definitely tells us that we must not do so. When two balls A, B collide on a billiard-table, A may go to the right and B to the left. When two electrons A, B collide, we might also expect to be able to say that A would go to the right and B to the left; actually we cannot, because we have no right to identify the two electrons which went into the collision with the two which come out; we must rather think of the two electrons A and B which entered into collision as combining into a drop of electric fluid, which then breaks up again to form two new electrons C and D. If we ask which way A will go after collision, the true answer is that A no longer exists. The superficial answer is that it is an even chance whether A goes to the right or to the left, for it is a toss-up whether we identify A with C or D. But the toss-up is not in nature; it is in our minds.

We see, then, that the particle-picture goes wrong in attributing indeterminism to nature; it is not a property of nature, but of our way of looking at nature. The particle-picture further goes wrong in attributing atomicity to the ingredients of the material world, whether matter or radiation; the atomicity does not reside in these ingredients but in the events which affect them. To return to our former analogy, all payments into and out of a bank account are by complete mathematical pence, but they do not consist of bronze pennies flying hither and thither. But we can now carry this train of ideas a little further; we know matter only through the energy or particles it emits, but this provides no warrant for assuming that matter itself consists of atoms either of substance or of energy—this would be like assuming that our balance at the bank must consist of a pile of bronze pennies.

New Philosophical Principles

We have seen that efforts to discover the true nature of reality are necessarily doomed to failure, so that if we are to progress further it must be by taking some other objective and utilizing some new philosophical principles of which we have not so far made use. Two such suggest themselves. The first is the principle of what Leibniz described as *probable reasoning;* we give up the quest for certain knowledge, and concentrate on that one of the various alternatives before us which seems to be most probably true. But how are we to decide which of the alternatives is most likely to be true?

This question has been much discussed of late, particularly by H. Jeffreys. For our purpose it is sufficient to rely on what may be described as the *simplicity postulate;* this asserts that of two alternatives, the simpler is likely to be the nearer to the truth.

Let us try to illustrate these new principles by considering a simple, although very artificial, analogy.

Let us imagine that in the centre of Europe there lives a peasant who has never seen or heard of the sea, and cannot even read about it, but is in possession of a super-perfect radio-set which can pick up messages from every ship in the world. Suppose further that every ship is continually sending out its position in a standard form, such as

$$\text{"Queen Mary," } + 41^\circ \ 10', - 72^\circ \ 26'$$

this meaning that, at the moment of speaking, the ship "Queen Mary" is in latitude $41^\circ \ 10'$ north and longitude $72^\circ \ 26'$ west.

At first he may merely amuse himself by listening to the various messages, but after a time he may take to recording them and, if he is of an inquiring turn of mind, he may try to discover some method or order in them. He will soon notice that all latitudes lie between $+ 90^\circ$ and $- 90^\circ$, and all longitudes between $+ 180^\circ$ and $- 180^\circ$. If he then tries plotting out these numbers on squared paper, he will find that successive positions of any one ship form a continuous chain, and may begin to construct a mental picture for himself by thinking of the senders of the messages as moving objects. He will then find that each supposed object moves at an approximately uniform rate on his chart, although this law is not exact or universal. A ship may move from longitude $+ 170^\circ$ to $+ 174^\circ$ in one day, and on to $+ 178^\circ$ the next, but the third day may take it to $- 178^\circ$, an apparent journey of 356°. Further, a ship may move at a regular 4° a day when its latitude is near to 0°, but this daily motion will increase as the latitude increases, and may shoot up almost beyond limits if ever the latitude approaches to 90°.

If, notwithstanding their peculiar nature, our listener succeeds in formulating exact laws, he will then be able to predict the motions of the ships. Or, to be more precise, he will be able, without assuming that he is dealing with either motions or ships, to predict what he will hear when he turns on his radio. He can predict the result of every experiment he can perform, since the only experiment within his power is to turn a knob and listen.

Those who are content with a positivist conception of the aims of science will feel that he is in an entirely satisfactory position; he has discovered the pattern of events, and so can predict accurately; what more can he want? A mental picture would be an added luxury, but also a useless luxury. For if the picture did not bear any resemblance at all to the reality it would be valueless, and if it did it would be unintelligible, since we are supposing that our listener cannot imagine either sea or ships.

PROBABLE REASONING

At this point, let us notice that the supposition that the signals came from moving objects was hypothetical in the sense that nothing in the observations compelled it—from the nature of the case the observer is debarred from knowing whether the signals come from moving objects or not. It expresses a possibility and not certain knowledge, and can never be proved true. In real science also a hypothesis can never be proved true. If it is negatived by future observations we shall know it is wrong, but if future observations confirm it we shall never be able to say it is right, since it will always be at the mercy of still further observations. A science which confines itself to correlating the phenomena can never learn anything about the reality underlying the phenomena, while a science which goes further than this, and introduces hypotheses about reality, can never acquire certain knowledge of a positive kind about reality; in whatever way we proceed, this is for ever denied us.

Certain knowledge is, however, equally beyond our reach in most departments of life. Oftener than not, we cannot wait for certain knowledge, but order our affairs in the light of probabilities. There is no reason why we should not do the same in our efforts to understand the universe, provided we always bear in mind that we are discussing probabilities and not certainties.

The philosopher does it as much as the rest of us. I am conscious only of my own thoughts and sensations, so that, for aught I know to the contrary, I may be the only conscious being in the universe. If I choose on these grounds to become a solipsist—i.e. one who supposes that he is the only conscious being in the whole universe—nothing can definitely prove me wrong. But my sensations inform me of other objects that look like my body, and seem to experience sensations and thoughts like my own. I assume, although only on grounds of probable reasoning, that these other objects are beings essentially similar to myself. If we refused to admit probability considerations, we ought all to be solipsists; with things as they are, any genuine solipsists there may be are kept safely shut up.

The physicist also relies on probability considerations every day of his life. He measures the wave-lengths of spectral lines in the light emitted by Sirius, and finds they are identical with those in the light emitted by hydrogen at a temperature of $10,000°$ C. He concludes without more ado that there are atoms of hydrogen at $10,000°$ in Sirius. There is no proof of this and never can be, for we shall never be able to go to Sirius to find out. But the probabilities against the agreement being a mere coincidence are so overwhelming that the physicist feels justified in disregarding this possibility, and announces that this part of the light of Sirius comes from hydrogen at a temperature of $10,000°$.

In these two instances, the philosopher and physicist are both guided by probable reasoning rather than by certain deductions. If our radio listener allows himself to be guided by similar considerations, he may decide provisionally that his signals come from moving objects. This idea may lead him to think of pasting together his $+180°$ and $-180°$ lines, thus transforming his plane diagram into a cylinder. This simplifies the situation enormously, for it now seems the most natural thing in the world that a sequence of readings equidistant in time should read 170°, 174°, 178°, — 178°, etc. But he is still faced with the peculiarity that his moving objects traverse more degrees of longitude per day in high latitudes than in low. With a little ingenuity, he may further think of crumpling in the two ends of his cylinder, and so making the degrees of longitude smaller in higher latitudes. If he finally tries the experiment of replacing his cylinder by a sphere, he will find that his laws assume an exceedingly simple form from which all oddity has disappeared. Each ship takes the shortest course from point to point, and performs its journey at a uniform speed.

Even the original laws were true laws, since they enabled the listener to predict accurately. But they were not simple, because their discoverer had expressed them against a bad background. As soon as he changed from one background to another—from a rectangular projection to a spherical surface —the laws changed from being strange but true to being simple and true. Precisely for this reason, most men will consider that the second set of laws was preferable. Without assigning any special attributes to the Designer of the universe, we probably feel that the simpler laws are likely to be in some way closer to that reality which we can never understand, than complicated and odd laws—in brief, that artificiality comes from man, and not from nature. In the example just considered, it is certainly more true to say that the earth's surface is spherical than to picture it as plane.

And in the real problems of science also, it is true, as Einstein has remarked, that "In every important advance the physicist finds that the fundamental laws are simplified more and more as experimental research advances. He is astonished to notice how sublime order emerges from what appeared to be chaos. And this cannot be traced back to the workings of his own mind but is due to a quality that is inherent in the world of perception."

This not only shows that our minds are in some way in harmony with the workings of nature—a harmony which

Einstein compares with the pre-established harmony of Leibniz—but also that our investigations of nature are proceeding on the right lines; it further shows that the simplicity which is inherent in nature is of the kind which *our minds* adjudge to be simple. Indeed any other kind of simplicity would probably escape our notice.

THE SIMPLICITY POSTULATE

This suggests the introduction of a further principle, if not into the technique of scientific investigation at least into the practice of philosophical discussion—the principle of simplicity. When two hypotheses are possible, we provisionally choose that which our minds adjudge to be the simpler, on the supposition that this is the more likely to lead in the direction of the truth. It includes as a special case the principle of Occam's razor—*entia non multiplicanda praeter necessitatem.*

There can of course be no absolute criterion as to which of two hypotheses is the simpler; in the last resort this must be a matter of private judgment. In the fictitious example we have just been discussing there could be no room for doubt, but in actual scientific practice there have been cases in which two investigators have differed as to which of two hypotheses was the simpler, as for example with the one-fluid and two-fluid theories of electricity.

The history of science provides many instances of situations such as we have been discussing. To begin with the most obvious, Ptolemy and his Arabian successors built up the famous system of cycles and epicycles which enabled them to predict the future positions of the planets with almost perfect precision. At first, the sun, moon and stars were supposed to revolve round the fixed central earth, while the planets revolved about other centres which themselves revolved about the earth. It was soon found that this did not quite fit the facts, and the orbits had to be changed to slightly eccentric circles—neither the earth nor the moving centres were any longer at the exact centres of the circles which were described around them. Finally, as the planetary motions came to be known to a still higher degree of accuracy, epicycle was piled on epicycle until the system became exceedingly complex.

Many, indeed, felt that it was too complex to correspond to the ultimate facts. In the thirteenth century, Alphonso X of Castile is reported to have said that if the heavens were really like that, "I could have given the Deity good advice, had He consulted me at their creation." At a later date Copernicus also thought the Ptolemaic system too complex to be true and, after years of thought and labour, showed that the planetary motions could be described much more simply if the background of the motions were changed: Ptolemy had assumed a fixed earth; Copernicus substituted a fixed sun. We now know that the sun can no more be said to be at rest, in any absolute sense, than the earth; it is one of the thousands of millions of stars which together form the galactic system, and it moves round the centre of this system just as the earth moves round the centre of the solar system. And even this centre of the galactic system cannot be said to be at rest. For millions of galactic systems can be seen in the sky, all pretty much like our own, and all in motion relative to our own galaxy and to one another. No one of all these galaxies has a better claim than any other to constitute a standard of "rest" from which the "motions" on the others can be measured. Nevertheless, many complications are avoided by imagining that the sun and not the earth is at rest. Neither the sun nor the earth is at rest in any absolute sense, and yet it is, in a sense, nearer to the truth to say that the earth moves round a fixed sun than to say that the sun moves round a fixed earth.

Copernicus had still to retain a few minor epicycles to make his system agree with the facts of observation. This, as we now know, was the inevitable consequence of his assumption that the planetary orbits were circular: neither he nor anyone else had so far dared to challenge Aristotle's dictum that the planets must necessarily move in circular orbits, because the circle was the only perfect curve. As soon as Kepler substituted ellipses for the Copernican circles, epicycles were seen to be unnecessary, and the theory of planetary motions assumed an exceedingly simple form—the form it was to retain for more than three centuries, until an even greater simplicity was imparted to it by the relativity theory of Einstein, to which we shall come in a moment.

The restricted (or physical) theory of relativity provides a second illustration of the same thing. The Newtonian mechanics, with its background of absolute space and time, had explained the motion of objects well enough so long as their speeds of motion were not comparable with that of light. But, as experiment ultimately showed, it could only explain the motion of rapidly moving objects at the price of introducing extreme complications. Objects in rapid motion had to contract and assume new shapes, while no one could ever quite say what happened to objects in rapid rotation. The theory of relativity introduced a tremendous simplification into the whole subject when it discarded Newton's absolute space and time as a background, and substituted the new space-time unity.

The generalized (or gravitational) theory of relativity provides an even more striking instance of the same thing. The Newtonian theory of gravitation, which required the planets to move round the sun in elliptical orbits, gave an excellent account of the movements of the outer planets, but failed with the inner. Attempts were made to remedy this by slightly altering the Newtonian law of gravitation, by supposing the sun to be surrounded by clouds of gas or dust which impeded the free motion of the inner planets, and in a variety of other ways. The relativity theory of gravitation then cleared up the whole situation at one stroke by rejecting Newton's force of gravitation altogether, and impressing a curvature on the space-time unity in which the motions of the planets were depicted. Once again the change was from an unsuitable to a suitable background. The whole motion of planets and other bodies, as well as of rays of light, could now be described by the simple statement that they all described geodesics—i.e. took the shortest possible course from point to point—in the new curved space-time unity.

The simplification which this change introduced was not only tremendous in itself, but was in line with a number of earlier simplifications, all based on the idea of a length of path or some similar quantity assuming the smallest value which was possible for it.

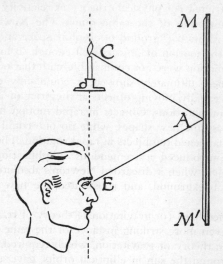

The principle made its first appearance in optics. If a candle is burning at *C*, and my eye at *E* looks at a mirror *MM'*, I shall seem to see the candle at some point *A* in the mirror. This shows that rays of light are travelling along the path *CAE* from the candle to my eye, and along no others; for if they travelled along any other path *CBE* as well, I should seem to see candles at both *A* and *B*, which I do not. Hero of Alexandria set himself the problem of finding what it was that specially distinguished the path *CAE* which the light actually took from every other possible path such as *CBE* which it might have taken, but did not. He found that *CAE* was the shortest path from *C* to *E* which touched the mirror on its way. Even though the light is reflected from hundreds of mirrors, the path is still determined by the same principle; it is the shortest path that can be found, subject to the condition of its touching all the mirrors in turn. Alternatively the path may be described as the quickest from *C* to *E*; the light chooses its path on the principle of wasting as little time as possible on the way.

Fermat (1601–1665) showed that this latter principle still determines the path when the light travels through water, glass, or other refracting substances of any kind whatever. Thus it is true under all circumstances that light always travels by the quickest route; this provides another instance of the tremendous simplifications to which Einstein refers.

Maupertuis (1698–1759) subsequently conjectured that the motions of tangible objects must conform to some similar principle, arguing that Divine perfection would be opposed to any expenditure of energy by moving bodies, beyond the absolute minimum necessary to get from one place to another. In time such a principle was found to govern the motion of all bodies of tangible size—the principle of "Least Action." This principle includes the Newtonian mechanics and the classical mechanics as special cases, so that it covers not only mechanical activities but those of electricity and magnetism as well. It can best be understood through a simple analogy.

When I hire a taxicab, the taximeter piles up the charges against me at a rate which depends both on where I am, and on how fast I am travelling. I have to pay one sum per five minutes when I am at rest in a city, some other sum per five minutes when I travel at 15 miles an hour in the city, twice as much when I travel at 30 miles an hour in the city, and so on, and on an entirely different tariff when I am outside the city limits. Now let us imagine a taximeter attached to every moving object in the universe, piling up charges at a rate which depends on both the speed of motion and the position of the object. Let all the objects move for some specified time, such as an hour, and at the end of the motion let all the charges shown on the various taximeters be added up. The principle of Least Action tells us that the actual objects in nature will have chosen their paths so as to make the total charge shown by all the taximeters a minimum—Nature, setting her face against unnecessary expenditure on taxicabs, always chooses the cheapest route.

Suppose, for instance, that a single particle has to be trans-

ferred, within a specified time, from one point A to another
point B, through a region in which conditions are absolutely
uniform, so that the taxicab tariff is of course uniform also.
The cheapest way of making the journey will be to travel in
a perfectly straight line at a perfectly uniform speed, which
is what Newton's law of motion tells the particle to do. Or
again, suppose that a planet has to be transported from its
present position to the corresponding position at the other
side of the sun. The shortest route would be straight through
the centre of the sun, but, as the tariff in intense gravitational
fields is exorbitant, the charges by this route would be pro-
hibitive. We find we can avoid these excessive charges by
taking a curved path round the sun, even though this length-
ens the journey somewhat. If part of the route still goes near
to the sun, it is cheapest to perform this part of the journey at
high speed, so as to spend as little time as possible in the
region of exorbitant tariffs. Exact mathematical analysis is
needed to find exactly what combination of path and speed
reduces the total charge to an absolute minimum; it tells us
that the path must be an ellipse having the sun in one of its
foci. This is precisely the path demanded by the Newtonian
mechanics, but we notice that it is no longer mapped out by
the action of "forces" of the Newtonian kind.

Logically, and to some extent chronologically also, the
principle of Least Action forms a direct successor to the principle of Least Time of Hero and Fermat. The principle of
Least Distance, or geodesics, in the curved space-time of
relativity is clearly in the same line of succession. It introduces
a great simplicity by changing to the new background of a
curved space—like the change of background of our radio
listener when he changed from a rectangular projection to a
curved spherical surface. Like the principles of Least Time
and of Least Action, this principle of Least Distance shows an
extreme simplicity which suggests that we are keeping in close
touch with the true significance of natural processes.

The old quantum theory did not show any such simplicity.
We need not concern ourselves with it any further since it
has now become clear that it was only an unsatisfactory
hybrid between the classical mechanics and the new quantum

theory, being, in fact, a last desperate effort to represent nature against a background of time and space.

In the new quantum theory the same simplicity reappears in full strength and almost in the same form. So far as its formal mathematical description goes, the theory is a genuine extension of the old Newtonian mechanics, so much so that the same mathematical equations will serve for the description of both, namely the canonical equations of which we spoke, these in turn being an expression of the principle of Least Action.

But the pictorial representations that must be given to these equations differ widely in the two cases. The classical mechanics came into existence as an effort to describe the continuous motions of objects under pushes and pulls; it is in this way that it is usually interpreted. But the new quantum mechanics must be interpreted rather as a description of steady states in which either there is no motion or else the state of motion does not change. Now and then, as we have seen, a jump occurs from one of these steady states to another, and it is with jumps of this kind rather than with gradual changes that the new mechanics is concerned. Are these jumps final, or will they ultimately be resolved into some kind of rapid continuous motions of which we have so far no knowledge, either observational or theoretical? We simply cannot form a judgment.

The main difference between the old mechanics and the new is, however, once again a difference of background. The classical mechanics and the old quantum theory had both assumed that the whole world existed in time and space; the new mechanics is most simply expressed in terms of symbols which are best interpreted by passing beyond space and time. In transcending space and time, the new quantum mechanics finds a new background which makes for far greater simplicity and so probably comes nearer to ultimate truth. In passing from the old mechanics to the new, the mathematical description of the pattern of events stands almost unaltered, while the interpretation we put upon the symbols is utterly changed.

The history of theoretical physics is a record of the clothing of mathematical formulae which were right, or very nearly right, with physical interpretations which were often very badly wrong. When Newton had found laws of motion of a mechanical system which were true (apart from the minor refinements of the theory of relativity), he put science on a wrong track for two centuries by interpreting them in terms of forces and absolute space and time. It was much the same with his supposed force of gravitation. Again, when the true laws of the propagation of light had been discovered, they were interpreted as applying to the propagation of waves in an ether which was supposed to fill all space, and again science was started along a wrong road which it was to follow for nearly two centuries.

Now when philosophy has availed itself of the results of science, it has not been by borrowing the abstract mathematical description of the pattern of events, but by borrowing the then current pictorial description of this pattern; thus it has not appropriated certain knowledge but conjectures. These conjectures were often good enough for the man-sized world, but not, as we now know, for those ultimate processes of nature which control the happenings of the man-sized world, and bring us nearest to the true nature of reality.

One consequence of this is that the standard philosophical discussions of many problems, such as those of causality and free-will or of materialism or mentalism, are based on an interpretation of the pattern of events which is no longer tenable. The scientific basis of these older discussions has been washed away, and with their disappearance have gone all the arguments, such as they were, that seemed to require the acceptance of materialism and determinism and the renunciation of human free-will. This does not mean that the conclusions previously reached were necessarily wrong, for a bad argument may lead to a good conclusion. But it does mean that the situation must be reviewed afresh. Everything is back in the melting-pot, and we must start anew and try to discover truth on the basis of the new physics. Apart from our knowledge of the pattern of events, our tools can only be probable reasoning and the principle of simplicity.

The New Picture of Modern Physics

We may appropriately start from those things of which we have the most certain knowledge, namely ourselves and our sensations. These sensations come to us through our senses, the most important of which is the sense of seeing. We see through the impact of radiation on the retina, this arriving in the form of the individual units we call photons. Other sense-organs act in a similar way, the smallest unit of sensation being produced by the arrival of a single quantum of energy from the world outside.

We have seen that photons may be represented as travelling in a space of three dimensions. This we may at once identify with the space of ordinary everyday life, because by space the ordinary man means the space through which photons travel to his eyes, the space in which he seems to see things shining or reflecting light, moving or standing still, the space in which he meets his friends.

These photons end their journeys by falling into our eyes, and so affecting our consciousness. But they are far from being projectiles falling at random. If we stand in the open on a clear night, we shall find that there are some directions of space from which photons arrive in a continuous stream and others from which no photons arrive. From such observations as this we deduce the existence of certain permanent sources of photons, or, more generally, of permanent sources of sensations; these we designate as matter.

This leads us to postulate the existence of a world of photons and matter, existing in ordinary space; it is what the plain man describes as the material world.

So far this material world has been nothing more than a mental construct private to ourselves; the space is our perceptual space, and may have no existence outside our own consciousness. If we now go asleep, or if our consciousness ceases for any other reason to function for a time, we shall find on awakening new sources of sensations which it is reasonable to identify with the old; the bedroom I find when

I waken in the morning is so exactly similar to the room I left when I fell asleep that a tremendous simplicity is introduced by assuming that it is the same, and that it has been in existence all the time.

On the same principle, the moon, planets and stars outside the room may be identified with those I left behind me when I fell asleep. These, however, are no longer in the same positions. If I study these changes of position, I shall find that they are precisely those that would have occurred if the bodies had described geodesics in a curved space-time unity of the kind described on p. 63. A tremendous gain in simplicity is now secured by supposing that a curved space-time has been in existence during my sleep, and that the astronomical bodies have moved in this. Thus we conclude, with a high degree of probability, that the space-time unity and the objects which figure in it cannot be mere constructs of our individual minds, but must have existences of their own, although we know that space and time separately are abstractions of our individual minds from the space-time unity. This does not of course touch the question, to which we shall return later, of whether space, time and the material world are or are not of a mental nature, being perhaps the constructs of a consciousness superior to our own. So long as we are concerned only with our sensations, it is all the same whether we regard the world as a mental construct or as having an existence of its own independent of mind—the essential point at the moment is that it cannot be a private mental construct of our own.

Appearance and Reality

The doctrine of materialism asserted that this space, time and material world comprised the whole of reality; it regarded consciousness as only a minor incident in the history of the material world, a somewhat exceptional episode in the haphazard muddle resulting from the chaotic movements of photons, electrons and matter in general. It interpreted thought as a mechanical motion in the brain, and emotion as a mechanical motion in the body. It seemed at one time to receive substantial support from science. For consciousness was never experienced except in conjunction with matter; a man's mental state was obviously influenced by the food, drink and drugs given to his body; and many thought it possible that all mental activities might be interpreted in terms of various physico-mental processes occurring in the associated body. At the same time astronomy was finding that only an inconceivably minute fraction of space provided any possibility for the existence of the kind of life we know, and it seemed impossible that the rest of the universe should contain anything but inanimate matter. It was hard to imagine that consciousness should be of fundamental importance in such a world.

The new physics suggests that, besides the matter and radiation which can be represented in ordinary space and time, there must be other ingredients which cannot be so represented. These are just as real as the material ingredients, but do not happen to make any direct appeal to our senses. Thus the material world as defined above constitutes the whole world of appearance, but not the whole world of reality; we may think of it as forming only a cross-section of the world of reality.

We may picture the world of reality as a deep-flowing stream; the world of appearance is its surface, below which we cannot see. Events deep down in the stream throw up bubbles and eddies on to the surface of the stream. These are the transfers of energy and radiation of our common life, which affect our senses and so activate our minds; below these lie deep waters which we can only know by inference. These bubbles and eddies show atomicity, but we know of no corresponding atomicity in the currents below.

Thus dualism of appearance and reality pervades the history of philosophy, again dating back to Plato. In a famous parable, Plato depicts mankind as chained in a cave in such a way that they can look only on the wall which forms the back of the cave; they cannot see the busy life outside, but only the shadows—the appearances—which objects moving in the sunshine cast on the walls of the cave. For the captives in the cave, the shadows constitute the whole world of appearance—the phenomenal world—while the world of reality lies for ever beyond their ken.

Our phenomenal world consists of the activities of matter and photons; the theatre of this activity is space and time. Thus the walls of the cave in which we are imprisoned are space and time; the shadows of reality which we see projected on the walls by the sunshine outside are the material particles which we see moving against a background of space and time, while the reality outside the cave which produces these shadows is outside space and time.

Many philosophers have regarded the world of appearance as a kind of illusion, some sort of creation or selection of our minds which had in some way less existence in its own right than the underlying world of reality. Modern physics does not confirm this view; the phenomena are seen to be just as much a part of the real world as the causes which produce them, being simply those parts of the real world which affect our senses, while the space and time in which they occur have the same sort of reality as the substratum which orders their motions. The walls of the cave and the shadows are just as real as the objects outside in the sunshine.

As the new physics has shown, all earlier systems of physics, from the Newtonian mechanics down to the old quantum theory, fell into the error of identifying appearance with reality; they confined their attention to the walls of the cave, without even being conscious of a deeper reality beyond. The new quantum theory has shown that we must probe the deeper substratum of reality before we can understand the world of appearance, even to the extent of predicting the results of experiment.

For, whatever may happen in reality, there is no reason why the shadows on the wall should change in accordance with a causal law. There will be many different arrangements of the figures out in the sunshine which all produce the same arrangement of shadows on the wall; these many arrangements will be followed by new arrangements which will not only be different in themselves but are likely to produce different shadows on the wall. It is the same with the happenings in the world of appearance; experiments that are precisely identical so far as the phenomena go may produce entirely different results. In this way causality disappears from the world of phenomena.

It comes back when we explore the substratum of reality, although in a strange new guise. Because we have only complete photons at our disposal, and these form blunt probes, the world of phenomena can never be seen clearly and distinctly, either by us or by our instruments. Instead of seeing clearly defined particles clearly located in space and executing clear-cut motions, we see only a collection of blurs—like a badly focused lantern slide. As we have seen, this is enough of itself to prevent our ever observing strict causality in the world of phenomena.

Each blur represents the unknown entity which the particle-picture depicts as a particle, or perhaps a group of such entities. The blurs may be pictured as wave-disturbances, the intensity of the waves at any point representing the probability that, with infinitely refined probes at our disposal, we should find a particle at that point. Or again we may interpret the waves as representations of knowledge—they do not give us a picture of a particle, but of what we know as to the position and speed of motion of the particle. Now these waves of knowledge exhibit complete determinism; as they roll on, they show us knowledge growing out of knowledge and uncertainty following uncertainty according to a strict causal law. But this tells us nothing we do not already know. If we had found new knowledge appearing, not out of previous knowledge but spontaneously and of its own accord, we should have come upon something very startling and of profound philosophical significance; actually what we find is merely what was to be expected; and the problem of causality is left much where it was.

Mentalism or Materialism

In addition to the dualism of appearance and reality, many pictures of the world have exhibited a second dualism, that of mind and matter or of body and soul.

This also, so far as our knowledge carries us, started with Plato. We have seen how his picture of the world consisted of forms, which exist only in our minds, and of sensible objects which, on Plato's view, display the imprint of the forms and so exemplify the qualities embodied in the forms. Plato maintained that the forms possessed a higher degree of reality than the material objects which exemplify them, so that the world was primarily a world of ideas and only secondarily a world of material objects.

We have further seen how Descartes, two thousand years later, drew a picture of the world in which mind and matter again figured, but they were now so distinct in their natures that neither could act on the other.

Then came the Idealist (or Mentalist) philosophers, who still divided the world into mind and matter, but argued that matter had no existence in its own right; it was of the same nature as mind, and existed only so far as it was a creation of mind. Under the leadership of Bishop Berkeley, they reached their conclusions by a twofold argument.

THE FIRST ARGUMENT FOR MENTALISM

The first was an argument we have already noticed. Galileo, Descartes, Locke and others divided the qualities of objects and substances into the two classes which Locke designated as primary and secondary. Secondary qualities are those which are perceived by the senses, and so may be differently estimated by different percipients; primary qualities are those which are essential to the object or substance and so are inherent in it whether they are perceived or not.

We have seen that physics gives no support to this division of qualities into primary and secondary. The idealists were at one with the physicists in this, but whereas the physicists consider that all physical qualities are primary, in Locke's sense of being "utterly inseparable from the body in what state soever it be," the idealists argued that all qualities were secondary since they could be differently estimated by different percipients, a flower looking scarlet to one man but purple to another, the leg of a cheese-mite looking minute to a man but of quite a decent size to the cheese-mite, and so on. This being so, they argued, colour and size cannot be objective properties of objects; they cannot reside in the objects themselves, but in the minds perceiving the objects. And if an object is nothing but the sum of its qualities, then when all qualities reside only in percipient minds, the object itself must do the same. In brief, the object is of the nature of an idea; existence consists in being perceived by a mind.

If so, of course, an object would be non-existent when it was not being perceived by a mind. Yet the planet Pluto was certainly in existence, and impressing its image on photographic plates, many years before anyone suspected its existence. And to all appearances things go on happening inside an empty room—the fire continues to burn and the clock to keep time; when we return we find no reason for suspecting that the clock and fire have been out of existence in our absence. Berkeley got over difficulties of this kind by supposing that an object, even though it might at times not be perceived by any human mind, was yet kept permanently in existence through being continually perceived by the mind of God. Thus the whole world became an idea in the mind of God.

We have already found reasons why science can give no countenance to any arguments which suppose objects to be the sum of their secondary qualities; they are, in brief, as follows.

Whatever capacity a red flower may have for producing a sensation of redness in a man's mind, it also has a capacity for reflecting red light whether there is anyone to see it or not, as may be very simply proved by photography. This capacity is obviously a primary quality, being "utterly inseparable from the body in what state soever it be," and Berkeley's argument cannot touch it. Berkeley's argument fails through his not seeing that each quality such as redness must have primary ingredients as well as its alleged secondary ingredients; there is an objective scientific redness as well as the subjective philosophic redness.

THE SECOND ARGUMENT FOR MENTALISM

The second line of argument ran somewhat as follows. When I hear a bell, a hammer has given a mechanical blow to a piece of metal and set it into vibration. The vibrations have been communicated in turn to the surrounding air, to my eardrums, and to a succession of elaborate pieces of mechanism and fluids inside my ears, with the result that a sequence of minute electric currents finally reaches my brain and produces certain physical changes there. These changes result in something crossing the mysterious mind-body bridge and producing certain happenings in the mind on the far side. These happenings we describe as the hearing of a bell, a purely mental idea because we might equally well experience it in a dream when there was no bell to produce it. Berkeley argued that effects must always be of the same general nature as their causes, a mechanical effect being traceable to a mechanical cause, and so on. Or, to put it rather more precisely, whatever crosses the mind-body bridge must be of the same general nature as its cause on the one side of the bridge and as its effect on the other. Thus Berkeley maintained that as the effects A on the mind side of the mind-body bridge are purely mental, their causes B on the body side must also be purely mental. In brief, as A is an idea, and "an idea can be like nothing but an idea," therefore B also must be an idea, or of course a set of ideas.

The argument is obviously double-edged, and just as effective when reversed. For if B must be of the same nature as A, it is equally valid to argue that A must be of the same nature as B. Since A is purely material, the argument would now prove that our mental processes must be material in their nature, as the materialists claim.

Berkeley was only able to see one side of the argument; he wished to serve theology by proving the existence of God. Before him, Descartes had been unable to see either side, claiming that mind and matter were so dissimilar, as a matter of experience, that they could have nothing in common; he too desired to serve theology—by establishing the freedom of the will. Disregarding all its theological implications, Berkeley's argument seems to provide a valid proof that mind and matter must have something in common; we can see how much real substance there is in it if we reflect on the straits to which Descartes and Leibniz were reduced when they tried to show how the opposite might be true.

In more recent times, Bertrand Russell has expressed what is essentially the same argument in the words: "So long as we adhere to the conventional notions of mind and matter, we are condemned to a view of perception which is miraculous. We suppose that a physical process starts from a visible object, travels to the eye, there changes into another physical process, causes yet another physical process in the optic nerve, and finally produces some effect in the brain, simultaneously with which we see the object from which the process started, the seeing being something "mental," totally different in character from the physical processes which precede and accompany it. This view is so queer that metaphysicians have invented all sorts of theories designed to substitute something less incredible. . . ."

"Everything that we can directly observe of the physical world happens inside our heads, and consists of *mental* events in at least one sense of the word *mental*. It also consists of events which form part of the physical world. The development of this point of view will lead us to the conclusion that the distinction between mind and matter is illusory. The stuff of the world may be called physical or mental or both or neither as we please; in fact the words serve no purpose."

If we accept this argument, the dualism of Descartes drops out of the picture altogether, and the only question left is whether we ought to say with the materialists that mind is material, or with the mentalists that matter is mental.

Whole libraries have, as Jeffreys pungently remarks, been filled with bad arguments on both sides. The materialists felt very sure, partly because of the success of science, that there was an external world of small hard atoms existing and moving in space and time, and concluded that mind must be material, and consciousness an activity of small hard atoms in space and time. The small hard atoms have now departed from science, and we picture matter as consisting mostly of empty space. Some writers have seemed to consider that this involves far-reaching philosophical consequences, and in particular, that it carries us in the direction of mentalism. It is hard to see why. Being hit by a golf-ball hurts just as much now that we know that it is little more than empty space; we realize that its material properties of solidity and hardness have not been demolished, but are merely explained in a new way.

The materialists also felt sure, partly on account of the success of science, that the absolute space and time of Newton had real existences in their own right. The physical theory of relativity now indicates—to a high degree of probability, although without absolute certainty—that space and time do not exist separately in their own right, but are subjective selections from a wider space-time unity. Some writers have argued as though this too implied a drift towards mentalism, but again it is hard to see why. Whatever degree of reality was possessed by the space and time of the older physics has not been banished from the world, but merely transferred to the space-time unity; this joint structure is every bit as objective, and may be every bit as real, as its components, space and time were once thought to be separately. The two components have simply entered into a partnership, so that they now form a single entity in the eyes of the law of science, but this makes them neither less real nor more mental than before.

The physical theory of relativity has, however, other considerations to bring forward. For the materialists, space was filled with real particles, exercising on one another forces which were electric or magnetic or gravitational in their nature; these directed the motions of the particles and so were responsible for all the activity of the world. These forces were of course as real as the particles they moved.

But the physical theory of relativity has now shown that electric and magnetic forces are not real at all; they are mere mental constructs of our own, resulting from our rather misguided efforts to understand the motions of the particles. It is the same with the Newtonian force of gravitation, and with energy, momentum and other concepts which were introduced to help us understand the activities of the world—all prove to be mere mental constructs, and do not even pass the test of objectivity. If the materialists are pressed to say how much of the world they now claim as material, their only possible answer would seem to be: Matter itself. Thus their whole philosophy is reduced to a tautology, for obviously matter must be material. But the fact that so much of what used to be thought to possess an objective physical existence now proves to consist only of subjective mental constructs must surely be counted a pronounced step in the direction of mentalism.

The gravitational theory of relativity again brings considerations of a new kind into play. It provides an outstanding example of the truth of Einstein's general remark that, as experimental research advances, the fundamental laws of nature become simplified more and more, and, as in many other departments of physics, we find this simplicity residing neither in the physical facts nor in their pictorial representations, but solely in the mathematical formulae which describe the pattern of events. These seem simple to our minds because they are expressible in the kind of mathematics to which we take naturally, and studied for the pure intellectual interest we found in it before we saw it would help us to understand nature—in brief, in pure and not in applied mathematics. Thus the pure mathematician finds it much easier to interpret gravitation in terms of his science than does the mechanic or engineer. But the pure mathematician deals with the mental sphere, the mechanic and the engineer with the material. Thus the relativity theory of gravitation, because of its close association with pure mathematics, seems to carry us yet further along the road from materialism to mentalism, and the same may be said of most of the recent developments of physical science.

The new quantum theory brings still further factors into the situation. We have seen how it puts before us the two pictures which we have described as the particle-picture and the wave-picture.

The particle-picture depicts the phenomena; its ingredients are those of the ordinary picture of the material world, namely matter and radiation existing and moving in time and space.

The ingredients of the wave-picture are wave-like disturbances. Whatever a particle may be in itself, we can never experience it as a point, but if we insist on picturing it as such, then the relative intensities of the waves indicate the relative proprieties of supposing it to exist at the various points of space.

Proprieties relative to what? The answer is: Relative to our knowledge. If we know nothing about a particle except that it exists, all places are equally likely for it, so that its waves are uniformly spread throughout the whole of space. By experiment after experiment we can restrict the extent of the waves, but we can never reduce it to a point, or indeed below a certain minimum; the coarse-grainedness of our probes precludes this, so that there must always be a finite region of wave-disturbance left. The waves in this region depict our knowledge and its imperfections exactly and precisely.

Thus the ingredients of the particle-picture are particles existing and moving in physical space, while the ingredients of the wave-picture are mental constructs existing and moving in conceptual spaces; the ingredients of the particle-picture are material, those of the wave-picture mental.

The first complete particle-picture was provided by Newton's mechanics in conjunction with his corpuscular theory of light. The mechanics supposed that those permanent sources of sensation which we call matter consisted of particles moving in physical space, while the corpuscular theory of light further supposed that the radiation by which our sense-organs are affected also consisted of particles. This scheme was found not to give an adequate account of the facts of observation, and in due course the corpuscular picture of light was replaced by the present wave-picture. This resulted in complete agreement with the facts of observation so far as optical phenomena were concerned. But, until the theory of relativity appeared, it was not suspected that the ingredients of this picture were purely mental constructs.

Thus physics continued to believe that it was studying an objective nature which existed in its own right independently of the mind which perceived it, and had existed from all eternity whether it was perceived or not; this belief was the soil in which materialism had its roots. Physics would have gone on holding this belief to this day, had the electron which the physicist observed behaved as, on this supposition, it ought to have done.

But it did not so behave, and the new quantum theory was brought into existence to make good the defects. It discovered what we believe to be the true pattern of events, with the wave-picture of matter as its pictorial representation. The particle-picture of radiation had already given place to a wave-picture; it now appeared that the particle-picture of matter must also be replaced by a wave-picture. The result was a complete agreement with experiment. In this progress towards the truth, let us notice that each step was from particles to waves, or from the material to the mental; the final picture consists wholly of waves, and its ingredients are wholly mental constructs.

We must remember that this picture is not a picture of reality, it is a picture we draw to help us imagine the course of events in reality. Thus we are not entitled to argue that reality is like the ingredients of the picture, although there is a certain presumption that the two are not altogether dissimilar in their natures; the pictorial representation does not take us into the mansion of reality, but does take us to its doorstep. Thus, when it was believed that the course of events could be most easily understood in terms of forces and mechanical models, most people thought that the picture or model must be like the reality, and jumped to the conclusion that reality was mechanical in its nature. Before this, when the course of events had seemed to be governed by the caprices and passions of gods and demons, it had been assumed that reality was of a similar nature; we have seen how Thales maintained that all things must be full of gods. And now that we find that we can best understand the course of events in terms of waves of knowledge, there is a certain presumption—although certainly no proof—that reality and knowledge are similar in their natures, or, in other words, that reality is wholly mental.

Apart from arguments of this type, we can have no means of knowing the true nature of reality. The most we can say is that the cumulative evidence of various pieces of probable reasoning makes it seem more and more likely that reality is better described as mental than as material.

Even if the two entities which we have hitherto described as mind and matter are of the same general nature, there remains the question as to which is the more fundamental of the two. Is mind only a by-product of matter, as the materialists claimed? Or is it, as Berkeley claimed, the creator and controller of matter?

Before the latter alternative can be seriously considered, some answer must be found to the problem of how objects can continue to exist when they are not being perceived in any human mind. There must, as Berkeley says, be "some other mind in which they exist." Some will wish to describe this, with Berkeley, as the mind of God; others with Hegel as a universal or Absolute mind in which all our individual minds are comprised. The new quantum mechanics may perhaps give a hint, although nothing more than a hint, as to how this can be.

In the particle-picture, which depicts the phenomenal world, each particle and each photon is a distinct individual going its own way. When we pass one stage further towards reality we come to the wave-picture. Photons are no longer independent individuals, but members of a single organization or whole—a beam of light—in which their separate individualities are merged, not merely in the superficial sense in which an individual is lost in a crowd, but rather as a raindrop is lost in the sea. The same is true of electrons; in the wave-picture these lose their separate individualities and become simply fractions of a continuous current of electricity. In each case, space and time are inhabited by distinct individuals, but when we pass beyond space and time, from the world of phenomena towards reality, individuality is replaced by community.

It seems at least conceivable that what is true of perceived objects may also be true of perceiving minds; just as there are wave-pictures for light and electricity, so there may be a corresponding picture for consciousness. When we view ourselves in space and time, our consciousnesses are obviously the separate individuals of a particle-picture, but when we pass beyond space and time, they may perhaps form ingredients of a single continuous stream of life. As it is with light and electricity, so it may be with life; the phenomena may be individuals carrying on separate existences in space and time, while in the deeper reality beyond space and time we may all be members of one body. In brief, modern physics is not altogether antagonistic to an objective idealism like that of Hegel.

The new dualism of the particle- and wave-pictures is in many ways reminiscent of the old dualism of Descartes. There is no longer a dualism of mind and matter, but of waves and particles; these seem to be the direct, although almost unrecognizable, descendants of the older mind and matter, the waves replacing mind and the particles matter. The two members of this dualism are no longer antagonistic or mutually exclusive; rather they are complementary. We need no longer devise elaborate mechanisms, as Descartes and Leibniz did, to keep the two in step, for one controls the other—the waves control the particles, or in the old terminology the mental controls the material.

The Problem of Free-Will

We have seen how the materialists interpreted thought and emotion as mechanical activities of the brain and body respectively, and imagined that if all the physical and chemical changes in a brain and body could be traced out, it would be possible, at least in principle, to deduce all the mental and emotional experiences of the associated mind. Thus, if material changes were bound by a causal chain, mental and emotional experiences would also be so bound, and there could be no room left for free-will.

There were nevertheless two schools of thought—the *determinists* who maintained that all events, including human acts, were causally determined and so compelled by past events and acts, including such events as those of heredity, environment, acquired habits and so forth; and the *indeterminists* who maintained that human acts are not entirely determined by the past, but that at every moment we can exercise a certain amount of guidance through a fiat which is our own.

On the determinist view, a man's actions would of course be completely predictable in principle by one who had a sufficiently intimate knowledge of his nature, of his past and of the character he has acquired in the past. On the indeterminist view, this is not so; a man can falsify all predictions by a capricious, and so unpredictable, choice.

THE DETERMINISTS

Practically all modern philosophers of the first rank—Descartes, Spinoza, Leibniz, Locke, Hume, Kant, Hegel, Mill, Alexander, as well as many others—have been determinists in the sense of admitting the cogency of the arguments for determinism, but many have at the same time been indeterminists in the sense of hoping to find a loophole of escape from these arguments. Often they conceded that our apparent freedom is an illusion, so that the only loophole they could hope to find would be an explanation as to how the illusion could originate.

Descartes and Kant, as we have seen, may fairly be described as determinists trying to shed their determinism, while Leibniz, Locke and Hume are perhaps better described as determinists trying to explain their determinism. Spinoza, Mill and Alexander were out-and-out determinists, although like many other determinists they were not always consistent in their determinism.

Leibniz thought that there are always sufficient reasons in the nature and character of each one of us to determine for us any decision we may be called upon to make. We are, then, never free, because our acts at every moment are completely determined by our nature which came to us in the past, and by our character which was formed in the past. Hume also thought that our decisions are always determined by our characters, so that to make a different decision we should need to be a different person. Locke thought our decisions are based on our desires to enjoy pleasure and avoid pain, and so are determined by our estimates of future pleasure and pain—although of course our judgments may be wrong. Spinoza thought that our actions and experiences are in actual fact determined by a sort of mathematical necessity, like that of a wheel in a machine, but that we feel ourselves free if we enjoy doing what actually we are doing under compulsion; a stone in the air, he said, would think itself free if it could forget the hand that had thrown it. Or, to take a more homely illustration which is not Spinoza's, I know that I choose jam-roll because I like it, and I feel myself free in so choosing because I do not stop to think that my liking is the inevitable result of my inheritance and upbringing, of the present state of my health and of my sugar metabolism, and of all sorts of things which it is quite beyond my power to change at the moment. Hegel and, at a later period, Alexander held very similar opinions. Kant thought that we feel ourselves free just in so far as our actions appear rational to us; if I rationally run downstairs to welcome a friend, my action seems free to me, but if I run downstairs irrationally because I am afraid of a ghost, it will seem to me that I acted under compulsion. Mill believed that all human actions are so completely determinate that sociology could be made into a perfectly exact science, in which the future of a society would be seen to follow from its past with a mechanical certainty and after unvarying laws. He then, with the characteristic irrationality of the thoroughgoing determinist, wanted these laws to be studied with a view to improving the future of the race!

The average plain man who is no philosopher will probably consider that the springs of human action are too varied, too intricate and too complex to be summed up in any single formula. His own philosophy is not very clear-cut, but may perhaps be described as one of determinism for others and freedom for himself. Yet this supposed freedom applies only to his present acts, and not to the past; we see our past selves as other men. For, as Henry Sidgwick says: "We always explain the voluntary action of all men except ourselves on the principle of causation by character and circumstances. We infer generally the future actions of those whom we know from their past actions; and if our forecast turns out in any case to be erroneous, we do not attribute the discrepancy to the disturbing influence of free-will, but to our incomplete acquaintance with their character and motives. . . . Nay even as regards our own actions, however free we feel ourselves at any moment, however unconstrained by present motives and circumstances and unfettered by the result of what we have previously been and felt our volitional choice may appear, still when it is once well past, and we survey it in the series of our actions, its relations of causation and resemblance to other parts of our life appear, and we naturally explain it as an effect of our nature, education and circumstances."

Not only so, but the freedom we claim for our present selves is almost indistinguishable from the determinism we attribute to others. We usually claim no freedom for ourselves beyond that of being able to do what we want to do, which simply means yielding to the strongest impulse, the freedom of the beam of the weighing scale to incline to the heavier side, the kind of freedom which philosopher and scientist agree in describing as determinism—since, under it, the future is fully determined; it follows from the past with the inevitability of a machine.

We can see this by examining special instances. Mr. Average Man thinks over his past, and proclaims that if he were young again, he would choose a different profession. He may insist that he would be free to make his own choice, but all he means is that if, at the age of eighteen, he had had the knowledge and experience of life which he now has at fifty, he would have acted differently. Of course he would, and so would we all, but this is no evidence of freedom. If Mr. Man now had to make his choice again, with precisely the same knowledge and experience as he had at eighteen, he would review the situation in the same way as he did before, the same considerations would be thrown into the scales, and the balance would again swing in the same direction as before. He will not claim a freedom to act from pure caprice, but only a freedom to yield to the strongest motive—the freedom of Newton's apple to fall towards the earth rather than towards the moon, because the earth attracted it more forcibly than the moon. And this is not freedom of any kind; it is pure determinism. As Hume said, to have made a different decision, he would have had to be a different man.

Or perhaps he may claim he is free to choose in trivial matters, as for instance whether he will ask for black or white coffee. Perhaps he usually asks for black, and if on some rare occasion he asks for white, he may imagine that in so trivial a matter his choice was wholly undetermined. But a psychologist will tell him that, even here, he can only yield to the strongest motive, no matter how weak these motives may be. When he made his unusual choice, his mind may have been far away from food and drink, absorbed in the pages of a book he was looking at, so that, when politeness compelled him to make a choice, he merely mentioned the colour suggested by the pages of his book. Or he may have felt a temporary but unconscious aversion to black and blackness through some association, such as mourning or a funeral. There are endless possibilities and only one impossibility, which is that he said "white" out of pure caprice, without having any guiding motive in his mind. The presence of milk in his coffee in two minutes' time will be a direct consequence of the state of his mind now, just as surely as the state of the material universe in two minutes' time will, on the deterministic view, be a direct consequence of its state now.

Although Mr. Average Man may occasionally protest that he is incapable of acting meanly or dishonourably, yet in general he would hate to think that he is not free to choose his own course of action at every moment of his life. Thus he likes to think that his own actions are wholly unpredictable, and yet, when other men behave in a wholly unpredictable way, he describes them as weak fools. In brief, freedom in ourselves is a virtue, but in others a vice; freedom is something we possess, but that others do not.

Not only plain men, but philosophical writers also, seem to confuse free-will with determinism of this unconscious kind. Thus Henry Sidgwick (*Methods of Ethics*) says that the question at issue in the free-will controversy, as he understands it, is whether his action at any moment is completely determined by his character and the external influences, including his bodily condition, which act on him at the moment, "or is there always a possibility of my choosing to act in the manner that I now judge to be reasonable and right, whatever my previous actions and experiences may have been?"

But a judgment as to what is reasonable and right cannot be based on nothing at all—if it is, it is no judgment but pure caprice. And it cannot be based on anything other than a man's character, which is founded on his previous actions and experiences, and the external influences acting on him at the moment—in brief, on the past and the present, or on what is inside him and on what is outside him. Thus Sidgwick's second alternative, which is clearly intended to represent free-will, is that our actions are determined by our judgments, and our judgments by our inner character and external influences—which brings us round to precisely his description of determinism. Thus his two alternatives are not determinism and freedom at all, but merely conscious and unconscious determinism, and he never reaches the real issue of free-will.

The same is true of theological attempts to solve the problem by adding Divine intervention to the external influences acting on a man—"We have no power to do good works . . . without the grace of God by Christ preventing us, that we may have a good will, and working with us when we have that good will." Such Divine intervention does not add to a man's freedom, but to the restrictions on it.

Attempts have been made to find an alternative to determinism in what is described as "teleological causation," according to which the future determines the present, or at least influences it, like the legendary carrot held in front of the donkey's nose. If a student is working hard in the hope of passing an examination, it is argued that the present spell of hard work is the effect of a future cause, namely an examination which is to be held at some future date. But it is surely more true to say that the cause is not the examination —which after all may never take place, and so can hardly be the cause of something which has already taken place—but the hope of passing the examination. This hope is not in the future; a man will not be working for an examination at this moment unless the hope of passing it has been in his mind at some previous moment, so that the proximate cause of his hard work is in the past, and not in the future. To some extent, the whole matter is one of juggling with words, but in whatever sense words are used, ideas such as teleological causation can throw no new light on the ultimate problem.

THE INDETERMINISTS

On the other side, Lotze (1817–1881) and William James (1842–1910) were consistent and logical indeterminists. Lotze agreed with the determinists that both natural events and human acts lie on strings of causal chains, and that such causal chains when once started have no end in future time, but he thought that such chains may have capricious beginnings. William James advocated the doctrine which C. S. Peirce had described as tychism—chance playing its part in ordering the course of events. According to him, the pattern of events is not unalterably fixed; we introduce novelties when we make choices (but it is not explained why one novelty rather than another is introduced).

We have already seen that modern physics is not entirely hostile to such ideas in their application to inanimate nature, although we also saw that they should not be applied to the underlying realities, but only to the phenomena as seen and understood by us—in other words, the indeterminacy does not reside in objective nature, but only in our subjective interpretation of nature.

Let us, however, ignore the distinction, and state the case in the form most favourable to indeterminism and freedom by imagining that an assigned state A of the inanimate world may be followed by any one of a number of different states $B, C, D, \ldots$ all of which lead to different future states of the world. In the inanimate world we find no apparent reason why A should be followed by B rather than by C or D. But suppose that in situations in which the human mind is concerned, the mind has some power of directing minute bits of the world to any one of the states, $B, C, D, \ldots$ as it chooses. Since all the transitions $A \rightarrow B, A \rightarrow C, A \rightarrow D$, etc. conform to the conservation of energy and momentum, we have mind acting on matter without the exercise of any material force or any transfer of energy, and moulding the universe within limits to its choice. This brings us to something very like Descartes's original explanation of the action of mind on matter, but it is no longer open to the objections raised by Leibniz.

Essentially the same solution was propounded by Clerk Maxwell. The course of a railway train is uniquely prescribed for it at most points of its journey by the rails on which it runs. Here and there, however, it comes to a junction at which alternative courses are open to it, and it may be turned on to one or the other by the quite negligible expenditure of energy involved in moving the points. Maxwell thought that the human body might come to similar junctions, at which it could be turned into one course or another by the action of the mind, without any expenditure of mechanical energy— the body is the train, the mind is the pointsman. The indeterminacy of atomic motions has seemed to many to provide just the kind of junction, and possibly also of points, that Maxwell needed.

This may suggest a possible way in which mind can act on matter, but it leaves the deeper problem of freedom of choice untouched. Even if the pointsman can move the points and divert the motion of the train in so doing, the question of why he moves the points in one direction rather than in another remains. If he moves them according to a prearranged plan, the train is simply following a schedule, which makes its motion as determinate as if the points and junction were non-existent. If, as most people would say, he moves them in a particular direction "because he chooses to," the question is why he chooses this direction rather than the other. If something determines his choice, we are back to determinism; if nothing, he acts from pure caprice, and this leads to a free-will which is neither of the kind we want to find nor of the kind we feel we do find. We like to imagine that we hold determinism at bay by our wisdom or virtue or foresight, and not through a mere random caprice over which we have no control and so for which we are in no way responsible. A man who has done a foolish deed may find comfort in thinking that he was the plaything of capricious forces, but not so the man who has been prudent or generous or has put his money on a winner.

Neither does a capricious indeterminism give us a free-will at all resembling that of our experience or imagined experience. If every event were not determined by a sufficient reason, the whole world would, as Leibniz remarked, be a chaos. A mind endowed with free-will of the capricious variety would be a prey to spontaneous and wholly irrational impulses; we should describe it as the mind of a madman, although in actual fact no madman's mind is ever quite so crazy. The further psychology and common sense probe into the question, the more necessary they find it to accept orthodox determinism—our acts are determined by our volitions, our volitions by our motives, and our motives by our past. The psychologist will think of this past in terms of heredity and environment, the moralist in terms of ethical and spiritual influences, and the physiologist in terms of physico-chemical activities. But all will agree that the relative strength of the various motives is determined by past events, so that a man never chooses for himself; his past always chooses for him.

PRESENT-DAY OPINION

Notwithstanding the apparent want of determinism disclosed in inanimate nature by the quantum theory, this is still the opinion of the vast majority of present-day physicists. Thus in his book, *Where is science going?* Planck, the founder of the quantum theory, writes: "No biographer will attempt to solve the question of the motives that govern the acts of his hero by attributing these to mere chance. He will rather attribute his inability to the lack of source materials, or he will admit that his own powers of spiritual penetration are not capable of reaching down into the depths of these motives. And in practical everyday life our attitude to our fellow-beings is based on the assumption that their words and actions are determined by distinct causes, which lie in the individual nature itself or in the environment, even though we admit that the source of these causes cannot be discovered by ourselves. . . . The principle of causality must be held to extend even to the highest achievements of the human soul. We must admit that the mind of each one of our great geniuses—Aristotle, Kant or Leonardo, Goethe or Beethoven, Dante or Shakespeare—even at the moments of its highest flights of thought or in the most profound inner workings of his soul—was subject to the causal fiat and was an instrument in the hands of an almighty law which governs the world."

In the same book, Einstein is reported as saying: "Honestly I cannot understand what people mean when they talk about the freedom of the will. I feel that I will to light my pipe and I do it, but how can I connect this up with the idea of freedom? What is behind the act of willing to light the pipe? Another act of willing? Schopenhauer once said: Der Mensch kann was er will; er kann aber nicht wollen was er will."

Modern philosophy also seems to have come to the conclusion that there is no real alternative to determinism, with the result that the question now discussed is no longer whether we are free but why we think we are free. We have seen how Alexander divides the world into levels which are at different stages of evolution—space-time, matter, life, mind, Deity. While conceding that all events are in actual fact deterministic, he considers that the inhabitants of each level may feel themselves free, while noting the absence of freedom prevailing in the levels lower than their own. Thus atoms, in the lowest level but one, feel themselves free when they contemplate space-time in which no freedom is possible; we have already quoted Spinoza's remark that a stone in the air would think itself free if it could forget the hand that had thrown it. In the same way, we think ourselves free, but think that machines and even plants—the levels just beneath us— are determinate. And again God, contemplating our activities from His higher level, feels Himself free but sees that we are not.

Without accepting any such scheme in detail, many philosophers would agree that we are able to do what we wish within limits, and so feel ourselves free, but this is only because we do not pause to reflect that our wishes themselves—the springs of our actions—are thrust on us by our pasts. On the other hand, as we have no immediate experience of this feeling of freedom in others, we see that their acts are thrust on them by their pasts, and so regard these acts as determinate.

In brief, neither the philosophical study nor the physical

research of the last 300 years has shown any cause for changing Descartes's dicta that "nothing cannot be the efficient
cause of anything" and that "the power of the will consists
only in this, that . . . we so act that we are not conscious of
being determined to a particular action by any external force."
Thus free-will is only our name for unconscious determinism. But Kant would presumably have argued that all this
does not prove that we are devoid of freedom, so much as
that a deterministic way of looking at things is ingrained in
our minds; it is our way of interpreting the temporal sequence of events.

And of course it may be. After a few individual experiences of the type "I have bumped my head, and I feel a pain,"
the growing child generalizes to such propositions as "I have
bumped my head, and *therefore* I feel a pain" and "If I bump
my head, I shall feel a pain." Such associations of ideas prove
helpful in avoiding further misadventures, and so are extended, and the habit of finding cause-effect relations grows.
But there is a continuous transition from cases such as those
just mentioned to "It is night, so it will soon be day" or "I am
hungry, so shall soon get something to eat," which are not
cause-effect relations at all. In these and similar ways the
post hoc ergo propter hoc habit of mind may become ingrained, and it may be possible to find a perfectly simple
psychological explanation of the cause-effect habit of the
human mind without even calling upon any inborn mental
"category."

In any case there can be no question that all our conscious
experiences of inanimate nature, which are limited to the
man-sized world, show that determinism does prevail here.
It may be that, because of this, we are unable to imagine how
anything but determinism can govern the inanimate world—
although modern physics shows that it does so far as the
phenomena are concerned—and that we then transfer this
inhibition from the material to the mental world. If so, it is
neither abstract physics nor concrete experience that thrusts
determinism upon us, but rather the inability of our minds to
imagine anything other than determinism.

Before the era of modern physics, it was a simple matter to define what we meant by causality and free-will. We supposed the world to consist of atoms and radiation; we imagined that precise positions could be assigned, in principle, to every atom and to every element of radiation, and the question of causality was simply whether, knowing these positions, it was possible in principle to predict the future course of events with certainty. The question of free-will was whether it was still possible to predict this course when consciousness and human volitions intervened in the picture.

But modern physics shows that these formulations of the questions have become meaningless. It is no longer possible to know the exact positions of particles or of elements of radiation, and, even if we could, it would still be impossible to predict what was going to happen next. So far as the inanimate world is concerned, we may picture a substratum below space and time in which the springs of events are concealed, and it may be that the future already lies hidden, but uniquely and inevitably determined, in this substratum. Such a hypothesis at least fits all the known facts of physics. But as we pass from the phenomenal world of space and time to this substratum, we seem, in some way we do not understand, to be passing from materialism to mentalism, and so possibly also from matter to mind. It may be then that the springs of events in this substratum include our own mental activities, so that the future course of events may depend in part on these mental activities.

At least the new physics has shown that the problems of causality and free-will are in need of a new formulation. If those who believe in freedom of the will could explain what they mean by freedom, and could show precisely where it differs from what we have called unconscious determinism, it is at least conceivable that what they want would be found in modern physics. The classical physics seemed to bolt and bar the door leading to any sort of freedom of the will; the new physics hardly does this; it almost seems to suggest that the door may be unlocked—if only we could find the handle. The old physics showed us a universe which looked more like a prison than a dwelling-place. The new physics shows us a universe which looks as though it might conceivably form a suitable dwelling-place for free men, and not a mere shelter for brutes—a home in which it may at least be possible for us to mould events to our desires and live lives of endeavour and achievement.

Conclusion

There is a temptation to try to round off our discussion by summarizing the conclusions we have reached. But the plain fact is that there are no conclusions. If we must state a conclusion, it would be that many of the former conclusions of nineteenth-century science on philosophical questions are once again in the melting-pot.

Just because of this, we cannot state any positive conclusions of any kind, as for instance that materialism is dead, or that a deterministic interpretation of the world is obsolete, but we can say that determinism and freedom, matter and materialism need to be redefined in the light of our new scientific knowledge. When this has been done, the materialist must decide for himself whether the only kind of materialism which science now permits can be suitably labelled materialism, and whether the ghostly remains of matter should be labelled as matter or as something else; it is mainly a question of terminology.

What remains is in any case very different from the full-blooded matter and the forbidding materialism of the Victorian scientist. His objective and material universe is proved to consist of little more than constructs of our own minds. In this and in other ways, modern physics has moved in the direction of mentalism.

Again we can hardly say that the new physics justifies any new conclusions on determinism, causality or free-will, but we can say that the argument for determinism is in some respects less compelling than it seemed to be fifty years ago. There appears to be a case for reopening the whole question as soon as anyone can discover how to do so.

This may seem a disappointing harvest to have garnered from so extensive a field of new scientific activity, and from one, moreover, which comes so close to the territory of philosophy. Yet we may reflect that physics and philosophy are at most a few thousand years old, but probably have lives of thousands of millions of years stretching away in front of them. They are only just beginning to get under way, and we are still, in Newton's words, like children playing with pebbles on the sea-shore, while the great ocean of truth rolls, unexplored, beyond our reach. It can hardly be a matter for surprise that our race has not succeeded in solving any large part of its most difficult problems in the first millionth part of its existence. Perhaps life would be a duller affair if it had, for to many it is not knowledge but the quest for knowledge that gives the greatest interest to thought—to travel hopefully is better than to arrive.

A. S. Eddington

REALITY, CAUSATION,
SCIENCE AND MYSTICISM

Sir Arthur Stanley Eddington
[1882–   ]

In his Preface to *The Nature of the Physical World* A. S. Eddington asserts, "The idealistic tinge in my conception of the physical world arose out of mathematical researches in the relativity theory." The British astronomer, famous for his studies in the motions of the stars, stellar evolution and relativity, seeks from science inferential concepts as they apply to human experience. He maintains that the physicist-philosopher must look beyond physics to the borderland of the material and spiritual worlds. Eddington insists that religion has become possible for a man of science within the last twenty years mainly because the philosophic trend of scientific thought has been startlingly re-directed by the discoveries of men like Einstein, Heisenberg and Bohr in the fields of relativity and quantum physics. "Reality, Causation, Science and Mysticism" is from Eddington's *The Nature of the Physical World*.

REALITY, CAUSATION, SCIENCE
AND MYSTICISM

A. S. EDDINGTON

Reality

The Real and the Concrete. ✥ One of our ancestors, taking arboreal exercise in the forest, failed to reach the bough intended and his hand closed on nothingness. The accident might well occasion philosophical reflections on the distinctions of substance and void—to say nothing of the phenomenon of gravity. However that may be, his descendants down to this day have come to be endowed with an immense respect for substance arising we know not how or why. So far as familiar experience is concerned, substance occupies the centre of the stage, rigged out with the attributes of form, colour, hardness, etc., which appeal to our several senses. Behind it is a subordinate background of space and time permeated by forces and unconcrete agencies to minister to the star performer.

Our conception of substance is only vivid so long as we do not face it. It begins to fade when we analyse it. We may dismiss many of its supposed attributes which are evidently projections of our sense-impressions outwards into the external world. Thus the colour which is so vivid to us is in our minds and cannot be embodied in a legitimate conception of the substantial object itself. But in any case colour is no part of the essential nature of substance. Its supposed nature is that which we try to call to mind by the word "concrete," which is perhaps an outward projection of our sense of touch. When I try to abstract from the bough everything but its substance or concreteness and concentrate on an effort to apprehend this, all ideas elude me; but the effort brings with it an instinctive tightening of the fingers—from which perhaps I might infer that my conception of substance is not very different from my arboreal ancestor's.

So strongly has substance held the place of leading actor on the stage of experience that in common usage *concrete* and *real* are almost synonymous. Ask any man who is not a philosopher or a mystic to name something typically real; he is almost sure to choose a concrete thing. Put the question to him whether Time is real; he will probably decide with some hesitation that it must be classed as real, but he has an inner feeling that the question is in some way inappropriate and that he is being cross-examined unfairly.

In the scientific world the conception of substance is wholly lacking, and that which most nearly replaces it, viz. electric charge, is not exalted as star-performer above the other entities of physics. For this reason the scientific world often shocks us by its appearance of unreality. It offers nothing to satisfy our demand for the concrete. How should it, when we cannot formulate that demand? I tried to formulate it; but nothing resulted save a tightening of the fingers. Science does not overlook the provision for tactual and muscular sensation. In leading us away from the concrete, science is reminding us that our contact with the real is more varied than was apparent to the ape-mind, to whom the bough which supported him typified the beginning and end of reality.

It is not solely the scientific world that will now occupy our attention. In accordance with the last chapter we are taking a larger view in which the cyclical schemes of physics are embraced with much besides. But before venturing on this more risky ground I have to emphasise one conclusion which is definitely scientific. The modern scientific theories have broken away from the common standpoint which identifies the real with the concrete. I think we might go so far as to say that time is more typical of physical reality than matter, because it is freer from those metaphysical associations which physics disallows. It would not be fair, being given an inch, to take an ell, and say that having gone so far physics may as well admit at once that reality is spiritual. We must go more warily. But in approaching such questions we are no longer tempted to take up the attitude that everything which lacks concreteness is thereby self-condemned.

The cleavage between the scientific and the extra-scientific domain of experience is, I believe, not a cleavage between the concrete and the transcendental but between the metrical and the non-metrical. I am at one with the materialist in feeling a repugnance towards any kind of pseudo-science of the extra-scientific territory. Science is not to be condemned as narrow because it refuses to deal with elements of experience which are unadapted to its own highly organised method; nor can it be blamed for looking superciliously on the comparative disorganisation of our knowledge and methods of reasoning about the non-metrical part of experience. But I think we have not been guilty of pseudo-science in our attempt to show in the last two chapters how it comes about that within the whole domain of experience a selected portion is capable of that exact metrical representation which is requisite for development by the scientific method.

Mind-Stuff. ⌐§ I will try to be as definite as I can as to the glimpse of reality which we seem to have reached. Only I am well aware that in committing myself to details I shall probably blunder. Even if the right view has here been taken of the philosophical trend of modern science, it is premature to suggest a cut-and-dried scheme of the nature of things. If the criticism is made that certain aspects are touched on which come more within the province of the expert psychologist, I must admit its pertinence. The recent tendencies of science do, I believe, take us to an eminence from which we can look down into the deep waters of philosophy; and if I rashly plunge into them, it is not because I have confidence in my powers of swimming, but to try to show that the water is really deep.

To put the conclusion crudely—the stuff of the world is mind-stuff. As is often the way with crude statements, I shall have to explain that by "mind" I do not here exactly mean mind and by "stuff" I do not at all mean stuff. Still this is about as near as we can get to the idea in a simple phrase. The mind-stuff of the world is, of course, something more general than our individual conscious minds; but we may think of its nature as not altogether foreign to the feelings in our consciousness. The realistic matter and fields of force of former physical theory are altogether irrelevant—except in so far as the mind-stuff has itself spun these imaginings. The symbolic matter and fields of force of present-day theory are more relevant, but they bear to it the same relation that the bursar's accounts bear to the activity of the college. Having granted this, the mental activity of the part of the world constituting ourselves occasions no surprise; it is known to us by direct self-knowledge, and we do not explain it away as something other than we know it to be—or, rather, it knows itself to be. It is the physical aspects of the world that we have to explain, presumably by some such method as that set forth in our discussion on world-building. Our bodies are more mysterious than our minds—at least they would be, only that we can set the mystery on one side by the device of the cyclic scheme of physics, which enables us to study their phenomenal behaviour without ever coming to grips with the underlying mystery.

The mind-stuff is not spread in space and time; these are part of the cyclic scheme ultimately derived out of it. But we must presume that in some other way or aspect it can be differentiated into parts. Only here and there does it rise to the level of consciousness, but from such islands proceeds all knowledge. Besides the direct knowledge contained in each self-knowing unit, there is inferential knowledge. The latter includes our knowledge of the physical world. It is necessary to keep reminding ourselves that all knowledge of our environment from which the world of physics is constructed, has entered in the form of messages transmitted along the nerves to the seat of consciousness. Obviously the messages travel in code. When messages relating to a table are travelling in the nerves, the nerve-disturbance does not in the least resemble either the external table that originates the mental impression or the conception of the table that arises in consciousness.[1] In the central clearing station the incoming messages are sorted and decoded, partly by instinctive image-building inherited from the experience of our ancestors, partly by scientific comparison and reasoning. By this very indirect and hypothetical inference all our supposed acquaintance with and our theories of a world outside us have been built up. We are acquainted with an external world because its fibres run into our consciousness; it is only our own ends of the fibres that we actually know; from those ends we more or less successfully reconstruct the rest, as a palaeontologist reconstructs an extinct monster from its footprint.

The mind-stuff is the aggregation of relations and relata which form the building material for the physical world. Our account of the building process shows, however, that much that is implied in the relations is dropped as unserviceable for the required building. Our view is practically that urged in 1875 by W. K. Clifford—

"The succession of feelings which constitutes a man's consciousness is the reality which produces in our minds the perception of the motions of his brain."

That is to say, that which the man himself knows as a

---

[1] I mean, resemble in intrinsic nature. It is true (as Bertrand Russell has emphasised) that the symbolic description of structure will be identical for the table in the external world and for the conception of the table in consciousness if the conception is scientifically correct. If the physicist does not attempt to penetrate beneath the structure he is indifferent as to which of the two we imagine ourselves to be discussing.

succession of feelings is the reality which when probed by the appliances of an outside investigator affects their readings in such a way that it is identified as a configuration of brain-matter. Again Bertrand Russell writes— [2]

"What the physiologist sees when he examines a brain is in the physiologist, not in the brain he is examining. What is in the brain by the time the physiologist examines it if it is dead, I do not profess to know; but while its owner was alive, part, at least, of the contents of his brain consisted of his percepts, thoughts, and feelings. Since his brain also consisted of electrons, we are compelled to conclude that an electron is a grouping of events, and that if the electron is in a human brain, some of the events composing it are likely to be some of the 'mental states' of the man to whom the brain belongs. Or, at any rate, they are likely to be parts of such 'mental states'—for it must not be assumed that part of a mental state must be a mental state. I do not wish to discuss what is meant by a 'mental state'; the main point for us is that the term must include percepts. Thus a percept is an event or a group of events, each of which belongs to one or more of the groups constituting the electrons in the brain. This, I think, is the most concrete statement that can be made about electrons; everything else that can be said is more or less abstract and mathematical."

I quote this partly for the sake of the remark that it must not be assumed that part of a mental state must necessarily be a mental state. We can no doubt analyse the content of consciousness during a short interval of time into more or less elementary constituent feelings; but it is not suggested that this psychological analysis will reveal the elements out of whose measure-numbers the atoms or electrons are built. The brain-matter is a partial aspect of the whole mental state; but the analysis of the brain-matter by physical investigation does not run at all parallel with the analysis of the mental state by psychological investigation. I assume that Russell meant to warn us that, in speaking of part of a mental

[2] *Analysis of Matter*, p. 320.

state, he was not limiting himself to parts that would be recognised as such psychologically, and he was admitting a more abstract kind of dissection.

This might give rise to some difficulty if we were postulating complete identity of mind-stuff with consciousness. But we know that in the mind there are memories not in consciousness at the moment but capable of being summoned into consciousness. We are vaguely aware that things we cannot recall are lying somewhere about and may come into the mind at any moment. Consciousness is not sharply defined, but fades into subconsciousness; and beyond that we must postulate something indefinite but yet continuous with our mental nature. This I take to be the world-stuff. We liken it to our conscious feelings because, now that we are convinced of the formal and symbolic character of the entities of physics, there is nothing else to liken it to.

It is sometimes urged that the basal stuff of the world should be called "neutral stuff" rather than "mind-stuff," since it is to be such that both mind and matter originate from it. If this is intended to emphasise that only limited islands of it constitute actual minds, and that even in these islands that which is known mentally is not equivalent to a complete inventory of all that may be there, I agree. In fact I should suppose that the self-knowledge of consciousness is mainly or wholly a knowledge which eludes the inventory method of description. The term "mind-stuff" might well be amended; but neutral stuff seems to be the wrong kind of amendment. It implies that we have two avenues of approach to an understanding of its nature. We have only one approach, namely, through our direct knowledge of mind. The supposed approach through the physical world leads only into the cycle of physics, where we run round and round like a kitten chasing its tail and never reach the world-stuff at all.

I assume that we have left the illusion of substance so far behind that the word "stuff" will not cause any misapprehension. I certainly do not intend to materialise or substantialise mind. Mind is—but you know what mind is like, so why should I say more about its nature? The word "stuff" has reference to the function it has to perform as a basis of world-building and does not imply any modified view of its nature.

It is difficult for the matter-of-fact physicist to accept the view that the substratum of everything is of mental character. But no one can deny that mind is the first and most direct thing in our experience, and all else is remote inference—inference either intuitive or deliberate. Probably it would never have occurred to us (as a serious hypothesis) that the world could be based on anything else, had we not been under the impression that there was a rival stuff with a more comfortable kind of "concrete" reality—something too inert and stupid to be capable of forging an illusion. The rival turns out to be a schedule of pointer readings; and though a world of symbolic character can well be constructed from it, this is a mere shelving of the inquiry into the nature of the world of experience.

This view of the relation of the material to the spiritual world perhaps relieves to some extent a tension between science and religion. Physical science has seemed to occupy a domain of reality which is self-sufficient, pursuing its course independently of and indifferent to that which a voice within us asserts to be a higher reality. We are jealous of such independence. We are uneasy that there should be an apparently self-contained world in which God becomes an unnecessary hypothesis. We acknowledge that the ways of God are inscrutable; but is there not still in the religious mind something of that feeling of the prophets of old, who called on God to assert his kingship and by sign or miracle proclaim that the forces of Nature are subject to his command? And yet if the scientist were to repent and admit that it was necessary to include among the agents controlling the stars and the electrons an omnipresent spirit to whom we trace the sacred things of consciousness, would there not be even graver apprehension? We should suspect an intention to reduce God to a system of differential equations, like the other agents which at various times have been introduced to restore order in the physical scheme. That fiasco at any rate is avoided.

For the sphere of the differential equations of physics is the metrical cyclic scheme extracted out of the broader reality. However much the ramifications of the cycles may be extended by further scientific discovery, they cannot from their very nature trench on the background in which they have their being—their actuality. It is in this background that our own mental consciousness lies; and here, if anywhere, we may find a Power greater than but akin to consciousness. It is not possible for the controlling laws of the spiritual substratum, which in so far as it is known to us in consciousness is essentially nonmetrical, to be analogous to the differential and other mathematical equations of physics which are meaningless unless they are fed with metrical quantities. So that the crudest anthropomorphic image of a spiritual deity can scarcely be so wide of the truth as one conceived in terms of metrical equations.

The Definition of Reality. ⋨ It is time we came to grips with the loose terms Reality and Existence, which we have been using without any inquiry into what they are meant to convey. I am afraid of this word Reality, not connoting an ordinarily definable characteristic of the things it is applied to but used as though it were some kind of celestial halo. I very much doubt if any one of us has the faintest idea of what is meant by the reality or existence of anything but our own Egos. That is a bold statement, which I must guard against misinterpretation. It is, of course, possible to obtain consistent use of the word "reality" by adopting a conventional definition. My own practice would probably be covered by the definition that a thing may be said to be real if it is the goal of a type of inquiry to which I personally attach importance. But if I insist on no more than this I am whittling down the significance that is generally assumed. In physics we can give a cold scientific definition of reality which is free from all sentimental mystification. But this is not quite fair play, because the word "reality" is generally used *with the*

intention of evoking sentiment. It is a grand word for a pero-
ration. "The right honourable speaker went on to declare
that the concord and amity for which he had unceasingly
striven had now become a reality (loud cheers)." The conception which it is so troublesome to apprehend is not "reality" but "reality (loud cheers)."

Let us first examine the definition according to the purely
scientific usage of the word, although it will not take us far
enough. The only subject presented to me for study is the
content of my consciousness. You are able to communicate
to me part of the content of your consciousness which thereby
becomes accessible in my own. For reasons which are generally admitted, though I should not like to have to prove
that they are conclusive, I grant your consciousness equal
status with my own; and I use this second-hand part of my
consciousness to "put myself in your place." Accordingly my
subject of study becomes differentiated into the contents of
many consciousnesses, each content constituting a *view-point.*
There then arises the problem of combining the view-
points, and it is through this that the external world of physics arises. Much that is in any one consciousness is individual,
much is apparently alterable by volition; but there is a
stable element which is common to other consciousnesses.
That common element we desire to study, to describe as
fully and accurately as possible, and to discover the laws by
which it combines now with one view-point, now with another. This common element cannot be placed in one man's
consciousness rather than in another's; it must be in neutral
ground—an external world.

It is true that I have a strong impression of an external
world apart from any communication with other conscious
beings. But apart from such communication I should have no
reason to trust the impression. Most of our common impressions of substance, world-wide instants, and so on, have
turned out to be illusory, and the externality of the world
might be equally untrustworthy. The impression of externality is equally strong in the world that comes to me in
dreams; the dream-world is less rational, but that might be

used as an argument in favour of its externality as showing its dissociation from the internal faculty of reason. So long as we have to deal with one consciousness alone, the hypothesis that there is an external world responsible for part of what appears in it is an idle one. All that can be asserted of this external world is a mere duplication of the knowledge that can be much more confidently asserted of the world appearing in the consciousness. The hypothesis only becomes useful when it is the means of bringing together the worlds of many consciousnesses occupying different view-points.

The external world of physics is thus a symposium of the worlds presented to different view-points. There is general agreement as to the principles on which the symposium should be formed. Statements made about this external world, if they are unambiguous, must be either true or false. This has often been denied by philosophers. It is quite commonly said that scientific theories about the world are neither true nor false but merely convenient or inconvenient. A favourite phrase is that the gauge of value of a scientific theory is that it economises thought. Certainly a simple statement is preferable to a circumlocutory one; and as regards any current scientific theory, it is much easier to show that it is convenient or that it economises thought than that it is true. But whatever lower standards we may apply in practice we need not give up our ideals; and so long as there is a distinction between true and false theories our aim must be to eliminate the false. For my part I hold that the continual advance of science is not a mere utilitarian progress; it is progress towards ever purer truth. Only let it be understood that the truth we seek in science is the truth about an external world propounded as the theme of study, and is not bound up with any opinion as to the status of that world —whether or not it wears the halo of reality, whether or not it is deserving of "loud cheers."

Assuming that the symposium has been correctly carried out, the external world and all that appears in it are called real without further ado. When we (scientists) assert of anything in the external world that it is real and that it exists, we are expressing our belief that the rules of the symposium have been correctly applied—that it is not a false concept introduced by an error in the process of synthesis, or a hallucination belonging to only one individual consciousness, or an incomplete representation which embraces certain viewpoints but conflicts with others. We refuse to contemplate the awful contingency that the external world, after all our care in arriving at it, might be disqualified by failing to exist; because we have no idea what the supposed qualification would consist in, nor in what way the prestige of the world would be enhanced if it passed the implied test. The external world is the world that confronts that experience which we have in common, and for us no other world could fill the same rôle, no matter how high honours it might take in the qualifying examination.

This domestic definition of existence for scientific purposes follows the principle now adopted for all other definitions in science, namely, that a thing must be defined according to the way in which it is in practice recognised and not according to some ulterior significance that we imagine it to possess. Just as matter must shed its conception of substantiality, so existence must shed its halo, before we can admit it into physical science. But clearly if we are to assert or to question the existence of anything not comprised in the external world of physics, we must look beyond the physical definition. The mere questioning of the reality of the physical world implies some higher censorship than the scientific method itself can supply.

The external world of physics has been formulated as an answer to a particular problem encountered in human experience. Officially the scientist regards it as a problem which he just happened across, as he might take up a cross-word problem encountered in a newspaper. His sole business is to see that the problem is correctly solved. But questions may be raised about a problem which play no part and need not be considered in connection with the solving of the problem. The extraneous question naturally raised about the problem of the external world is whether there is some higher justification for embarking on this world-solving competition rather than on other problems which our experience might suggest to us. Just what kind of justification the scientist would claim for his quest is not very clear, because it is not within the province of science to formulate such a claim. But certainly he makes claims which do not rest on the aesthetic perfection of the solution or on material benefits derived from scientific research. He would not allow his subject to be shoved aside in a symposium on truth. We can scarcely say anything more definite than that science claims a "halo" for its world.

If we are to find for the atoms and electrons of the external world not merely a conventional reality but "reality (loud cheers)" we must look not to the end but to the beginning of the quest. It is at the beginning that we must find that sanction which raises these entities above the mere products of an arbitrary mental exercise. This involves some kind of assessment of the impulse which sets us forth on the voyage of discovery. How can we make such assessment? Not by any reasoning that I know of. Reasoning would only tell us that the impulse might be judged by the success of the adventure—whether it leads in the end to things which really exist and wear the halo in their own right; it takes us to and fro like a shuttle along the chain of inference in vain search for the elusive halo. But, legitimately or not, the mind is confident that it can distinguish certain quests as sanctioned by indisputable authority. We may put it in different ways; the impulse to this quest is part of our very nature; it is the expression of a purpose which has possession of us. Is this precisely what we meant when we sought to affirm the reality of the external world? It goes some way towards giving it a meaning but is scarcely the full equivalent. I doubt if we really satisfy the conceptions behind that demand unless we make the bolder hypothesis that the quest and all that is reached by it are of worth in the eyes of an Absolute Valuer.

Whatever justification at the source we accept to vindicate the reality of the external world, it can scarcely fail to admit on the same footing much that is outside physical science.

Although no long chains of regularised inference depend from them we recognise that other fibres of our being extend in directions away from sense-impressions. I am not greatly concerned to borrow words like "existence" and "reality" to crown these other departments of the soul's interest. I would rather put it that any raising of the question of reality in its transcendental sense (whether the question emanates from the world of physics or not) leads us to a perspective from which we see man not as a bundle of sensory impressions, but conscious of purpose and responsibilities to which the external world is subordinate.

From this perspective we recognise a spiritual world alongside the physical world. Experience—that is to say, the self *cum* environment—comprises more than can be embraced in the physical world, restricted as it is to a complex of metrical symbols. The physical world is, we have seen, the answer to one definite and urgent problem arising in a survey of experience; and no other problem has been followed up with anything like the same precision and elaboration. Progress towards an understanding of the non-sensory constituents of our nature is not likely to follow similar lines, and indeed is not animated by the same aims. If it is felt that this difference is so wide that the phrase spiritual *world* is a misleading analogy, I will not insist on the term. All I would claim is that those who in the search for truth start from consciousness as a seat of self-knowledge with interests and responsibilities not confined to the material plane, are just as much facing the hard facts of experience as those who start from consciousness as a device for reading the indications of spectroscopes and micrometers.

Physical Illustrations. ✍ If the reader is unconvinced that there can be anything indefinite in the question whether a thing exists or not, let him glance at the following problem. Consider a distribution of matter in Einstein's spherical "finite but unbounded" space. Suppose that the matter is so arranged

that every particle has an exactly similar particle at its antipodes. (There is some reason to believe that the matter
would *necessarily* have this arrangement in consequence of
the law of gravitation; but this is not certain.) Each group
of particles will therefore be exactly like the antipodal group
not only in its structure and configuration but in its entire
surroundings; the two groups will in fact be indistinguishable
by any possible experimental test. Starting on a journey
round the spherical world we come across a group A, and
then after going half round we come to an exactly similar
group A' indistinguishable by any test; another half circle
again brings us to an exactly similar group, which, however,
we decide is the original group A. Now let us ponder a little.
We realise that in any case by going on far enough we come
back to the same group. Why do we not accept the obvious
conclusion that this happened when we reached A'; everything was exactly as though we had reached the starting-
point again? We have encountered a succession of precisely
similar phenomena but for some arbitrary reason have decided that only the alternate ones are *really* the same. There
is no difficulty in identifying all of them; in that case the
space is "elliptical" instead of "spherical." But which is the
real truth? Disregard the fact that I introduced A and A' to
you as though they were not the same particles, because that
begs the question; imagine that you have actually had this
adventure in a world you had not been told about. You cannot find out the answer. Can you conceive what the question
means? I cannot. All that turns on the answer is whether we
shall provide two separate haloes for A and A' or whether
one will suffice.

Descriptions of the phenomena of atomic physics have an
extraordinary vividness. We see the atoms with their girdles
of circulating electrons darting hither and thither, colliding
and rebounding. Free Electrons torn from the girdles hurry
away a hundred times faster, curving sharply round the atoms
with side slips and hairbreadth escapes. The truants are caught
and attached to the girdles and the escaping energy shakes the
aether into vibration. X-rays impinge on the atoms and toss

the electrons into higher orbits. We see these electrons falling back again, sometimes by steps, sometimes with a rush,
caught in a cul-de-sac of metastability, hesitating before "for-
bidden passages." Behind it all the quantum h regulates each
change with mathematical precision. This is the sort of picture that appeals to our understanding—no insubstantial pag-
eant to fade like a dream.

The spectacle is so fascinating that we have perhaps forgotten that there was a time when we wanted to be told what
an electron is. The question was never answered. No familiar
conceptions can be woven round the electron; it belongs to
the waiting list. Similarly the description of the processes
must be taken with a grain of salt. The tossing up of the electron is a conventional way of depicting a particular change
of state of the atom which cannot really be associated with
movements in space as macroscopically conceived. *Something
unknown is doing we don't know what*—that is what our
theory amounts to. It does not sound a particularly illuminating theory. I have read something like it elsewhere—

The slithy toves
Did gyre and gimble in the wabe.

There is the same suggestion of activity. There is the same
indefiniteness as to the nature of the activity and of what it
is that is acting. And yet from so unpromising a beginning we
really do get somewhere. We bring into order a host of apparently unrelated phenomena; we make predictions, and our
predictions come off. The reason—the sole reason—for this
progress is that our description is not limited to unknown
agents executing unknown activities, but *numbers* are scattered freely in the description. To contemplate electrons
circulating in the atom carries us no further; but by contemplating eight circulating electrons in one atom and seven
circulating electrons in another we begin to realise the difference between oxygen and nitrogen. Eight slithy toves gyre
and gimble in the oxygen wabe; seven in nitrogen. By admitting a few numbers even "Jabberwocky" may become scien-

tific. We can now venture on a prediction; if one of its toves escapes, oxygen will be masquerading in a garb properly belonging to nitrogen. In the stars and nebulae we do find such wolves in sheep's clothing which might otherwise have startled us. It would not be a bad reminder of the essential unknownness of the fundamental entities of physics to translate it into "Jabberwocky"; provided all numbers—all metrical attributes—are unchanged, it does not suffer in the least. Out of the numbers proceeds that harmony of natural law which it is the aim of science to disclose. We can grasp the tune but not the player. Trinculo might have been referring to modern physics in the words, "This is the tune of our catch, played by the picture of Nobody."

Causation

In the old conflict between freewill and predestination it has seemed hitherto that physics comes down heavily on the side of predestination. Without making extravagant claims for the scope of natural law, its moral sympathy has been with the view that whatever the future may bring forth is already foretold in the configurations of the past—

> Yea, the first Morning of Creation wrote
> What the Last Dawn of Reckoning shall read.

I am not so rash as to invade Scotland with a solution of a problem which has rent her from the synod to the cottage. Like most other people, I suppose, I think it incredible that the wider scheme of Nature which includes life and conscious can be completely predetermined; yet I have not been able to form a satisfactory conception of any kind of law or causal sequence which shall be other than deterministic. It seems contrary to our feeling of the dignity of the mind to suppose that it merely registers a dictated sequence of thoughts and emotions; but it seems equally contrary to its dignity to put it at the mercy of impulses with no causal antecedents. I shall not deal with this dilemma. Here I have to set forth the position of physical science on this matter so far as it comes into her territory. It does come into her territory, because that which we call human will cannot be entirely dissociated from the consequent motions of the muscles and disturbance of the material world. On the scientific side a new situation has arisen. It is a consequence of the advent of the quantum theory that *physics is no longer pledged to a scheme of deterministic law*. Determinism has dropped out altogether in the latest formulations of theoretical physics and it is at least open to doubt whether it will ever be brought back.

The foregoing paragraph is from the manuscript of the original lecture delivered in Edinburgh. The attitude of physics at that time was one of indifference to determinism. If there existed a scheme of strictly causal law at the base of phenomena the search for it was not at present practical politics, and meanwhile another ideal was being pursued. The fact that a causal basis had been lost sight of in the new theories was fairly well known; many regretted it, and held that its restoration was imperative.[3]

In rewriting this chapter a year later I have had to mingle with this attitude of indifference an attitude more definitely hostile to determinism which has arisen from the acceptance of the Principle of Indeterminacy. There has been no time for more than a hurried examination of the far-reaching consequences of this principle; and I should have been reluctant to include "stop-press" ideas were it not that they appear to clinch the conception towards which the earlier developments were leading. The future is a combination

---

[3] A few days after the course of lectures was completed, Einstein wrote in his message on the Newton Centenary, "It is only in the quantum theory that Newton's differential method becomes inadequate, and indeed strict causality fails us. But the last word has not yet been said. May the spirit of Newton's method give us the power to restore unison between physical reality and the profoundest characteristic of Newton's teaching—strict causality." (*Nature*, 1927, March 26, p. 467.)

of the causal influences of the past together with unpredictable elements—unpredictable not merely because it is impracticable to obtain the data of prediction, but because no data connected causally with our experience exist. It will be necessary to defend so remarkable a change of opinion at some length. Meanwhile we may note that science thereby withdraws its moral opposition to free-will. Those who maintain a deterministic theory of mental activity must do so as the outcome of their study of the mind itself and not with the idea that they are thereby making it more conformable with our experimental knowledge of the laws of inorganic nature.

Causation and Time's Arrow. ✍§ Cause and effect are closely bound up with time's arrow; the cause must precede the effect. The relativity of time has not obliterated this order. An event Here-Now can only cause events in the cone of absolute future; it can be caused by events in the cone of absolute past; it can neither cause nor be caused by events in the neutral wedge, since the necessary influence would in that case have to be transmitted with a speed faster than light. But curiously enough this elementary notion of cause and effect is quite inconsistent with a strictly causal scheme. How can I cause an event in the absolute future, if the future was predetermined before I was born? The notion evidently implies that something may be born into the world at the instant Here-Now, which has an influence extending throughout the future cone but no corresponding linkage to the cone of absolute past. The primary laws of physics do not provide for any such one-way linkage; any alteration in a prescribed state of the world implies alterations in its past state symmetrical with the alterations in its future state. Thus in primary physics, which knows nothing of time's arrow, there is no discrimination of cause and effect; but events are connected by a *symmetrical* causal relation which is the same viewed from either end.

Primary physics postulates a strictly causal scheme, but the causality is a symmetrical relation and not the one-way relation of cause and effect. Secondary physics can distinguish cause and effect but its foundation does not rest on a causal scheme and it is indifferent as to whether or not strict causality prevails.

The lever in a signal box is moved and the signal drops. We can point out the relation of constraint which associates the positions of lever and signal; we can also find that the movements are not synchronous, and calculate the time-difference. But the laws of mechanics do not ascribe an absolute sign to this time-difference; so far as they are concerned we may quite well suppose that the drop of the signal causes the motion of the lever. To settle which is the cause, we have two options. We can appeal to the signalman who is confident that *he* made the mental decision to pull the lever; but this criterion will only be valid if we agree that there was a genuine decision between two possible courses and not a mere mental registration of what was already predetermined. Or we can appeal to secondary law which takes note of the fact that there was more of the random element in the world when the signal dropped than when the lever moved. But the feature of secondary law is that it ignores strict causation; it concerns itself not with what must happen but with what is likely to happen. Thus distinction of cause and effect has no meaning in the closed system of primary laws of physics; to get at it we have to break into the scheme, introducing considerations of volition or of probability which are foreign to it. This is rather analogous to the ten vanishing coefficients of curvature which could only be recognised if the closed system of the world were broken into by standards foreign to it.

For convenience I shall call the relation of effect to cause *causation*, and the symmetrical relation which does not distinguish between cause and effect *causality*. In primary physics causality has completely replaced causation. Ideally the whole world past and future is connected into a deterministic scheme by relations of causality. Up till very recently it was universally held that such a determinate scheme must exist (possibly subject to suspension by supernatural agencies outside the scope of physics); we may therefore call this the "orthodox" view. It was, of course, recognised that we were only acquainted with part of the structure of this causal scheme, but it was the settled aim of theoretical physics to discover the whole.

This replacement in orthodox science of causation by causality is important in one respect. We must not let causality borrow an intuitive sanction which really belongs only to causation. We may think we have an intuition that the same cause cannot have two alternative effects; but we do not claim any intuition that the same effect may not spring from two alternative causes. For this reason the assumption of a rigid determinateness enforced by relations of causality cannot be said to be insisted on by intuition.

What is the ground for so much ardent faith in the orthodox hypothesis that physical phenomena rest ultimately on a scheme of completely deterministic laws? I think there are two reasons—

(1) The principal laws of Nature which have been discovered are apparently of this deterministic type, and these have furnished the great triumphs of physical prediction. It is natural to trust to a line of progress which has served as well in the past. Indeed it is a healthy attitude to assume that nothing is beyond the scope of scientific prediction until the limits of prediction actually declare themselves.

(2) The current epistemology of science presupposes a deterministic scheme of this type. To modify it involves a much deeper change in our attitude to natural knowledge than the mere abandonment of an untenable hypothesis.

In explanation of the second point we must recall that knowledge of the physical world has to be inferred from the nerve-messages which reach our brains, and the current epistemology assumes that there exists a determinate scheme of inference (lying before us as an ideal and gradually being unravelled). But, as has already been pointed out, the chains of inference are simply the converse of the chains of physical causality by which distant events are connected to the nerve-messages. If the scheme of transmission of these messages through the external world is not deterministic then the scheme of inference as to their source cannot be deterministic, and our epistemology has been based on an impossible ideal. In that case our attitude to the whole scheme of natural knowledge must be profoundly modified.

These reasons will be considered at length, but it is convenient to state here our answers to them in equally summary form.

(1) In recent times some of the greatest triumphs of physical prediction have been furnished by admittedly statistical laws which do not rest on a basis of causality. Moreover the great laws hitherto accepted as causal appear on minuter examination to be of statistical character.

(2) Whether or not there is a causal scheme at the base of atomic phenomena, modern atomic theory is not now attempting to find it; and it is making rapid progress because it no longer sets this up as a practical aim. We are in the position of holding an epistemological theory of natural knowledge which does not correspond to actual aim of current scientific investigation.

Predictability of Events. ᴇ§ Let us examine a typical case of successful scientific prediction. A total eclipse of the sun visible in Cornwall is prophesied for 11 August 1999. It is generally supposed that this eclipse is already predetermined by the present configuration of the sun, earth and moon. I do not wish to arouse unnecessary misgiving as to whether the eclipse will come off. I expect it will; but let us examine the grounds of expectation. It is predicted as a consequence of the law of gravitation—a law which we found in chapter VII to be a mere truism. That does not diminish the value of the prediction; but it does suggest that we may not be able to pose as such marvellous prophets when we come up against laws which are not mere truisms. I might venture to predict that 2 + 2 will be equal to 4 even in 1999; but if this should prove correct it will not help to convince anyone that the universe (or, if you like, the human mind) is governed by laws of deterministic type. I suppose that in the most erratically governed world *something* can be predicted if truisms are not excluded.

But we have to look deeper than this. The law of gravitation is only a truism when regarded from a macroscopic point of view. It presupposes space, and measurement with gross material or optical arrangements. It cannot be refined to an accuracy beyond the limits of these gross appliances; so that it is a truism with a probable error—small, but not infinitely small. The classical laws hold good in the limit when exceedingly large quantum numbers are involved. The system comprising the sun, earth and moon has exceedingly high state-number and the predictability of its configurations is not characteristic of natural phenomena in general but of those involving great numbers of atoms of action—such that we are concerned not with individual but with average behaviour.

Human life is proverbially uncertain; few things are more certain than the solvency of a life-insurance company. The average law is so trustworthy that it may be considered predestined that half the children now born will survive the age of x years. But that does not tell us whether the span of life of young A. McB. is already written in the book of fate, or whether there is still time to alter it by teaching him not to run in front of motor-buses. The eclipse in 1999 is as safe as the balance of a life-insurance company; the next quantum jump of an atom is as uncertain as your life and mine.

We are thus in a position to answer the main argument for a predetermination of the future, viz. that observation shows the laws of Nature to be of a type which leads to definite predictions of the future, and it is reasonable to expect that any laws which remain undiscovered will conform to the same type. For when we ask what is the characteristic of the phenomena that have been successfully predicted, the answer is that they are effects depending on the average configurations

of vast numbers of individual entities. But averages are predictable because they are averages, irrespective of the type of
government of the phenomena underlying them.

Considering an atom alone in the world in State 3, the classical theory would have asked, and hoped to answer, the question, What will it do next? The quantum theory substitutes
the question, Which will it do next? Because it admits only
two lower states for the atom to go to. Further, it makes no
attempt to find a definite answer, but contents itself with
calculating the respective odds on the jumps to State 1 and
State 2. The quantum physicist does not fill the atom with
gadgets for directing its future behaviour, as the classical
physicist would have done; he fills it with gadgets determining
the odds on its future behaviour. He studies the art of the
bookmaker not of the trainer.

Thus in the structure of the world as formulated in the new
quantum theory it is predetermined that of 500 atoms now in
State 3, approximately 400 will go on to State 1 and 100 to
State 2—in so far as anything subject to chance fluctuations
can be said to be predetermined. The odds of 4 to 1 find their
appropriate representation in the picture of the atom; that
is to say, something symbolic of a 4 : 1 ratio is present in each
of the 500 atoms. But there are no marks distinguishing the
atoms belonging to the group of 100 from the 400. Probably
most physicists would take the view that although the marks
are not yet shown in the picture, they are nevertheless present
in Nature; they belong to an elaboration of the theory which
will come in good time. The marks, of course, need not be
in the atom itself; they may be in the environment which will
interact with it. For example, we may load dice in such a way
that the odds are 4 to 1 on throwing a 6. Both those dice
which turn up 6 and those which do not have these odds written in their constitution—by a displaced position of the centre
of gravity. The result of a particular throw is not marked in
the dice; nevertheless it is strictly causal (apart perhaps from
the human element involved in throwing the dice) being determined by the external influences which are concerned. Our
own position at this stage is that future developments of phys-

ics may reveal such causal marks (either in the atom or in the influences outside it) or it may not. Hitherto whenever we have thought we have detected causal marks in natural phenomena they have always proved spurious, the apparent determinism having come about in another way. Therefore we are inclined to regard favourably the possibility that there may be no causal marks anywhere.

But, it will be said, it is inconceivable that an atom can be so evenly balanced between two alternative courses that nowhere in the world as yet is there any trace of the ultimately deciding factor. This is an appeal to intuition and it may fairly be countered with another appeal to intuition. I have an intuition much more immediate than any relating to the objects of the physical world; this tells me that nowhere in the world as yet is there any trace of a deciding factor as to whether I am going to lift my right hand or my left. It depends on an unfettered act of volition not yet made or foreshadowed.[4] My intuition is that the future is able to bring forth deciding factors which are not secretly hidden in the past.

The position is that the laws governing the microscopic elements of the physical world—individual atoms, electrons, quanta—do not make definite predictions as to what the individual will do next. I am here speaking of the laws that have been actually discovered and formulated on the old quantum theory and the new. These laws indicate several possibilities in the future and state the odds on each. In general the odds are moderately balanced and are not tempting to an aspiring prophet. But short odds on the behaviour of individuals combine into very long odds on suitably selected statistics of a number of individuals; and the wary prophet can find predictions of this kind on which to stake his credit—without serious risk. All the successful predictions hitherto attributed to causality are traceable to this. It is quite true that the quan-

---

[4] It is fair to assume the trustworthiness of this intuition in answering an argument which appeals to intuition; the assumption would beg the question if we were urging the argument independently.

tum laws for individuals are not incompatible with causality; they merely ignore it. But if we take advantage of this indifference to reintroduce determinism at the basis of world structure it is because our philosophy predisposes us that way, not because we know of any experimental evidence in its favour.

We might for illustration make a comparison with the doctrine of predestination. That theological doctrine, whatever may be said against it, has hitherto seemed to blend harmoniously with the predetermination of the material universe. But if we were to appeal to the new conception of physical law to settle this question by analogy the answer would be:—The individual is not predestined to arrive at either of the two states, which perhaps may here be sufficiently discriminated as State 1 and State 2; the most that can be considered already settled is the respective odds on his reaching these states.

The New Epistemological Outlook. ✎ Scientific investigation does not lead to knowledge of the intrinsic nature of things. "Whenever we state the properties of a body in terms of physical quantities we are imparting knowledge of the response of various metrical indicators to its presence and nothing more." But if a body is not acting according to strict causality, if there is an element of uncertainty as to the response of the indicators, we seem to have cut away the ground for this kind of knowledge. It is not predetermined what will be the reading of the weighing-machine if the body is placed on it, therefore the body has no definite mass; nor where it will be found an instant hence, therefore it has no definite velocity; nor where the rays now being reflected from it will converge in the microscope, therefore it has no definite position; and so on. It is no use answering that the body really has a definite mass, velocity, position, etc., which we are unaware of; that statement, if it means anything, refers to an intrinsic nature of things outside the scope of scientific knowledge. We cannot infer these properties with precision from anything that we can be aware of, because the breach of causality has broken the chain of inference. Thus our knowledge of the response of indicators to the presence of the body is non-existent; therefore we cannot assert knowledge of it at all. So what is the use of talking about it? The body which was to be the abstraction of all these (as yet unsettled) pointer readings has become superfluous in the physical world. That is the dilemma into which the old epistemology leads us as soon as we begin to doubt strict causality.

In phenomena on a gross scale this difficulty can be got round. A body may have no definite position but yet have within close limits an extremely probable position. When the probabilities are large the substitution of probability for certainty makes little difference; it adds only a negligible haziness to the world. But though the practical change is unimportant there are fundamental theoretical consequences. All probabilities rest on a basis of *a priori* probability, and we cannot say whether probabilities are large or small without having assumed such a basis. In agreeing to accept those of our calculated probabilities which are very high as virtually equivalent to certainties on the old scheme, we are as it were making our adopted basis of *a priori* probability a constituent of the world-structure—adding to the world a kind of symbolic texture that cannot be expressed on the old scheme.

On the atomic scale of phenomena the probabilities are in general well-balanced, and there are no "naps" for the scientific punter to put his shirt on. If a body is still defined as a bundle of pointer readings (or highly probable pointer readings) there are no "bodies" on the atomic scale. All that we can extract is a bundle of probabilities. That is in fact just how Schrödinger tries to picture the atom—as a wave centre of his probability entity ψ.

We commonly have had to deal with probabilities which arise through ignorance. With fuller knowledge we should sweep away the references to probability and substitute the exact facts. But it appears to be a fundamental point in Schrödinger's theory that his probabilities are not to be replaced in that way. When his ψ is sufficiently concentrated it indi-

438

A. S. EDDINGTON

cates the point where the electron is; when it is diffused it gives only a vague indication of the position. But this vague indication is not something which ideally ought to be replaced by exact knowledge; it is ψ itself which acts as the source of the light emitted from the atom, the period of the light being that of the beats of ψ. I think this means that the spread of ψ is not a symbol for uncertainty arising through lack of information; it is a symbol for causal failure—an indeterminacy of behaviour which is part of the character of the atom.

We have two chief ways of learning about the interior of the atom. We can observe electrons entering or leaving, and we can observe light entering or leaving. Bohr has assumed a structure connected by strictly causal law with the first phenomenon, Heisenberg and his followers with the second. If the two structures were identifiable then the atom would involve a complete causal connection of the two types of phenomena. But apparently no such causal linkage exists. Therefore we have to be content with a correlation in which the entities of the one model represent probabilities in the second model. There are perhaps details in the two theories which do not quite square with this; but it seems to express the ideal to be aimed at in describing the laws of an incompletely causal world, viz. that the causal source of one phenomenon shall represent the probability of causal source of another phenomenon. Schrödinger's theory has given at least a strong hint that the actual world is controlled on this plan.

The Principle of Indeterminacy. Thus far we have shown that modern physics is drifting away from the postulate that the future is predetermined, ignoring it rather than deliberately rejecting it. With the discovery of the Principle of Indeterminacy its attitude has become more definitely hostile.

Let us take the simplest case in which we think we can predict the future. Suppose that we have a particle with known position and velocity at the present instant. Assuming that nothing interferes with it we can predict the position at a subsequent instant. (Strictly the noninterference would be a subject for another prediction, but to simplify matters we shall concede it.) It is just this simple prediction which the principle of indeterminacy expressly forbids. It states that we cannot know accurately both the velocity and position of a particle at the present instant.

At first sight there seems to be an inconsistency. There is no limit to the accuracy with which we may know the position, provided that we do not want to know the velocity also. Very well; let us make a highly accurate determination of position now, and after waiting a moment make another highly accurate determination of position. Comparing the two accurate positions we compute the accurate velocity— and snap our fingers at the principle of indeterminacy. This velocity, however, is of no use for prediction, because in making the second accurate determination of position we have rough-handled the particle so much that it no longer has the velocity we calculated. *It is a purely retrospective velocity.* The velocity does not exist in the present tense but in the future perfect; it never exists, it never will exist, but a time may come when it *will have* existed.

The velocity which we attribute to a particle now can be regarded as an anticipation of its future positions. To say that it is unknowable (except with a certain degree of inaccuracy) is to say that the future cannot be anticipated. Immediately the future is accomplished, so that it is no longer an anticipation, the velocity becomes knowable.

The classical view that a particle necessarily has a definite (but not necessarily knowable) velocity now, amounts to disguising a piece of the unknown future as an unknowable element of the present. Classical physics foists a deterministic scheme on us by a trick; it smuggles the unknown future into the present, trusting that we shall not press an inquiry as to whether it has become any more knowable that way.

The same principle extends to every kind of phenomenon that we attempt to predict, so long as the need for accuracy is not buried under a mass of averages. To every co-ordinate there corresponds a momentum, and by the principle of indeterminacy the more accurately the co-ordinate is known the less accurately the momentum is known. Nature thus provides that knowledge of one-half of the world will ensure ignorance of the other half—ignorance which, we have seen, may be remedied later when the same part of the world is contemplated retrospectively. We can scarcely rest content with a picture of the world which includes so much that cannot be known. We have been trying to get rid of unknowable things, i.e. all conceptions which have no causal connection with our experience. We have eliminated velocity through aether, "right" frames of space, etc., for this reason. This vast new unknowable element must likewise be swept out of the Present. Its proper place is in the Future because then it will no longer be unknowable. It has been put in prematurely as an anticipation of that which cannot be anticipated.

In assessing whether the symbols which the physicist has scattered through the external world are adequate to predetermine the future, we must be on our guard against retrospective symbols. It is easy to prophesy after the event.

Natural and Supernatural. ✒ A rather serious consequence of dropping causality in the external world is that it leaves us with no clear distinction between the Natural and the Supernatural. In an earlier chapter I compared the invisible agent invented to account for the tug of gravitation to a "demon." Is a view of the world which admits such an agent any more scientific than that of a savage who attributes all that he finds mysterious in Nature to the work of invisible demons? The Newtonian physicist had a valid defence. He could point out that his demon Gravitation was supposed to act according to fixed causal laws and was therefore not to be compared with the irresponsible demons of the savage. Once a deviation from strict causality is admitted the distinction melts away. I suppose that the savage would admit that his demon was to some extent a creature of habit and that it would be possible to make a fair guess as to what he would do in the future; but that sometimes he would show a will of his own. It is that imperfect consistency which formerly disqualified him from admission as an entity of physics along with his brother Gravitation.

That is largely why there has been so much bother about "me"; because I have, or am persuaded that I have, "a will of my own." Either the physicist must leave his causal scheme at the mercy of supernatural interference from me, or he must explain away my supernatural qualities. In self-defence the materialist favoured the latter course; he decided that I was not supernatural—only complicated. We on the other hand have concluded that there is no strict causal behaviour anywhere. We can scarcely deny the charge that in abolishing the criterion of causality we are opening the door to the savage's demons. It is a serious step, but I do not think it means the end of all true science. After all if they try to enter we can pitch them out again, as Einstein pitched out the respectable causal demon who called himself Gravitation. It is a privation to be no longer able to stigmatise certain views as *unscientific* superstition; but we are still allowed, if the circumstances justify it, to reject them as *bad science*.

Volition. From the philosophic point of view it is of deep interest to consider how this affects the freedom of the human mind and spirit. A complete determinism of the material universe cannot be divorced from determinism of the mind. Take, for example, the prediction of the weather this time next year. The prediction is not likely ever to become practicable, but "orthodox" physicists are not yet convinced that it is theoretically impossible; they hold that next year's weather is already predetermined. We should require extremely detailed knowledge of present conditions, since a small local deviation can exert an ever-expanding influence. We must examine the state of the sun so as to predict the fluctuations in the heat and corpuscular radiation which it sends us. We must dive into the bowels of the earth to be forewarned of volcanic eruptions which may spread a dust screen over the atmosphere as Mt. Katmai did some years ago. But further we must penetrate into the recesses of the human mind. A coal strike, a great war, may directly change the conditions of the atmosphere; a lighted match idly thrown away may cause deforestation which will change the rainfall and climate. There can be no fully deterministic control of inorganic phenomena unless the determinism governs mind itself. Conversely if we wish to emancipate mind we must to some extent emancipate the material world also. There appears to be no longer any obstacle to this emancipation.

Let us look more closely into the problem of how the mind gets a grip on material atoms so that movements of the body and limbs can be controlled by its volition. I think we may now feel quite satisfied that the volition is genuine. The materialist view was that the motions which appear to be caused by our volition are really reflex actions controlled by the material processes in the brain, the act of will being an inessential side phenomenon occurring simultaneously with the physical phenomena. But this assumes that the result of applying physical laws to the brain is fully determinate. It is meaningless to say that the behaviour of a conscious brain is precisely the same as that of a mechanical brain if the behaviour of a mechanical brain is left undetermined. If the laws of physics are not strictly causal the most that can be said is that the behaviour of the conscious brain is one of the possible behaviours of a mechanical brain. Precisely so; and the decision between the possible behaviours is what we call volition.

Perhaps you will say, When the decision of an atom is made between its possible quantum jumps, is that also "volition"? Scarcely; the analogy is altogether too remote. The position is that both for the brain and the atom there is nothing in the physical world, i.e. the world of pointer readings, to predetermine the decision; the decision is a fact of the physical world with consequences in the future but not causally connected to the past. In the case of the brain we have an insight into a mental world behind the world of pointer readings and in that world we get a new picture of the fact of decision which must be taken as revealing its real nature—if the words *real nature* have any meaning. For the atom we have no such insight into what is behind the pointer readings. We believe that behind all pointer readings there is a background continuous with the background of the brain; but there is no more ground for calling the background of the spontaneous behaviour of the atom "volition" than for calling the background of its causal behaviour "reason." It should be understood that we are not attempting to reintroduce in the background the strict causality banished from the pointer readings. In the one case in which we have any insight—the background of the brain—we have no intention of giving up the freedom of the mind and will. Similarly we do not suggest that the marks of predestination of the atom, not found in the pointer readings, exist undetectable in the unknown background. To the question whether I would admit that the cause of the decision of the atom has something in common with the cause of the decision of the brain, I would simply answer that there is no cause. In the case of the brain I have a deeper insight into the decision; this insight exhibits it as volition, i.e. something outside causality.

A mental decision to turn right or turn left starts one of two alternative sets of impulses along the nerves to the feet. At some brain centre the course of behaviour of certain atoms or elements of the physical world is directly determined for them by the mental decision—or, one may say, the scientific description of that behaviour is the metrical aspect of the decision. It would be a possible though difficult hypothesis to assume that very few atoms (or possibly only one atom) have this direct contact with the conscious decision, and that these few atoms serve as a switch to deflect the material world from one course to the other. But it is physically improbable that each atom has its duty in the brain so precisely allotted that the control of its behaviour would prevail over all possible irregularities of the other atoms. If I have at all rightly understood the processes of my own mind, there is no finicking with individual atoms.

I do not think that our decisions are precisely balanced on the conduct of certain key-atoms. Could we pick up one atom in Einstein's brain and say that if it had made the wrong quantum jump there would have been a corresponding flaw in the theory of relativity? Having regard to the physical influences of temperature and promiscuous collision it is impossible to maintain this. It seems that we must attribute to the mind power not only to decide the behaviour of atoms individually but to affect systematically large groups—in fact to tamper with the odds on atomic behaviour. This has always been one of the most dubious points in the theory of the interaction of mind and matter.

Interference with Statistical Laws. ᴈ Has the mind power to set aside *statistical laws* which hold in inorganic matter? Unless this is granted its opportunity of interference seems to be too circumscribed to bring about the results which are observed to follow from mental decisions. But the admission involves a genuine physical difference between inorganic and organic (or, at any rate, conscious) matter. I would prefer to avoid this hypothesis, but it is necessary to face the issue squarely. The indeterminacy recognised in modern quantum theory is only a partial step towards freeing our actions from deterministic control. To use an analogy—we have admitted an uncertainty which may take or spare human lives; but we have yet to find an uncertainty which may upset the expectations of a life-insurance company. Theoretically the one uncertainty might lead to the other, as when the fate of millions turned on the murders at Sarajevo. But the hypothesis that the mind operates through two or three key-atoms in the brain is too desperate a way of escape for us, and I reject it for the reasons already stated.

It is one thing to allow the mind to direct an atom between

two courses neither of which would be improbable for an inorganic atom; it is another thing to allow it to direct a crowd of atoms into a configuration which the secondary laws of physics would set aside as "too improbable." Here the improbability is that a large number of entities each acting independently should conspire to produce the result; it is like the improbability of the atoms finding themselves by chance all in one half of a vessel. We must suppose that in the physical part of the brain immediately affected by a mental decision there is some kind of interdependence of behaviour of the atoms which is not present in inorganic matter.

I do not wish to minimise the seriousness of admitting this difference between living and dead matter. But I think that the difficulty has been eased a little, if it has not been removed. To leave the atom constituted as it was but to interfere with the probability of its undetermined behaviour, does not seem quite so drastic an interference with natural law as other modes of mental interference that have been suggested. (Perhaps that is only because we do not understand enough about these probabilities to realise the heinousness of our suggestion.) Unless it belies its name, probability can be modified in ways which ordinary physical entities would not admit of. There can be no unique probability attached to any event or behaviour; we can only speak of "probability in the light of certain given information," and the probability alters according to the extent of the information. It is, I think, one of the most unsatisfactory features of the new quantum theory in its present stage that it scarcely seems to recognise this fact, and leaves us to guess at the basis of information to which its probability theorems are supposed to refer.

Looking at it from another aspect—if the unity of a man's consciousness is not an illusion, there must be some corresponding unity in the relations of the mind-stuff which is behind the pointer readings. Applying our measures of relation structure, we shall build matter and fields of force obeying identically the principal field-laws; the atoms will individually be in no way different from those which are without this unity in the background. But it seems plausible that when we consider their collective behaviour we shall have to take account of the broader unifying trends in the mind-stuff, and not expect the statistical results to agree with those appropriate to structures of haphazard origin.

I think that even a materialist must reach a conclusion not unlike ours if he fairly faces the problem. He will need in the physical world something to stand for a symbolic unity of the atoms associated with an individual consciousness, which does not exist for atoms not so associated—a unity which naturally upsets physical predictions based on the hypothesis of random disconnection. For he has not only to translate into material configurations the multifarious thoughts and images of the mind, but must surely not neglect to find some kind of physical substitute for the Ego.

Science and Mysticism

One day I happened to be occupied with the subject of "Generation of Waves by Wind." I took down the standard treatise on hydrodynamics, and under that heading I read—

The equations (12) and (13) of the preceding Art. enable us to examine a related question of some interest, viz. the generation and maintenance of waves against viscosity, by suitable forces applied to the surface.

If the external forces p'_{yy}, p'_{xy} be given multiples of e^{ikx+at}, where k and a are prescribed, the equations in question determine A and C, and thence, by (9) the value of η. Thus we find

$$\frac{p'_{yy}}{g\rho\eta} = \frac{(a^2 + 2\nu k^2 a + \sigma^2)A - i(\sigma^2 + 2\nu kma)C}{gk(A - iC)},$$

$$\frac{p'_{xy}}{g\rho\eta} = \frac{a}{gk} \cdot \frac{2i\nu k^2 A + (a + 2\nu k^2)C}{(A - iC)},$$

where σ^2 has been written for $gk + T' k^3$ as before. . . .

And so on for two pages. At the end it is made clear that

a wind of less than half a mile an hour will leave the surface unruffled. At a mile an hour the surface is covered with minute corrugations due to capillary waves which decay immediately the disturbing cause ceases. At two miles an hour the gravity waves appear. As the author modestly concludes, "Our theoretical investigations give considerable insight into the incipient stages of wave-formation."

On another occasion the same subject of "Generation of Waves by Wind" was in my mind; but this time another book was more appropriate, and I read—

There are waters blown by changing winds to laughter
And lit by the rich skies, all day. And after,
   Frost, with a gesture, stays the waves that dance
And wandering loveliness. He leaves a white
   Unbroken glory, a gathered radiance,
A width, a shining peace, under the night.

The magic words bring back the scene. Again we feel Nature drawing close to us, uniting with us, till we are filled with the gladness of the waves dancing in the sunshine, with the awe of the moonlight on the frozen lake. These were not moments when we fell below ourselves. We do not look back on them and say, "It was disgraceful for a man with six sober senses and a scientific understanding to let himself be deluded in that way. I will take Lamb's *Hydrodynamics* with me next time." It is good that there should be such moments for us. Life would be stunted and narrow if we could feel no significance in the world around us beyond that which can be weighed and measured with the tools of the physicist or described by the metrical symbols of the mathematician.

Of course it was an illusion. We can easily expose the rather clumsy trick that was played on us. Aethereal vibrations of various wave-lengths, reflected at different angles from the disturbed interface between air and water, reached our eyes, and by photoelectric action caused appropriate stimuli to travel along the optic nerves to a brain-centre. Here the mind set to work to weave an impression out of the stimuli. The incoming material was somewhat meagre; but the mind is a great storehouse of associations that could be used to clothe the skeleton. Having woven an impression the mind surveyed all that it had made and decided that it was very good. The critical faculty was lulled. We ceased to analyse and were conscious only of the impression as a whole. The warmth of the air, the scent of the grass, the gentle stir of the breeze, combined with the visual scene in one transcendent impression, around us and within us. Associations emerging from their storehouse grew bolder. Perhaps we recalled the phrase "rippling laughter." Waves—ripples—laughter—gladness— the ideas jostled one another. Quite illogically we were glad; though what there can possibly be to be glad about in a set of aethereal vibrations no sensible person can explain. A mood of quiet joy suffused the whole impression. The gladness in ourselves was in Nature, in the waves, everywhere. That's how it was.

It was an illusion. Then why toy with it longer? These airy fancies which the mind, when we do not keep it severely in order, projects into the external world should be of no concern to the earnest seeker after truth. Get back to the solid substance of things, to the material of the water moving under the pressure of the wind and the force of gravitation in obedience to the laws of hydrodynamics. But the solid substance of things is another illusion. It too is a fancy projected by the mind into the external world. We have chased the solid substance from the continuous liquid to the atom, from the atom to the electron, and there we have lost it. But at least, it will be said, we have reached something real at the end of the chase—the protons and electrons. Or if the new quantum theory condemns these images as too concrete and leaves us with no coherent images at all, at least we have symbolic co-ordinates and momenta and Hamiltonian functions devoting themselves with single-minded purpose to ensuring that $qp - pq$ shall be equal to $ih/2\pi$.

In a previous chapter I have tried to show that by following this course we reach a cyclic scheme which from its very nature can only be a partial expression of our environment. It is not reality but the skeleton of reality. "Actuality" has been lost in the exigencies of the chase. Having first rejected the mind as a worker of illusion we have in the end to return to the mind and say, "Here are worlds well and truly built on a basis more secure than your fanciful illusions. But there is nothing to make any one of them an actual world. Please choose one and weave your fanciful images into it. That alone can make it actual." We have torn away the mental fancies to get at the reality beneath, only to find that the reality of that which is beneath is bound up with its potentiality of awakening these fancies. It is because the mind, the weaver of illusion, is also the only guarantor of reality that reality is always to be sought at the base of illusion. Illusion is to reality as the smoke to the fire. I will not urge that hoary untruth "There is no smoke without fire." But it is reasonable to inquire whether in the mystical illusions of man there is not a reflection of an underlying reality.

To put a plain question—Why should it be good for us to experience a state of self-deception such as I have described? I think everyone admits that it is good to have a spirit sensitive to the influences of Nature, good to exercise an appreciative imagination and not always to be remorselessly dissecting our environment after the manner of the mathematical physicists. And it is good not merely in a utilitarian sense, but in some purposive sense necessary to the fulfilment of the life that is given us. It is not a dope which it is expedient to take from time to time so that we may return with greater vigour to the more legitimate employment of the mind in scientific investigation. Just possibly it might be defended on the ground that it affords to the non-mathematical mind in some feeble measure that delight in the external world which would be more fully provided by an intimacy with its differential equations. (Lest it should be thought that I have intended to pillory hydrodynamics, I hasten to say in this connection that I would not rank the intellectual (scientific) appreciation on a lower plane than the mystical appreciation; and I know of passages written in mathematical symbols which in their sublimity might vie with Rupert Brooke's sonnet.) But I think you will agree with me that it is impossible to allow that the one kind of appreciation can adequately fill the place of the other. Then how can it be deemed good if there is *nothing* in it but self-deception? That would be an upheaval of all our ideas of ethics. It seems to me that the only alternatives are either to count all such surrender to the mystical contact of Nature as mischievous and ethically wrong, or to admit that in these moods we catch something of the true relation of the world to ourselves—a relation not hinted at in a purely scientific analysis of its content. I think the most ardent materialist does not advocate, or at any rate does not practice, the first alternative; therefore I assume the second alternative, that there is some kind of truth at the base of the illusion.

But we must pause to consider the extent of the illusion. Is it a question of a small nugget of reality buried under a mountain of illusion? If that were so it would be our duty to rid our minds of some of the illusion at least, and try to know the truth in purer form. But I cannot think there is much amiss with our appreciation of the natural scene that so impresses us. I do not think a being more highly endowed than ourselves would prune away much of what we feel. It is not so much that the feeling itself is at fault as that our introspective examination of it wraps it in fanciful imagery. If I were to try to put into words the essential truth revealed in the mystic experience, it would be that our minds are not apart from the world; and the feelings that we have of gladness and melancholy and our yet deeper feelings are not of ourselves alone, but are glimpses of a reality transcending the narrow limits of our particular consciousness—that the harmony and beauty of the face of Nature is at root one with the gladness that transfigures the face of man. We try to express much the same truth when we say that the physical entities are only an extract of pointer readings and beneath them is a nature continuous with our own. But I do not willingly put it into words or subject it to introspection. We have seen how in the physical world the meaning is greatly changed when we contemplate it as surveyed from without instead of, as it essentially must be, from within. By introspection we drag out the truth for external survey; but in the mystical feeling the truth is apprehended from within and is, as it should be, a part of ourselves.

Symbolic Knowledge and Intimate Knowledge. May I elaborate this objection to introspection? We have two kinds of knowledge which I call symbolic knowledge and intimate knowledge. I do not know whether it would be correct to say that reasoning is only applicable to symbolic knowledge, but the more customary forms of reasoning have been developed for symbolic knowledge only. The intimate knowledge will not submit to codification and analysis; or, rather, when we attempt to analyse it the intimacy is lost and it is replaced by symbolism.

For an illustration let us consider Humour. I suppose that humour can be analysed to some extent and the essential ingredients of the different kinds of wit classified. Suppose that we are offered an alleged joke. We subject it to scientific analysis as we would a chemical salt of doubtful nature, and perhaps after careful consideration of all its aspects we are able to confirm that it really and truly is a joke. Logically, I suppose, our next procedure would be to laugh. But it may certainly be predicted that as the result of this scrutiny we shall have lost all inclination we may ever have had to laugh at it. It simply does not do to expose the inner workings of a joke. The classification concerns a symbolic knowledge of humour which preserves all the characteristics of a joke except its laughableness. The real appreciation must come spontaneously, not introspectively. I think this is a not unfair analogy for our mystical feeling for Nature, and I would venture even to apply it to our mystical experience of God. There are some to whom the sense of a divine presence irradiating the soul is one of the most obvious things of experience. In their view a man without this sense is to be regarded as we regard a man without a sense of humour. The absence is a kind of mental deficiency. We may try to analyse the experience as we analyse humour, and construct a theology, or it may be an atheistic philosophy, which shall put into scientific form what is to be inferred about it. But let us not forget that the theology is symbolic knowledge whereas the experience is intimate knowledge. And as laughter cannot be compelled by the scientific exposition of the structure of a joke, so a philosophic discussion of the attributes of God (or an impersonal substitute) is likely to miss the intimate response of the spirit which is the central point of the religious experience.

Defence of Mysticism. ◄§ A defence of the mystic might run something like this. We have acknowledged that the entities of physics can from their very nature form only a partial aspect of the reality. How are we to deal with the other part? It cannot be said that that other part concerns us less than the physical entities. Feelings, purpose, values, make up our consciousness as much as sense-impressions. We follow up the sense-impressions and find that they lead into an external world discussed by science; we follow up the other elements of our being and find that they lead—not into a world of space and time, but surely somewhere. If you take the view that the whole of consciousness is reflected in the dance of electrons in the brain, so that each emotion is a separate figure of the dance, then all features of consciousness alike lead into the external world of physics. But I assume that you have followed me in rejecting this view, and that you agree that consciousness as a whole is greater than those quasi-metrical aspects of it which are abstracted to compose the physical brain. We have then to deal with those parts of our being unamenable to metrical specification, that do not make contact —jut out, as it were—into space and time. By dealing with them I do not mean make scientific inquiry into them. The first step is to give acknowledged status to the crude conceptions in which the mind invests them, similar to the status of those crude conceptions which constitute the familiar material world.

Our conception of the familiar table was an illusion. But if some prophetic voice had warned us that it was an illusion and therefore we had not troubled to investigate further we should never have found the scientific table. To reach the reality of the table we need to be endowed with sense-organs to weave images and illusions about it. And so it seems to me that the first step in a broader revelation to man must be the awakening of image-building in connection with the higher faculties of his nature, so that these are no longer blind alleys but open out into a spiritual world—a world partly of illusion, no doubt, but in which he lives no less than in the world, also of illusion, revealed by the senses.

The mystic, if haled before a tribunal of scientists, might perhaps end his defence on this note. He would say, "The familiar material world of everyday conception, though lacking somewhat in scientific truth, is good enough to live in; in fact the scientific world of pointer readings would be an impossible sort of place to inhabit. It is a symbolic world and the only thing that could live comfortably in it would be a *symbol*. But I am not a symbol; I am compounded of that mental activity which is from your point of view a nest of illusion, so that to accord with my own nature I have to transform even the world explored by my senses. But I am not merely made up of senses; the rest of my nature has to live and grow. I have to render account of that environment into which it has its outlet. My conception of my spiritual environment is not to be compared with your scientific world of pointer readings; it is an everyday world to be compared with the material world of familiar experience. I claim it as no more real and no less real than that. Primarily it is not a world to be analysed, but a world to be lived in."

Granted that this takes us outside the sphere of exact knowledge, and that it is difficult to imagine that anything corresponding to exact science will ever be applicable to this part of our environment, the mystic is unrepentant. Because we are unable to render exact account of our environment it does not follow that it would be better to pretend that we live in a vacuum.

If the defence may be considered to have held good against

the first onslaught, perhaps the next stage of the attack will be an easy tolerance. "Very well. Have it your own way. It is a harmless sort of belief—not like a more dogmatic theology. You want a sort of spiritual playground for those queer tendencies in man's nature, which sometimes take possession of him. Run away and play then; but do not bother the serious people who are making the world go round." The challenge now comes not from the scientific materialism which professes to seek a natural explanation of spiritual power, but from the deadlier moral materialism which despises it. Few deliberately hold the philosophy that the forces of progress are related only to the material side of our environment, but few can claim that they are not more or less under its sway. We must not interrupt the "practical men," these busy moulders of history carrying us at ever-increasing pace towards our destiny as an ant-heap of humanity infesting the earth. But is it true in history that material forces have been the most potent factors? Call it of God, of the Devil, fanaticism, unreason; but do not underrate the power of the mystic. Mysticism may be fought as error or believed or inspired, but it is no matter for easy tolerance—

> We are the music-makers
>   And we are the dreamers of dreams
> Wandering by lone sea-breakers
>   And sitting by desolate streams;
>
> World-losers and world-forsakers,
>   On whom the pale moon gleams:
> Yet we are the movers and shakers
>   Of the world for ever, it seems.

Reality and Mysticism. ✎ But a defence before the scientists may not be a defence to our own self-questionings. We are haunted by the word *reality*. I have already tried to deal with the questions which arise as to the meaning of reality;

but it presses on us so persistently that, at the risk of repetition, I must consider it once more from the standpoint of religion. A compromise of illusion and reality may be all very well in our attitude towards physical surroundings; but to admit such a compromise into religion would seem to be a trifling with sacred things. Reality seems to concern religious beliefs much more than any others. No one bothers as to whether there is a reality behind humour. The artist who tries to bring out the soul in his picture does not really care whether and in what sense the soul can be said to exist. Even the physicist is unconcerned as to whether atoms or electrons really exist; he usually asserts that they do, but, as we have seen, existence is there used in a domestic sense and no inquiry is made as to whether it is more than a conventional term. In most subjects (perhaps not excluding philosophy) it seems sufficient to agree on the things that we shall call real, and afterwards try to discover what we mean by the word. And so it comes about that religion seems to be the one field of inquiry in which the question of reality and existence is treated as of serious and vital importance.

But it is difficult to see how such an inquiry can be profitable. When Dr. Johnson felt himself getting tied up in argument over "Bishop Berkeley's ingenious sophistry to prove the non-existence of matter, and that everything in the universe is merely ideal," he answered, "striking his foot with mighty force against a large stone, till he rebounded from it,—'I refute it *thus*.'" Just what that action assured him of is not very obvious; but apparently he found it comforting. And to-day the matter-of-fact scientist feels the same impulse to recoil from these flights of thought back to something kickable, although he ought to be aware by this time that what Rutherford has left us of the large stone is scarcely worth kicking.

There is still the tendency to use "reality" as a word of magic comfort like the blessed word "Mesopotamia." If I were to assert the reality of the soul or of God, I should certainly not intend a comparison with Johnson's large stone— a patent illusion—or even with the p's and q's of the quantum theory—an abstract symbolism. Therefore I have no right

to use the word in religion for the purpos
its behalf that comfortable feeling which (p
has become associated with stones and qua

Scientific instincts warn me that any atte
question "What is real?" in a broader sense
for domestic purposes in science, is likely
dering among vain words and high-soundin
know that there are regions of the human s
by the world of physics. In the mystic sen
around us, in the expression of art, in a year
the soul grows upward and finds the fulfil
implanted in its nature. The sanction for th
within us, a striving born with our conscio
Light proceeding from a greater power than
scarcely question this sanction, for the p
springs from a striving which the mind is i
a questioning that will not be suppressed. W
tellectual pursuits of science or in the mysti
spirit, the light beckons ahead and the purp
nature responds. Can we not leave it at tha
essary to drag in the comfortable word "rea
istered like a pat on the back?

The problem of the scientific world is
problem—the problem of all experience. Ex
regarded as a combination of self and envi
part of the problem to disentangle these two
ponents. Life, religion, knowledge, truth a
this problem, some relating to the finding o
to the finding of our environment from th
fronting us. All of us in our lives have to
of this problem; and it is an important condi
have to solve the problem are ourselves par
Looking at the very beginning, the initial f
of purpose in ourselves which urges us to em
lem. We are meant to fulfil something by
are faculties with which we are endowed, or
to attain, which must find a status and an o
tion. It may seem arrogant that we should

on moulding truth to our own nature; but it is rather that the problem of truth can only spring from a desire for truth which is in our nature.

A rainbow described in the symbolism of physics is a band of aethereal vibrations arranged in systematic order of wavelength from about .000040 cm. to .000072 cm. From one point of view we are paltering with the truth whenever we admire the gorgeous bow of colour, and should strive to reduce our minds to such a state that we receive the same impression from the rainbow as from a table of wave-lengths. But although that is how the rainbow impresses itself on an impersonal spectroscope, we are not giving the whole truth and significance of experience—the starting-point of the problem —if we suppress the factors wherein we ourselves differ from a spectroscope. We cannot say that the rainbow, as part of the world, was meant to convey the vivid effects of colour; but we can perhaps say that the human mind as part of the world was meant to perceive it that way.

Significance and Values. ✥ When we think of the sparkling waves as moved with laughter we are evidently attributing a significance to the scene which was not there. The physical elements of the water—the scurrying electric charges—were guiltless of any intention to convey the impression that they were happy. But so also were they guiltless of any intention to convey the impression of substance, of colour, or of geometrical form of the waves. If they can be held to have had any intention at all it was to satisfy certain differential equations—and that was because they are the creatures of the mathematician who has a partiality for differential equations. The physical no less than the mystical significance of the scene is not there; it is *here*—in the mind.

What we make of the world must be largely dependent on the sense-organs that we happen to possess. How the world must have changed since man came to rely on his eyes rather than his nose! You are alone on the mountains wrapt in a great silence; but equip yourself with an extra artificial sense-organ and, lo! the aether is hideous with the blare of the Savoy bands. Or—

The isle is full of noises,
Sounds, and sweet airs, that give delight, and hurt not.
Sometimes a thousand twangling instruments
Will hum about mine ears; and sometimes voices.

So far as broader characteristics are concerned we see in Nature what we look for or are equipped to look for. Of course, I do not mean that we can arrange the details of the scene; but by the light and shade of our values we can bring out things that shall have the broad characteristics we esteem. In this sense the value placed on permanence creates the world of apparent substance; in this sense, perhaps, the God within creates the God in Nature. But no complete view can be obtained so long as we separate our consciousness from the world of which it is a part. We can only speak speculatively of that which I have called the "background of the pointer readings"; but it would at least seem plausible that if the values which give the light and shade of the world are absolute they must belong to the background, unrecognised in physics because they are not in the pointer readings but recognised by consciousness which has its roots in the background. I have no wish to put that forward as a theory; it is only to emphasise that, limited as we are to a knowledge of the physical world and its points of contact with the background in isolated consciousness, we do not quite attain that thought of the unity of the whole which is essential to a complete theory. Presumably human nature has been specialised to a considerable extent by the operation of natural selection; and it might well be debated whether its valuation of permanence and other traits now apparently fundamental are essential properties of consciousness or have been evolved through interplay with the external world. In that case the values given by mind to the external world have originally come to it from the external world-stuff. Such a tossing to and fro of values is, I think, not foreign to our view that the world-stuff behind the pointer readings is of nature continuous with the mind.

In viewing the world in a practical way values for normal human consciousness may be taken as standard. But the evident possibility of arbitrariness in this valuation sets us hankering after a standard that could be considered final and absolute. We have two alternatives. Either there are no absolute values, so that the sanctions of the inward monitor in our consciousness are the final court of appeal beyond which it is idle to inquire. Or there are absolute values; then we can only trust optimistically that our values are some pale reflection of those of the Absolute Valuer, or that we have insight into the mind of the Absolute from whence come those strivings and sanctions whose authority we usually forbear to question.

I have naturally tried to make the outlook reached in these lectures as coherent as possible, but I should not be greatly concerned if under the shafts of criticism it becomes very ragged. Coherency goes with finality; and the anxious question is whether our arguments have begun right rather than whether they have had the good fortune to end right. The leading points which have seemed to me to deserve philosophic consideration may be summarised as follows:

(1) The symbolic nature of the entities of physics is generally recognised; and the scheme of physics is now formulated in such a way as to make it almost self-evident that it is a partial aspect of something wider.

(2) Strict causality is abandoned in the material world. Our ideas of the controlling laws are in process of reconstruction and it is not possible to predict what kind of form they will ultimately take; but all the indications are that strict causality has dropped out permanently. This relieves the former necessity of supposing that mind is subject to deterministic law or alternatively that it can suspend deterministic law in the material world.

(3) Recognising that the physical world is entirely abstract and without "actuality" apart from its linkage to conscious-

ness, we restore consciousness to the fundamental position instead of representing it as an inessential complication occasionally found in the midst of inorganic nature at a late stage of evolutionary history.

(4) The sanction for correlating a "real" physical world to certain feelings of which we are conscious does not seem to differ in any essential respect from the sanction for correlating a spiritual domain to another side of our personality.

It is not suggested that there is anything new in this philosophy. In particular the essence of the first point has been urged by many writers, and has no doubt won individual assent from many scientists before the recent revolutions of physical theory. But it places a somewhat different complexion on the matter when this is not merely a philosophic doctrine to which intellectual assent might be given, but has become part of the scientific attitude of the day, illustrated in detail in the current scheme of physics.

Conviction. ⌘ Through fourteen chapters you have followed with me the scientific approach to knowledge. I have given the philosophical reflections as they have naturally arisen from the current scientific conclusions, I hope without distorting them for theological ends. In the present chapter the standpoint has no longer been predominantly scientific; I started from that part of our experience which is not within the scope of a scientific survey, or at least is such that the methods of physical science would miss the significance that we consider it essential to attribute to it. The starting-point of belief in mystical religion is a conviction of significance or, as I have called it earlier, the sanction of a striving in the consciousness. This must be emphasised because appeal to intuitive conviction of this kind has been the foundation of religion through all ages and I do not wish to give the impression that we have now found something new and more scientific to substitute. I repudiate the idea of proving the distinctive beliefs of religion either from the data of physical science or by the methods of physical science. Presupposing a mystical religion based not on science but (rightly or wrongly) on a self-known experience accepted as fundamental, we can proceed to discuss the various criticisms which science might bring against it or the possible conflict with scientific views of the nature of experience equally originating from self-known data.

It is necessary to examine further the nature of the conviction from which religion arises; otherwise we may seem to be countenancing a blind rejection of reason as a guide to truth. There is a hiatus in reasoning, we must admit; but it is scarcely to be described as a rejection of reasoning. There is just the same hiatus in reasoning about the physical world if we go back far enough. We can only reason from data and the ultimate data must be given to us by a non-reasoning process—a self-knowledge of that which is in our consciousness. To make a start we must be aware of something. But that is not sufficient; we must be convinced of the significance of that awareness. We are bound to claim for human nature that, either of itself or as inspired by a power beyond, it is capable of making legitimate judgments of significance. Otherwise we cannot even reach a physical world.[4]

Accordingly the conviction which we postulate is that certain states of awareness in consciousness have at least equal significance with those which are called sensations. It is perhaps not irrelevant to note that time by its dual entry into our minds to some extent bridges the gap between sense-impressions and these other states of awareness. Amid the latter must be found the basis of experience from which a spiritual religion arises. The conviction is scarcely a matter to be argued about, it is dependent on the forcefulness of the feeling of awareness.

But, it may be said, although we may have such a de-

---

[4] We can of course solve the problem arising from certain data without being convinced of the significance of the data—the "official" scientific attitude as I have previously called it. But a physical world which has only the status of the solution of a problem, arbitrarily chosen to pass an idle hour, is not what is intended here.

partment of consciousness, may we not have misunderstood altogether the nature of that which we believe we are experiencing? That seems to me to be rather beside the point. In regard to our experience of the physical world we have very much misunderstood the meaning of our sensations. It has been the task of science to discover that things are very different from what they seem. But we do not pluck out our eyes because they persist in deluding us with fanciful colourings instead of giving us the plain truth about wave-length. It is in the midst of such misrepresentations of environment (if you must call them so) that we have to live. It is, however, a very one-sided view of truth which can find in the glorious colouring of our surroundings nothing but misrepresentation—which takes the environment to be all important and the conscious spirit to be inessential. In our scientific chapters we have seen how the mind must be regarded as dictating the course of world-building; without it there is but formless chaos. It is the aim of physical science, so far as its scope extends, to lay bare the fundamental structure underlying the world; but science has also to explain if it can, or else humbly to accept, the fact that from this world have arisen minds capable of transmuting the bare structure into the richness of our experience. It is not misrepresentation but rather achievement—the result perhaps of long ages of biological evolution —that we should have fashioned a familiar world out of the crude basis. It is a fulfilment of the purpose of man's nature. If likewise the spiritual world has been transmuted by a religious colour beyond anything implied in its bare external qualities, it may be allowable to assert with equal conviction that this is not misrepresentation but the achievement of a divine element in man's nature.

May I revert again to the analogy of theology with the supposed science of humour which (after consultation with a classical authority) I venture to christen "geloeology." Analogy is not convincing argument, but it must serve here. Consider the proverbial Scotchman with strong leanings towards philosophy and incapable of seeing a joke. There is no reason why he should not take high honours in geloeology, and for example write an acute analysis of the differences between British and American humour. His comparison of our respective jokes would be particularly unbiased and judicial, seeing that he is quite incapable of seeing the point of either. But it would be useless to consider his views as to which was following the right development; for that he would need a sympathetic understanding—he would (in the phrase appropriate to the other side of my analogy) need to be *converted*. The kind of help and criticism given by the geloeologist and the philosophical theologian is to secure that there is method in our madness. The former may show that our hilarious reception of a speech is the result of a satisfactory dinner and a good cigar rather than a subtle perception of wit; the latter may show that the ecstatic mysticism of the anchorite is the vagary of a fevered body and not a transcendent revelation. But I do not think we should appeal to either of them to discuss the reality of the sense with which we claim to be endowed, nor the direction of its right development. That is a matter for our inner sense of values which we all believe in to some extent, though it may be a matter of dispute just how far it goes. If we have no such sense then it would seem that not only religion, but the physical world and all faith in reasoning totter in insecurity.

I have sometimes been asked whether science cannot now furnish an argument which ought to convince any reasonable atheist. I could no more ram religious conviction into an atheist than I could ram a joke into the Scotchman. The only hope of "converting" the latter is that through contact with merry-minded companions he may begin to realise that he is missing something in life which is worth attaining. Probably in the recesses of his solemn mind there exists inhibited the seed of humour, awaiting an awakening by such an impulse. The same advice would seem to apply to the propagation of religion; it has, I believe, the merit of being entirely orthodox advice.

We cannot pretend to offer proofs. *Proof* is an idol before whom the pure mathematician tortures himself. In physics we are generally content to sacrifice before the lesser shrine of

Plausibility. And even the pure mathematician—that stern logician—reluctantly allows himself some prejudgments; he is never quite convinced that the scheme of mathematics is flawless, and mathematical logic has undergone revolutions as profound as the revolutions of physical theory. We are all alike stumblingly pursuing an ideal beyond our reach. In science we sometimes have convictions as to the right solution of a problem which we cherish but cannot justify; we are influenced by some innate sense of the fitness of things. So too there may come to us convictions in the spiritual sphere which our nature bids us hold to. I have given an example of one such conviction which is rarely if ever disputed—that surrender to the mystic influence of a scene of natural beauty is right and proper for a human spirit, although it would have been deemed an unpardonable eccentricity in the "observer" contemplated in earlier chapters. Religious conviction is often described in somewhat analogous terms as a surrender; it is not to be enforced by argument on those who do not feel its claim in their own nature.

I think it is inevitable that these convictions should emphasise a personal aspect of what we are trying to grasp. We have to build the spiritual world out of symbols taken from our own personality, as we build the scientific world out of the metrical symbols of the mathematician. If not, it can only be left ungraspable—an environment dimly felt in moments of exaltation but lost to us in the sordid routine of life. To turn it into more continuous channels we must be able to approach the World-Spirit in the midst of our cares and duties in that simpler relation of spirit to spirit in which all true religion finds expression.

Mystical Religion. ✎ We have seen that the cyclic scheme of physics presupposes a background outside the scope of its investigations. In this background we must find, first, our own personality, and then perhaps a greater personality. The idea of a universal Mind or Logos would be, I think, a fairly plausible inference from the present state of scientific theory; at least it is in harmony with it. But if so, all that our inquiry justifies us in asserting is a purely colourless pantheism. Science cannot tell whether the world-spirit is good or evil, and its halting argument for the existence of a God might equally well be turned into an argument for the existence of a Devil.

I think that that is an example of the limitation of physical schemes that has troubled us before—namely, that in all such schemes opposites are represented by $+$ and $-$. Past and future, cause and effect, are represented in this inadequate way. One of the greatest puzzles of science is to discover why protons and electrons are not simply the opposites of one another, although our whole conception of electric charge requires that positive and negative electricity should be related like $+$ and $-$. The direction of time's arrow could only be determined by that incongruous mixture of theology and statistics known as the second law of thermodynamics; or, to be more explicit, the direction of the arrow could be determined by statistical rules, but its significance as a governing fact "making sense of the world" could only be deduced on theological assumptions. If physics cannot determine which way up its own world ought to be regarded, there is not much hope of guidance from it as to ethical orientation. We trust to some inward sense of fitness when we orient the physical world with the future on top, and likewise we must trust to some inner monitor when we orient the spiritual world with the good on top.

Granted that physical science has limited its scope so as to leave a background which we are at liberty to, or even invited to, fill with a reality of spiritual import, we have yet to face the most difficult criticism from science. "Here," says science, "I have left a domain in which I shall not interfere. I grant that you have some kind of avenue to it through the self-knowledge of consciousness, so that it is not necessarily a domain of pure agnosticism. But how are you going to deal with this domain? Have you any system of inference from mystic experience comparable to the system by which science develops a knowledge of the outside world? I do not insist on your employing my method, which I acknowledge is inapplicable; but you ought to have some defensible method. The alleged basis of experience may possibly be valid; but have I any reason to regard the religious interpretation currently given to it as anything more than muddle-headed romancing?"

The question is almost beyond my scope. I can only acknowledge its pertinency. Although I have chosen the lightest task by considering only mystical religion—and I have no impulse to defend any other—I am not competent to give an answer which shall be anything like complete. It is obvious that the insight of consciousness, although the only avenue to what I have called *intimate* knowledge of the reality behind the symbols of science, is not to be trusted implicitly without control. In history religious mysticism has often been associated with extravagances that cannot be approved. I suppose too that oversensitiveness to aesthetic influences may be a sign of a neurotic temperament unhealthy to the individual. We must allow something for the pathological condition of the brain in what appear to be moments of exalted insight. One begins to fear that after all our faults have been detected and removed there will not be any "us" left. But in the study of the physical world we have ultimately to rely on our sense-organs, although they are capable of betraying us by gross illusions; similarly the avenue of consciousness into the spiritual world may be beset with pitfalls, but that does not necessarily imply that no advance is possible.

A point that must be insisted on is that religion or contact with spiritual power if it has any general importance at all must be a commonplace matter of ordinary life, and it should be treated as such in any discussion. I hope that you have not interpreted my references to mysticism as referring to abnormal experiences and revelations. I am not qualified to discuss what evidential value (if any) may be attached to the stranger forms of experience and insight. But in any case to suppose that mystical religion is mainly concerned with these is like supposing that Einstein's theory is mainly concerned with the perihelion of Mercury and a few other exceptional observations. For a matter belonging to daily affairs the tone of current discussions often seems quite inappropriately pedantic.

As scientists we realise that colour is merely a question of the wave-lengths of aethereal vibrations; but that does not seem to have dispelled the feeling that eyes which reflect light near wave-length 4800 are a subject for rhapsody whilst those which reflect wave-length 5300 are left unsung. We have not yet reached the practice of the Laputans, who, "if they would, for example, praise the beauty of a woman, or any other animal, they describe it by rhombs, circles, parallelograms, ellipses, and other geometrical terms." The materialist who is convinced that all phenomena arise from electrons and quanta and the like controlled by mathematical formulae, must presumably hold the belief that his wife is a rather elaborate differential equation; but he is probably tactful enough not to obtrude this opinion in domestic life. If this kind of scientific dissection is felt to be inadequate and irrelevant in ordinary personal relationships, it is surely out of place in the most personal relationship of all—that of the human soul to a divine spirit.

We are anxious for perfect truth, but it is hard to say in what form perfect truth is to be found. I cannot quite believe that it has the form typified by an inventory. Somehow as part of its perfection there should be incorporated in it that which we esteem as a "sense of proportion." The physicist is not conscious of any disloyalty to truth on occasions when his sense of proportion tells him to regard a plank as continuous material, well knowing that it is "really" empty space containing sparsely scattered electric charges. And the deepest philosophical researches as to the nature of the Deity may give a conception equally out of proportion for daily life; so that we should rather employ a conception that was unfolded nearly two thousand years ago.

I am standing on the threshold about to enter a room. It is a complicated business. In the first place I must shove against an atmosphere pressing with a force of fourteen pounds on every square inch of my body. I must make sure of landing on a plank travelling at twenty miles a second round the sun —a fraction of a second too early or too late, the plank would be miles away. I must do this whilst hanging from a round planet head outward into space, and with a wind of aether blowing at no one knows how many miles a second through every interstice of my body. The plank has no solidity of substance. To step on it is like stepping on a swarm of flies. Shall I not slip through? No, if I make the venture one of the flies hits me and gives a boost up again; I fall again and am knocked upwards by another fly; and so on. I may hope that the net result will be that I remain about steady; but if unfortunately I should slip through the floor or be boosted too violently up to the ceiling, the occurrence would be, not a violation of the laws of Nature, but a rare coincidence. These are some of the minor difficulties. I ought really to look at the problem four-dimensionally as concerning the intersection of my world-line with that of the plank. Then again it is necessary to determine in which direction the entropy of the world is increasing in order to make sure that my passage over the threshold is an entrance, not an exit.

Verily, it is easier for a camel to pass through the eye of a needle than for a scientific man to pass through a door. And whether the door be barn door or church door it might be wiser that he should consent to be an ordinary man and walk in rather than wait till all the difficulties involved in a really scientific ingress are resolved.

Albert Einstein

THE PROBLEM OF SPACE,

ETHER, AND THE FIELD

IN PHYSICS

Albert Einstein
[1879–   ]

The contributions to modern science made by Albert Einstein cannot be fully evaluated in our time. Another age, more imaginatively adapted to his concepts of time-space, may see more than abstract logic in his theory of relativity —a theory which measures distance between events rather than objects and involves both time and space together. It is a system based upon relations, not things, and is mathematically verifiable. The man who, two hundred years after Sir Isaac Newton's death, changed our understanding of the law of gravity and gave to physics an entirely new perspective first published his work on relativity in 1905, when he announced his so-called restricted theory. In 1915 this work was amplified with his generalized theory. Since then corroboration of his new principles has been found in abundance, and now every aspect of the philosophy of science has been changed as a consequence of his investigations. "The Problem of Space, Ether and the Field in Physics" is from Albert Einstein's book, *The World As I See It*.

THE PROBLEM OF SPACE, ETHER, AND THE FIELD IN PHYSICS

ALBERT EINSTEIN

Scientific thought is a development of pre-scientific thought. As the concept of space was already fundamental in the latter, we must begin with the concept of space in pre-scientific thought. There are two ways of regarding concepts, both of which are necessary to understanding. The first is that of logical analysis. It answers the question, How do concepts and judgments depend on each other? In answering it we are on comparatively safe ground. It is the security by which we are so much impressed in mathematics. But this security is purchased at the price of emptiness of content. Concepts can only acquire content when they are connected, however indirectly, with sensible experience. But no logical investigation can reveal this connection; it can only be experienced. And yet it is this connection that determines the cognitive value of systems of concepts.

Take an example. Suppose an archaeologist belonging to a later culture finds a text-book of Euclidean geometry without diagrams. He will discover how the words "point," "straight-line," "plane" are used in the propositions. He will also see how the latter are deduced from each other. He will even be able to frame new propositions according to the known rules.

But the framing of these propositions will remain an empty word-game for him, as long as "point," "straight-line," "plane," etc., convey nothing to him. Only when they do convey something will geometry possess any real content for him. The same will be true of analytical mechanics, and indeed of any exposition of the logically deductive sciences.

What does this talk of "straight-line," "point," "intersection," etc., conveying something to one, mean? It means that one can point to the parts of sensible experience to which those words refer. This extra-logical problem is the essential problem, which the archaeologist will only be able to solve intuitively, by examining his experience and seeing if he can discover anything which corresponds to those primary terms of the theory and the axioms laid down for them. Only in this sense can the question of the nature of a conceptually presented entity be reasonably raised.

With our pre-scientific concepts we are very much in the position of our archaeologist in regard to the ontological problem. We have, so to speak, forgotten what features in the world of experience caused us to frame those concepts, and we have great difficulty in representing the world of experience to ourselves without the spectacles of the old-established conceptual interpretation. There is the further difficulty that our language is compelled to work with words which are inseparably connected with those primitive concepts. These are the obstacles which confront us when we try to describe the essential nature of the pre-scientific concept of space.

One remark about concepts in general, before we turn to the problem of space: concepts have reference to sensible experience, but they are never, in a logical sense, deducible from them. For this reason I have never been able to understand the quest of the *a priori* in the Kantian sense. In any ontological question, the only possible procedure is to seek out those characteristics in the complex of sense experiences to which the concepts refer.

Now as regards the concept of space: this seems to presuppose the concept of the solid object. The nature of the complexes and sense-impressions which are probably responsible for that concept has often been described. The correspondence between certain visual and tactile impressions, the fact that they can be continuously followed out through time, and that the impressions can be repeated at any movement (taste, sight), are some of those characteristics. Once the concept of the solid object is formed in connection with the experiences just mentioned—which concept by no means presupposes that of space or spatial relation—the desire to get an intellectual grasp of the relations of such solid bodies is bound to give rise to concepts which correspond to their spatial relations. Two solid objects may touch one another or be distant from one another. In the latter case, a third body can be inserted between them without altering them in any way, in the former not. These spatial relations are obviously real in the same sense as the bodies themselves. If two bodies are of equal value for the filling of *one* such interval, they will also prove of equal value for the filling of other intervals. The interval is thus shown to be independent of the selection of any special body to fill it; the same is universally true of spatial relations. It is plain that this independence, which is a principal condition of the usefulness of framing purely geometrical concepts, is not necessary *a priori*. In my opinion, this concept of the interval, detached as it is from the selection of any special body to occupy it, is the starting point of the whole concept of space.

Considered, then, from the point of view of sense experience, the development of the concept of space seems, after these brief indications, to conform to the following schema —solid body; spatial relations of solid bodies; interval; space. Looked at in this way, space appears as something real in the same sense as solid bodies.

It is clear that the concept of space as a real thing already existed in the extra-scientific conceptual world. Euclid's mathematics, however, knew nothing of this concept as such; they confined themselves to the concepts of the object, and the spatial relations between objects. The point, the plane, the straight line, length, are solid objects idealised. All spatial relations are reduced to those of contact (the intersection of straight lines and planes, points lying on straight lines, etc.). Space as a continuum does not figure in the conceptual system at all. This concept was first introduced by Descartes, when he described the point-in-space by its co-ordinates. Here for the first time geometrical figures appear, up to a point, as parts of infinite space, which is conceived as a three-dimensional continuum.

The great superiority of the Cartesian treatment of space is by no means confined to the fact that it applies analysis to the purposes of geometry. The main point seems rather to be this:—The geometry of the Greeks prefers certain figures (the straight line, the plane) in geometrical descriptions; other figures (e.g., the ellipse) are only accessible to it because it constructs or defines them with the help of the point, the straight line and the plane. In the Cartesian treatment on the other hand, all surfaces are, in principle, equally represented, without any arbitrary preference for linear figures in the construction of geometry.

In so far as geometry is conceived as the science of laws governing the mutual relations of practically rigid bodies in space, it is to be regarded as the oldest branch of physics. This science was able, as I have already observed, to get along without the concept of space as such, the ideal corporeal forms—point, straight line, plane, length—being sufficient for its needs. On the other hand, space as a whole, as conceived by Descartes, was absolutely necessary to Newtonian physics. For dynamics cannot manage with the concepts of the mass point and the (temporally variable) distance between mass points alone. In Newton's equations of motion the concept of acceleration plays a fundamental part, which cannot be defined by the temporally variable intervals between points alone. Newton's acceleration is only thinkable or definable in relation to space as a whole. Thus to the geometrical reality of the concept of space a new inertia-determining function of space was added. When Newton described space as absolute, he no doubt meant this real significance of space, which made it necessary for him to attribute to it a quite definite state of motion, which yet did not appear to be fully determined by the phenomena of mechanics. This space was conceived as absolute in another sense also; its inertia-determining effect was conceived as autonomous, i.e., not to be influenced by any physical circumstance whatever; it affected masses, but nothing affected it.

And yet in the minds of physicists space remained until the most recent time simply the passive container of all events, playing no part in physical happenings itself. Thought only began to take a new turn with the wave theory of light and the theory of the electromagnetic field of Faraday and Clerk Maxwell. It became clear that there existed in free space conditions which propagated themselves in waves, as well as localised fields which were able to exert force on electrical masses or magnetic poles brought to the spot. Since it would have seemed utterly absurd to the physicists of the nineteenth century to attribute physical functions or states to space itself, they invented a medium pervading the whole of space, on the model of ponderable matter—the ether, which was supposed to act as a vehicle for electro-magnetic phenomena, and hence for those of light also. The states of this medium, imagined as constituting the electro-magnetic fields, were at first thought of mechanically, on the model of the elastic deformations of rigid bodies. But this mechanical theory of the ether was never quite successful and so the idea of a closer explanation of the nature of the etheric fields was given up. The ether thus became a kind of matter whose only function was to act as a substratum for electrical fields which were by their very nature not further analysable. The picture was, then, as follows:—Space is filled by the ether, in which the material corpuscles or atoms of ponderable matter swim; the atomic structure of the latter had been securely established by the turn of the century.

Since the reciprocal action of bodies was supposed to be accomplished through fields, there had also to be a gravitational field in the ether, whose field-law had, however, assumed no clear form at that time. The ether was only accepted as the seat of all operations of force which make themselves effective across space. Since it had been realised that electrical masses in motion produce a magnetic field, whose energy acted as a model for inertia, inertia also appeared as a field-action localised in the ether.

The mechanical properties of the ether were at first a mystery. Then came H. A. Lorentz's great discovery. All the phenomena of electro-magnetism then known could be explained on the basis of two assumptions: that the ether is firmly fixed in space—that is to say, unable to move at all, and that electricity is firmly lodged in the mobile elementary particles. Today his discovery may be expressed as follows: —Physical space and the ether are only different terms for the same thing; fields are physical conditions of space. For if no particular state of motion belongs to the ether, there does not seem to be any ground for introducing it as an entity of a special sort alongside of space. But the physicists were still far removed from such a way of thinking; space was still, for them, a rigid, homogeneous something, susceptible of no change or conditions. Only the genius of Riemann, solitary and uncomprehended, had already won its way by the middle of last century to a new conception of space, in which space was deprived of its rigidity, and in which its power to take part in physical events was recognised as possible. This intellectual achievement commands our admiration all the more for having preceded Faraday's and Clerk Maxwell's field theory of electricity. Then came the special theory of relativity with its recognition of the physical equivalence of all inertial systems. The inseparableness of time and space emerged in connection with electrodynamics, or the law of the propagation of light. Hitherto it had been silently assumed that the four-dimensional continuum of events could be split up into time and space in an objective manner—i.e., that an absolute significance attached to the "now" in the world of events. With the discovery of the relativity of simultaneity, space and time were merged in a single continuum in the same way as the three-dimensions of space had been before. Physical space was thus increased to a four-dimensional space which also included the dimension of time. The four-dimensional space of the special theory of relativity is just as rigid and absolute as Newton's space.

The theory of relativity is a fine example of the fundamental character of the modern development of theoretical science. The hypotheses with which it starts become steadily more abstract and remote from experience. On the other hand it gets nearer to the grand aim of all science, which is to cover the greatest possible number of empirical facts by logical deduction from the smallest possible number of hypotheses or axioms. Meanwhile the train of thought leading from the axioms to the empirical facts or verifiable consequences gets steadily longer and more subtle. The theoretical scientist is compelled in an increasing degree to be guided by purely mathematical, formal considerations in his search for a theory, because the physical experience of the experimenter cannot lift him into the regions of highest abstraction. The predominantly inductive methods appropriate to the youth of science are giving place to tentative deduction. Such a theoretical structure needs to be very thoroughly elaborated before it can lead to conclusions which can be compared with experience. Here too the observed fact is undoubtedly the supreme arbiter; but it cannot pronounce sentence until the wide chasm separating the axioms from their verifiable consequences has been bridged by much intense, hard thinking. The theorist has to set about this Herculean task in the clear consciousness that his efforts may only be destined to deal the death blow to his theory. The theorist who undertakes such a labour should not be carped at as "fanciful"; on the contrary, he should be encouraged to give free rein to his fancy, for there is no other way to the goal. His is no idle day-dreaming, but a search for the logically simplest possibilities and their consequences. This plea was needed in order to make the hearer or reader more ready to follow the ensuing train of ideas with attention; it is the line of thought which has led from the special to the general theory of relativity and thence to its latest offshoot, the unitary field theory. In this exposition the use of mathematical symbols cannot be avoided.

We start with the special theory of relativity. This theory is still based directly on an empirical law, that of the constant velocity of light. Let P be a point in empty space, P' one separated from it by a length $d\sigma$ and infinitely near to it. Let a flash of light be emitted from P at a time t and reach P' at a time t + dt. Then

$$d\sigma^2 = C^2 dt^2$$

If dx_1, dx_2, dx_3 are the orthogonal projections of $d\sigma$, and the imaginary time co-ordinate $\sqrt{-1}\,ct = x_4$ is introduced, then the above-mentioned law of the constancy of the propagation of light takes the form

$$ds^2 = dx_1^2 + dx_2^2 + dx_3^2 + dx_4^2 = 0$$

Since this formula expresses a real situation, we may attribute a real meaning to the quantity ds, even supposing the neighbouring points of the four-dimensional continuum are selected in such a way that the ds belonging to them does not disappear. This is more or less expressed by saying that the four-dimensional space (with imaginary time-co-ordinates) of the special theory of relativity possesses a Euclidean metric.

The fact that such a metric is called Euclidean is connected with the following. The position of such a metric in a three-dimensional continuum is fully equivalent to the positions of the axioms of Euclidean geometry. The defining equation of the metric is thus nothing but the Pythagorean theorem applied to the differentials and the co-ordinates.

Such alteration of the co-ordinates (by transformation) is permitted in the special theory of relativity, since in the new co-ordinates too the magnitude ds^2 (fundamental invariant) is expressed in the new differentials of the co-ordinates by the sum of the squares. Such transformations are called Lorentz transformations.

The leuristic method of the special theory of relativity is characterised by the following principle:—Only those equations are admissible as an expression of natural laws which do not change their form when the co-ordinates are changed by means of a Lorentz transformation (co-variance of equations in relation to Lorentz transformations).

This method led to the discovery of the necessary connection between impulse and energy, the strength of an electric and a magnetic field, electrostatic and electro-dynamic forces, inert mass and energy; and the number of independent concepts and fundamental equations was thereby reduced.

This method pointed beyond itself. Is it true that the equations which express natural laws are co-variant in relation to Lorentz transformations only and not in relation to other transformations? Well, formulated in that way the question really means nothing, since every system of equations can be expressed in general co-ordinates. We must ask, Are not the laws of nature so constituted that they receive no real simplification through the choice of any one *particular* set of co-ordinates?

We will only mention in passing that our empirical principle of the equality of inert and heavy masses prompts us to answer this question in the affirmative. If we elevate the equivalence of all co-ordinate systems for the formulation of natural laws into a principle, we arrive at the general theory of relativity, provided we stick to the law of the constant velocity of light or to the hypothesis of the objective significance of the Euclidean metric at least for infinitely small portions of four-dimensional space.

This means that for finite regions of space the existence (significant for physics) of a general Riemannian metric is presupposed according to the formula

$$ds^2 = \sum_{\mu\nu} g\mu\nu \; dx^{\mu} \; dx^{\nu},$$

whereby the summation is to be extended to all index combinations from 11 to 44.

The structure of such a space differs absolutely radically in *one* respect from that of a Euclidean space. The coefficients $g\mu\nu$ are for the time being any functions whatever of the co-ordinates x_1 to x_4, and the structure of the space is not really determined until these functions $g_{\mu\nu}$ are really known. It is only determined more closely by specifying laws which the metrical field of the $g_{\mu\nu}$ satisfy. On physical grounds this gave rise to the conviction that the metrical field was at the same time the gravitational field.

Since the gravitational field is determined by the configuration of masses and changes with it, the geometric structure of this space is also dependent on physical factors. Thus according to this theory space is—exactly as Riemann guessed—no longer absolute; its structure depends on physical influences. Physical geometry is no longer an isolated self-contained science like the geometry of Euclid.

The problem of gravitation was thus reduced to a mathematical problem: it was required to find the simplest fundamental equations which are co-variant in relation to any transformation of co-ordinates whatever.

I will not speak here of the way this theory has been confirmed by experience, but explain at once why Theory could not rest permanently satisfied with this success. Gravitation had indeed been traced to the structure of space, but besides the gravitational field there is also the electro-magnetic field. This had, to begin with, to be introduced into the theory as an entity independent of gravitation. Additional terms which took account of the existence of the electro-magnetic field had to be included in the fundamental equations for the field. But the idea that there were two structures of space independent of each other, the metric-gravitational and the electro-magnetic, was intolerable to the theoretical spirit. We are forced to the belief that both sorts of field must correspond to verified structure of space.

The "unitary field-theory," which represents itself as a mathematically independent extension of the general theory of relativity, attempts to fulfil this last postulate of the field theory. The formal problem should be put as follows:—Is there a theory of the continuum in which a new structural element appears side by side with the metric such that it forms a single whole together with the metric? If so, what are the simplest field laws to which such a continuum can be made subject? And finally, are these field-laws well fitted to represent the properties of the gravitational field and the electro-magnetic field? Then there is the further question whether the corpuscles (electrons and protons) can be regarded as positions of particularly dense fields, whose movements are determined by the field equations. At present there is only one way of answering the first three questions. The space structure on which it is based may be described as follows, and the description applies equally to a space of any number of dimensions.

Space has a Riemannian metric. This means that the Euclidean geometry holds good in the infinitesimal neighbourhood of every point P. Thus for the neighbourhood of every point P there is a local Cartesian system of co-ordinates, in reference to which the metric is calculated according to the Pythagorean theorem. If we now imagine the length 1 cut off from the positive axes of these local systems, we get the orthogonal "local n-leg." Such a local n-leg is to be found in every other point P' of space also. Thus, if a linear element (PG or P'G') starting from the points P or P', is given, then the magnitude of this linear element can be calculated by the aid of the relevant local n-leg from its local co-ordinates by means of Pythagoras's theorem. There is therefore a definite meaning in speaking of the numerical equality of the linear elements PG and P'G'.

It is essential to observe now that the local orthogonal n-legs are not completely determined by the metric. For we can still select the orientation of the n-legs perfectly freely without causing any alteration in the result of calculating the size of the linear elements according to Pythagoras's theorem. A corollary of this is that in a space whose structure consists exclusively of a Riemannian metric, two linear elements PG and P'G', can be compared with regard to their magnitude but not their direction; in particular, there is no sort of point in saying that the two linear elements are parallel to one another. In this respect, therefore, the purely metrical (Riemannian) space is less rich in structure than the Euclidean.

Since we are looking for a space which exceeds Riemannian

space in wealth of structure, the obvious thing is to enrich Riemannian space by adding the relation of direction or parallelism. Therefore for every direction through P let there be a definite direction through P′, and let this mutual relation be a determinate one. We call the directions thus related to each other "parallel." Let this parallel relation further fulfil the condition of angular uniformity: If PG and PK are two directions in P, P′G′ and P′K′ the corresponding parallel directions through P′, then the angles KPG and K′P′G′ (measurable on Euclidean lines in the local system) should be equal.

The basic space-structure is thereby completely defined. It is most easily described mathematically as follows:—In the definite point P we suppose an orthogonal n-leg with definite, freely chosen orientation. In every other point P′ of space we so orient its local n-leg that its axes are parallel to the corresponding axes at the point P. Given the above structure of space and free choice in the orientation of the n-leg at one point P, all n-legs are thereby completely defined. In the space P let us now imagine any Gaussian system of co-ordinates and that in every point the axes of the n-leg there are projected on to it. This system of n^2 components completely describes the structure of space.

This spatial structure stands, in a sense, midway between the Riemannian and the Euclidean. In contrast to the former, it has room for the straight-line, that is to say a line all of whose elements are parallel to each other in pairs. The geometry here described differs from the Euclidean in the non-existence of the parallelogram. If at the ends P and G of a length PG two equal and parallel lengths PP′ and GG′ are marked off, P′G′ is in general neither equal nor parallel to PG.

The mathematical problem now solved so far is this:— What are the simplest conditions to which a space-structure of the kind described can be subjected? The chief question which still remains to be investigated is this:—To what extent can physical fields and primary entities be represented by solutions, free from singularities, of the equations which answer the former question?